Making Math Meaningful®

A Middle School Math Curriculum
for Teachers and Parents

Written By Jamie York

Jamie York Press

2012

Making Math Meaningful®

A Middle School Math Curriculum
for Teachers and Parents

Cover Design Copyright © 2003 by Catherine Douglas.

Catherine Douglas was a student at Shining Mountain Waldorf School when she designed the cover to this book. It is an impressive example of how equiangular spirals emerge from nested octagons.

JAMIE YORK
PRESS

Meaningful Math Books for Waldorf
Public, Private, and Home Schools

780 Quince Circle
Boulder, CO 80304
Toll-Free: 1-877-JYP-MATH (1-877-597-6284)
www.JamieYorkPress.com

Table of Contents

EIGHTH GRADE ARITHMETIC — 73

EIGHTH GRADE ALGEBRA — 90

EIGHTH GRADE COMPUTERS — 94

EIGHTH GRADE GEOMETRY — 96

−Introduction−

About this Book

Who is this for?

While most of my teaching experience is within the Waldorf school system, the curriculum presented here can be effectively used by any teacher wishing to bring meaningful, age-appropriate material to their students. The explanations in this book are also useful for parents (or tutors) who are helping their children in a math class that uses the curriculum laid out in this book.

While most of the material is not overly difficult, much of it is foreign, even for math majors. In writing this book, I have assumed that the reader may be weak in math. I hope that with some effort, even the most difficult topic is understandable.

A Word of Caution

This book should not be viewed as a recipe for teaching mathematics in a Waldorf school. Indeed there is no such recipe. This book is merely a resource that reflects the opinions of the author. There are other opinions as well that may also be called "Waldorf".

The reader (presumably a teacher) should not simply follow instructions or carry out a plan just because it is stated in this book. As always, it is the teacher's job to develop the inner sense of what is right at a particular moment for the class and to create an effective lesson. It is ultimately the teacher's love and creativity that will bring the material alive for the students. No book can give this to the teacher.

Things to keep in mind regarding this book

- *You can't cover all of this!* I have never, with any class, covered all the material listed in this book. How much material is covered will depend upon the teacher, the class, and the amount of time available. Obviously, it is important not to rush through the material for the sake of getting through the curriculum.

- *Main Lessons and Track Classes.* Some of the material presented here assumes familiarity with the Waldorf lesson structuring, known as main lesson (which is a three or four-week intensive course that meets up to two hours everyday) and track class (which meets throughout the whole year for 40-minutes each class). In Waldorf schools, we typically introduce a completely new topic in the main lesson and then work on developing skills in the track classes.

- *Order of topics.* The topics in this book are arranged by grade, according to subject area. It is not intended that a teacher should cover the topics in the order that they appear in this book. Teachers using my workbooks will likely find it best to cover topics in the order that they appear in the workbook. *Some topics don't appear in the workbooks at all.*

Our workbooks, puzzle and game book, and more!

The following *Making Math Meaningful* books are available from Jamie York Press:

- *Workbooks.* Our middle school workbooks are designed to bring this middle school curriculum to life.
- *Puzzle and Game Book.* Our puzzle and game book is intended as a resource for grades four through twelve, in order to supplement the normal classroom material, and provide for that "something different".
- *Source Book for Teaching Math in Grades One through Five.* This includes a wealth of ideas and resources for the lower grades class teacher.
- *High School Books.* Our high school workbooks are available for grades 9-12, covering everything from Algebra I to an introduction to calculus. Additionally, *A Teacher's Guide for our High School Workbooks*, and *A Source Book for Teaching High School Math* will soon be published.

Our website

Making Math Meaningful books has a website: **www.JamieYorkPress.com**. On this site, you can view full-color photos of children's main lesson book pages, download (for free!) a variety of practice sheets, and access other resources related to *Making Math Meaningful* books. You can also contact us there with questions and comments. We'd appreciate your feedback and suggestions.

Acknowledgements and permissions

- Thank you to Nettie Fabrie and Wim Gottenbos for many of the ideas included in the introduction.
- Drawings in this book have been reprinted with permission from the following:
  - *The Geometrical Foundation of Natural Structure,* by Robert Williams, Dover Publications, 1979.
  - *Geometric Drawing and the Waldorf School Plan,* by H. von Baravalle, Rudolf Steiner College Press.
  - *Platonic and Archimedean Solids,* by Daud Sutton, Walker & Company, 2001.

The challenge of teaching math today

The Math Tightrope

In teaching mathematics, perhaps like no other subject, we find ourselves walking a tightrope. If we step a bit to one side, a sizable portion of the class becomes perplexed and overwhelmed. If we correct ourselves to the other side, the quicker students get bored and the class as a whole doesn't progress enough. For many teachers, each step along this tightrope brings up unpleasant memories from their own childhood.

As Waldorf teachers, we are aware that the teaching of math is more than just an intellectual exercise. Rudolf Steiner, the founder of the first Waldorf school, spoke of the importance of "permeating the soul with mathematics in the right way" and how a healthy relationship to mathematics can benefit the student's later spiritual development.

Certainly, math in a Waldorf school is viewed differently and taught differently. Yet, the problems we face are often the same as in the mainstream. How can we do better?

Meaningless math

What is society's view of math? Math is often not seen as meaningful in and of itself. A widespread belief is that "good math" must be practical and useful. It then follows that the main reason to study math is that it can be useful for some other purpose or subject. All of these attitudes toward math can make it challenging to teach math in a meaningful way.

I believe that practical applications of math can be helpful, but I also feel that there is a higher purpose to learning math.

The *LIST*

If people believe that math should always be practical, then it stands to reason that skill development would become the primary focus. Over time this has degenerated into the *LIST* – a horrifically long list of skills that are supposedly necessary for our students to move to the next level (e.g., middle school, high school, or college). The *LIST* manages to put pressure on teachers at all levels of education. They fear that if they don't get through the entire *LIST*, then their students won't be prepared. We are led to believe that this *LIST* is getting longer and longer, and more and more daunting. Such an over-emphasis on skill development is boring or overwhelming (or both) for many students, and for the teacher as well.

I believe that basic skills are important, but the list of topics needed to move forward is not horrifically long; it is actually quite manageable (see *What skills are really needed?* below). I also believe there is much more to math than just learning skills. With so much emphasis going toward the mastery of a long list of skills, some of the more interesting aspects of mathematics become neglected.

Why this curriculum?

Previous to when I began teaching at Shining Mountain Waldorf School in 1994, my experiences as a math teacher had been fairly typical. I was to teach out of some textbook, and it was expected that my class would complete the majority of that book.

When I arrived at Shining Mountain and was given the task of teaching middle school math, I was surprised to find that there were no textbooks, and that very little existed in terms of a math curriculum guideline. I was expected to create my own materials. This newfound freedom was both exciting and daunting. I proceeded to research what was happening at other Waldorf schools regarding math curriculum. I spent a great deal of time creating my own worksheets. My original question ("What should I teach?") was soon transformed into, "What topics would best help in developing the thinking and imagination of my middle school students?"

This book is intended to share with others what I have discovered and developed during this journey.

Being a Waldorf teacher

All teachers have a tremendous responsibility to oversee the development of the children in their class. Additionally, all Waldorf teachers have a great deal of freedom in deciding what to bring into the classroom. They do not rely on textbooks; instead each child creates his own book for every main lesson.

It is important that we, as Waldorf teachers, are the authors of what comes into the classroom. It needs to be clear to us why we do what we do. We shouldn't just blindly do something because it's what everyone else does. We need to feel it's right for the students in front of us. In this way we take ownership of the curriculum.

A higher purpose

Rudolf Steiner spoke about how mathematics is a training in sense-free thinking. He also spoke of how the proper teaching of mathematics is an important part of the students' moral and spiritual development. By developing mathematical capacities in our students, we are helping to lay the foundation for the students' spiritual development later in life.

> "The student of mathematics must get rid of all arbitrary thinking and follow purely the demands of thought. In thinking in this way, the laws of the spiritual world flow into him. This regulated thinking leads to the most spiritual truths." -- Rudolf Steiner[1]

Imagination and math

In today's society, imagination is associated largely with fantasy and not viewed as very "useful". It is therefore not surprising that in mainstream education, the development of the child's imagination can be considered unimportant. In contrast, Waldorf education holds that the development of the child's imagination is a central aspect of developing the whole child.

In terms of the teaching of math, imagination can be woven into the lessons, not just by telling compelling stories, but also by showing students that math is a fascinating and creative human endeavor. In this way, math can be a springboard for thinking flexibly and creatively.

> "Imagination is more important than knowledge. Knowledge is limited. Imagination encircles the world." -- Albert Einstein

Will our students be prepared?

Preparation for high school and college math

Often we hear parents who worry about their children's math, say: "Will our children be prepared?" We may then ask, "Prepared for what?" Usually the anxiety is regarding preparation for the next step – whether this next step is to be middle school, high school, or college.

It is an interesting exercise to ask a group of parents who have this question – and perhaps the anxiety as well – what they think it would look like to have their children well prepared in math for the "next step". Surprisingly, when brought in this way, parents won't usually speak of the necessity for their child to learn a long list of math skills, nor will they say how important it is that their child be ahead of other students.

I believe that there are four critical ingredients that our students need in order to be prepared for their next step in their math education – be it middle school, high school, or college.

1. *Enthusiasm for learning.* Enthusiasm and love for learning math go a long way.
2. *Study skills.* The term "study skills" is broad; it includes organization, work habits, etc.
3. *Higher level thinking.* We want our students to be able to think for themselves, think analytically, and we hope that their thinking is heart-felt and imbued with imagination.
4. *Basic math skills.* Yes, skills are important. However, the list of necessary skills needed for the next step isn't as daunting as we might be led to believe.

Preparation for life

Of course, there is much more to education than preparing our students for math in middle school, high school, or college. Patrick Bassett, the head of NAIS (National Association of Independent Schools), asks the question: "What are the skills and values that will be necessary for students to succeed and prosper in the 21st century?"[2]

In order to answer this question, Bassett refers to several sources, including: a Harvard-based study; the government's commission on education; a think tank for higher education; the academic testing industry; public opinion surveys; Tony Wagner's *Seven Survival Skills*; and Howard Gardner's book, *Five Minds for the Future*. What Bassett finds is a surprisingly high degree of congruence between these very different sources.

In the end, Bassett's list of six skills and values needed for the 21st century is:

1. *Character.* This includes a variety of qualities, such as empathy, integrity, resilience, courage, etc.
2. *Creativity.* Later in life, this quality manifests itself as adaptability and developing an entrepreneurial spirit.
3. *Critical thinking.* This includes problem solving, the ability to analyze information (filtering, analysis, and synthesis), questioning what you are "told" in the media, and thinking for yourself.

---

[1] Rudolf Steiner, *Spiritual Ground of Education,* lecture given at Oxford, August 21 1922, GA 305
[2] Patrick Bassett, *Demonstrations of Learning for 21st Century Schools*, Independent Perspective (Journal), Fall 2009.

4. *Communication.* The emphasis here is public speaking. In today's information world of media and computer screens, children (and adults!) are losing their abilities to speak articulately.
5. *Teaming.* Working together productively and collaboratively has become more important than ever.
6. *Leadership.* Today, perhaps more than ever, the world is in need of inspirational leaders, who have strong values, and the courage and will to "stand up for the good".

I believe that the above six skills and values speak for the strength (and need!) of Waldorf education.

The major themes for math

Grades 1-4: Developing a sense of number. This is also when the arithmetic facts should be mastered. These early grades are <u>not</u> about the mastery of written procedural skills (e.g., long division, adding fractions, etc.).

Grades 5-6: Consolidating skills. We consolidate skills that were introduced in earlier grades and develop mastery with written procedural skills (e.g., long division, adding fractions, etc.).

Grades 7-9: Developing abstract thinking. Students start to develop confidence in their thinking.

Grades 10-12: Developing logical, analytical, synthetic thinking. "Real math" and independent thinking can all really take off at the end of high school as the student begins to find his own identity and destiny.

What math skills are really needed?

Math educators often agree that there is too much of an emphasis on procedural skills in math education today. They say that we need to find more time to develop problem-solving skills and creative thinking capabilities. Yet, many teachers complain that there is never enough time for these "extras". We can begin to feel that there is an overwhelming amount of material that the students must learn, and, if they don't learn it all, they won't be ready for the next step. As stated above, the actual list of necessary skills is relatively short.

(<u>Note</u>: The below lists are simply intended as benchmarks in two-year intervals. Any skill listed under a certain year may very well be mastered a year earlier.)

Skills needed by the end of <u>fourth grade</u>: Arithmetic facts learned "by heart", and a *sense of number*.

Skills needed by the end of <u>sixth grade</u>: The four processes. Fractions. Decimals. Measurement. Estimation.

Skills needed by the end of <u>eighth grade</u>: Percents. Ratios and proportions. Basic algebra (not too much!). Area and volume. Dimensional analysis (i.e., unit conversions).

In the math classroom

Two types of topics: Skills and Mathematical Experiences

As teachers, we sometimes think that the students are supposed to "learn" everything that we teach – that everything should be learned, tested, and retained. However, that's not true. It can be helpful to consider that math topics can be divided into two categories: *skills* (i.e., material that needs to be mastered) and *mathematical experiences*.

<u>Skills</u> (a topic that needs to be mastered). Here the teacher needs to create a dance between introducing, deepening, practicing, sleeping, and reviewing. The bigger the topic, the greater the number of times it needs to be put to sleep, and then later reviewed. It is quite typical to introduce a skills topic one year, but not to have the students reach mastery until the next year, or the year after.

<u>Mathematical experiences</u>. With a "pure" mathematical experience, there is often no expectation that the students remember the topic or learn it as a skill. Examples of such topics include puzzle problems, "Wonder of Number" topics, number bases (8th grade), and a variety of geometric topics. We teach these topics because they stretch our students' minds, teaching them to think mathematically, and they engender enthusiasm and wonder for math.

How much algebra?

In a Waldorf school, the basic fundamentals of algebra are presented in a three-week main lesson block in seventh grade. After this, the subject is "put to sleep" for up to a year, allowing the students to digest this important step before building on it. This is in direct contrast to the normal approach to algebra, which gives an initial introduction to algebra, and then immediately builds on this not-yet-firm foundation.

While I recognize that schools can feel pressured to give their eighth graders a full year of algebra – and each school needs to decide about this for themselves – I feel strongly that *the bulk of algebra belongs in ninth grade, when the child is most developmentally ready for it.* The goal is to have the students enter high school saying, "I love algebra, and I'm good at it!" Too much algebra in eighth grade is likely to be overwhelming for many of the students, and dampen their enthusiasm for this important subject.

The algebra curriculum during the middle school years should not have priority over other material. At the very least, it is necessary to review the algebra covered in seventh grade during the eighth grade year. However, any algebra topic that is not covered in eighth grade, will be covered as part of a standard ninth grade algebra course. In contrast, most of the topics listed here under *geometry* and *arithmetic* should be covered by the end of eighth grade, as it is generally not part of high school curricula.

Should math classes be divided into faster and slower paced sections?

Many schools split the middle school math track classes according to ability level. The argument is that this improves the teacher-student ratio, thereby allowing struggling students to receive more individual attention. It is also argued that it allows the more advanced students to go faster.

While I can understand both sides of this debate – and each school must decide about it according to its own situation – I am personally opposed to splitting the math classes in middle school.

First of all, the math curriculum in the middle school, as outlined in this book, is generally not sequential. In other words, success in one topic does not depend on the success of a previous unit. This allows a student to recover from a unit in which he/she did poorly.

Secondly, if the classes were tracked starting in sixth or seventh grade, the students would be "put in a box" that would be difficult to get out of. Middle school is the time that the students "wake up" in their thinking – and some students "wake up" later than others. I have seen many students who struggled at the start of seventh grade, but then "woke up", worked hard, and ended up entering high school very strong.

Having the whole class together is definitely more of a challenge for the teacher. It requires better classroom management skills, better organization, and a conscious effort to meet the needs of a more diverse class (i.e., finding ways to challenge those students who need to be challenged, and supporting those students who are struggling). But I feel that it can be well worth it!

Group Work

In my math classes, grades six through twelve, I have the students spend a significant amount of time working in groups. I assign the groups (of two or three students) carefully. Sometimes, a stronger student may be helping a classmate to understand a problem. At other times, I might group students together with similar ability and skill level in order to work on problems from a new topic (e.g., the group worksheets from the eighth grade workbook are specifically designed to guide the students to the discovery of new concepts).

Mental math

By "mental math", I am referring to doing calculations in your head without writing down the work. Mental math is an important skill to be developed from first grade up through eighth grade. It helps to strengthen the students' sense of number. Mental math can be worked on in a variety of ways, including orally with the whole class, or individually on paper (e.g., arithmetic facts practice sheets).

Another aspect of mental math, which the students love, is math tricks. I have listed all of these math tricks in *Appendix B*. You will find some that you already know, albeit subconsciously. Others will surprise you.

Repetition and review!

Waldorf education seems to be the antithesis of dull, repetitive rote learning. We tend to be strong at introducing things in an interesting and imaginative way, but often there is not enough repetition and drill when it is needed. The end result can be that our students don't retain what we've taught them – they can't remember how to do fractions; they don't have their multiplication facts down; and they are very slow at doing simple arithmetic. It shouldn't be this way. Through mental math, homework, and in-class math sheets, the teacher needs to systematically plan how to integrate repetition and review into the routine in order to strengthen the students' skills. For the students who need more of this than others, the teacher needs to work with the extra-lesson teacher, the parents, or a tutor, to ensure they get enough.

Arithmetic facts

Knowing the arithmetic facts has nothing to do with how "smart" a student is. In reality, a lack of confidence often causes students to do poorly in math during their middle school and high school years. This lack of confidence often starts from them not knowing their arithmetic facts, which makes them *think* that they must be bad at math, and in the end it can turn into a self-fulfilling prophecy.

There is a fairly narrow window – the center of which is third grade – for learning the arithmetic facts. It is much more difficult to learn these facts by heart after fourth grade. So how can we reach our goal of having all of our students learn their arithmetic facts by heart by the end of third grade? The real key to achieving this goal is working systematically and creatively with the children starting in first grade. To help in this effort, we have prepared *arithmetic facts sheets* that can be used in grades three through six. These sheets can be downloaded for free from our website: **www.JamieYorkPress.com**.

If a student hasn't learned the facts by sixth grade, then it is probably best to identify and work on the few facts that haven't been properly learned. This should be done *daily* by using flashcards (just for those facts) for several months. This flashcard work should then be continued even after these facts have been learned, in order to ensure that they are retained. But remember – it is quite possible to become good at math even if the facts aren't solid.

Word problems

At times, word problems are held up as being more important than they really are. Some say that word problems show how math can be useful in the real world, and that word problems help to develop problem-solving abilities. Neither is necessarily true. In truth, many students (especially in the upper grades) quickly learn to hate word problems; they shut down as soon as they see a word problem.

There are many different types of word problems, and many levels. It is helpful to keep in mind that the analytical thinking abilities needed for true problem solving only really blossom toward the end of high school.

My point here is not to say that word problems should be avoided until high school. Word problems should be brought into the classroom, starting in first grade, through stories and images. But we should be very careful! We need to keep in mind the pedagogical purpose of word problems. Word problems – if well chosen – can show how mathematics can appear in our everyday lives. We need to carefully consider how to bring word problems to the class in a way that isn't traumatizing. Keep it simple, and make it fun!

Calculators

I first allow my students to use calculators in the middle of eighth grade, when many of the calculations by hand can be overly tedious. In high school, calculators are used more and more each year.

Computers

I do a brief unit on computers in an effort to meet the needs of eighth graders who have a hunger for knowledge of the modern world as they prepare to enter high school. I believe that actual work with computers should be delayed until high school. In order to begin to understand about how computers store information, I do a unit on *number bases* and *ASCII code*, which gives a basic picture of how computer memory works.

One aspect of what I am proposing here – teaching about computer programming – is quite different from what is done in a typical Waldorf school. I call this unit *algorithms*; it is the "thinking" behind the computer. I have the students experience the thought process of computer programming without getting on a computer. Essentially, the students get to see algorithms, written in English, which are similar to computer programs.

The art of teaching math

What makes a good math teacher?

Many class teachers feel under-confident in their own math skills, and, in some cases, have had traumatic experiences with math when they were in school. Often, this results in the teacher developing an antipathy towards math. However, if such a teacher can find a way to rise above his antipathy toward math, then that teacher may find joy in math, which can result in bringing math lessons to the students with wonderful enthusiasm.

This is what I feel makes a good math teacher:

- <u>Enthusiasm for learning math</u>. For many teachers, this amounts to finding a new relationship to math. How wonderful it can be to find out that math can be interesting and rewarding!
- <u>Ability to present the material effectively</u>. This is the art of teaching.
- <u>Adequate preparation time for the math lessons</u>. With everything that is demanded of the class teacher, there often isn't enough time left to prepare adequately for the math lessons.
- <u>A healthy relationship to the students</u>. This helps create a safe and comfortable learning environment for the students.

The three myths of math

<u>Myth #1</u>. *Only people born with math ability can become good at math.* In reality, hard work can help develop math ability. A student in the upper grades who is seen as being strong in math, might very well have once struggled with math.

<u>Myth #2</u>. *Confusion is bad.* In reality, confusion is part of learning math. Every time we learn a new topic in math, we must go through a period of confusion as we gain clarity.

<u>Myth #3</u>. *Forgetting is bad.* In reality, forgetting is an important part of learning. In fact, for important topics, it can be said in order to learn it permanently, you need to forget it three times!

Four steps towards math trauma

1. <u>Confusion</u>. *Everyone experiences confusion* when learning math.
2. <u>Struggling</u>. *Most students struggle* with math at least occasionally.
3. <u>Frustration</u>. *Many students get frustrated* with math.
4. <u>Shutting down/trauma</u>. *Some students shut down and become "math traumatized".*

One of the jobs of the teacher is to guide the students through the challenges they encounter in school and in life. In today's world, our children are often shielded from discomfort; they come to expect that things should be easy. They have little patience. It is therefore not surprising that so many children have little tolerance for confusion and struggle. If we compound this with a variety of emotional issues, then we can see how important it is for us, as teachers, to *coach* these students through these challenges.

Teaching the "Big Topics"

The "big topics" in middle school math are fractions, decimals, percents, ratios, and (simple) algebra. Our students should have these topics mastered before entering high school. There are two common mistakes made with these big topics.

The first is to do *too much too soon*. The topic may have been introduced in a wonderful and effective way, but the mistake can be made to build too much on the new foundation, resulting in many of the students drowning. The second mistake is *not enough follow-up and review*. This often happens with percents. It is introduced and practiced (perhaps too much!) in sixth grade, and then the students might never see it again.

So how should percents, for example, be done? It should be introduced in a wonderful sixth grade main lesson – not too much, and kept very simple. Then, one year later, the topic is reviewed and deepened – again being careful that it isn't too much. And then, once again, it is put to sleep. Now the stage has been set for going into depth in eighth grade. A similar three-step plan can be followed with any "big topic". If we want the students to learn something well and permanently, then we need to create a "dance" between introducing, deepening, practicing, sleeping, and reviewing.

Be aware of using math in a competitive way!

While games and competition can be fun for many of the students, they can leave a few students feeling badly. For this reason, teachers should be very discerning about what games they bring into the classroom. Simply ask yourself, "Could this game make someone feel badly?" Students should not be required to stand up in front of the class (e.g., math-around-the-world, or math-baseball) and compete against one another. For some students, to lose in front of everyone in this way can be quite humiliating. On the other hand, a simple math board game played between friends could be fun and instructive.

What to do when things aren't going well…

- <u>Relax</u>. Parents are often fearful. This gets through to the students and pressures the teacher, who in turn becomes fearful and anxious. Try not to have your teaching driven by anxiety and fear.

- <u>Parent communication</u>. Speak to parents, in parent evenings, and individually. Parents need to understand clearly what you are doing and why, especially if it is different than the norm. Parents need to be well informed. They need to know what their child has achieved and what their child needs to work on.

- Ask yourself: "<u>Why am I doing this</u>?" The answer shouldn't be: "because that's how everyone does it." We should have a real pedagogical answer that we can give to ourselves, our parents, and our colleagues.

- <u>Give it a rest</u>. Re-evaluate what you're doing. Doing more isn't necessarily helpful. Maybe if a particular topic is put to rest for a month or two – or even until next year – then the class will really absorb it better at that later time.

- Make sure that the timing is right. When should we introduce a certain topic? The question shouldn't be "How soon can I do it?", but rather, "Is this the developmentally appropriate time to bring this topic?" Live into where the students are developmentally. If it seems that many of the students aren't ready for something, then it may be wise to listen to that instinct. *When in doubt, wait!*
- Remember your role. Remember that one of the most important roles of the math teacher is as "math coach" – to help these students through their emotional math issues.

Perfectionism and fear of failure

Some students have a tendency towards perfectionism. Often, it is one of the stronger students in the class. Perfectionists want life to be rhythmical and predictable. When faced with a task, they need to be confident that they can do it well.

The core of the difficulty is that math often violates these rules. Confusion and learning to overcome your struggles is part of doing math. To some degree, especially in middle school and above, math is about facing the unknown and figuring out how to solve unfamiliar problems. To a perfectionist, all of this is threatening.

Things become further complicated as the student enters adolescence, becomes more self-aware, and math becomes even more unpleasant and scary. Such a student may eventually just give up on math. Why? Because it is less painful to give up than it is to put forth effort and, in the end, perhaps fail anyway. This is known as "fear of failure".

So what can we do as teachers? Once again, our role as a coach is critical. And this is bigger than just math. We need to look for situations where *they feel they can't succeed*, but *we know they can*. Such a situation could be having a role in a class play, climbing a mountain, riding a bicycle (or a unicycle!), or solving a particularly daunting math problem. They think they can't, and we know they can. At the right time, and in the right way, we need to gently push them into these situations. Our role is to coach them through their challenges, and to help ensure their success. And once they succeed, celebrate! "Look at what you did! And you thought you couldn't do it!" After that, we can build on this success. In this way, the student's confidence is slowly built up, and, over time, the student becomes more comfortable with the challenges that life presents, and hopefully becomes more open to learning math.

Remediation[1]

Meeting the needs of a student with learning challenges can take a good deal of time and energy. In general, we can always expect to have a few students who are somewhat behind the rest of the class. It is especially important for the teacher to know where each one of these students is at, to understand why there is an issue, and to have a plan of how to move forward.

Confidence is an important factor. The student needs to know that his teacher believes in him. The student shouldn't feel that he is doing "dumbed-down math". If the student (or the class as a whole) is behind or has certain holes in his knowledge, then we still should find ways to bring the current material to him.

Individual *coaching* often makes a huge difference, but all of this shouldn't fall on the shoulders of the class teacher. The class teacher should ask the remedial teacher for help early on. Some students with remedial needs (especially if we are able to work with the situation effectively) can be behind the rest of the class for years, but then they can "wake up" to math as late as eighth grade.

Additionally, we need to be careful not to allow fear to set in with ourselves, the student, or the parents – fear exacerbates the situation. We need to work productively with the parents of a student with remedial needs. Clear communication with parents is critical. This includes having a written record (as a school document) of the student's progress and a written record of any modifications in the student's program (i.e., an ILP).

Depending upon a school's resources, it may not be feasible to keep a student with serious learning challenges in the school. Sometimes, in spite of our own emotional attachments to the student, we have to admit that we can't meet a student's needs.

---

[1] For more ideas on working with children with learning challenges, see Ernst Schuberth's book, *Teaching Mathematics for First and Second Grades in Waldorf Schools*, pages 59 and on.

Summary of Math Curriculum Topics

Sixth Grade

Arithmetic (75%)

The World of Numbers	Mental math & math tricks; casting out nines; exponents & roots; divisibility; prime factorization.
Division	Division and fractions; long division; why long division works; short division; checking answers.
Fractions	Thorough review; the relationship between fractions decimals & division; comparing fractions and decimals; compound fractions.
Decimals	Thorough review; converting between fractions and decimals; repeating decimals; converting repeating decimals to fractions.
Business Math &Percents	Introduction to percents; determining the percent of a given number; determining a percentage; percent increase and decrease; profit, commission & tax; simple interest; discount; loss; rate of pay; unit cost; temperature conversion formulas; business formulas; line graphs; pie charts.
Other Topics	Metric system; word problems (rates); statistics; introduction to ratios; significant digits; currency exchange rates.

Geometry (25%)

General Concepts	Circle & polygon terminology; angle measure; the three dimensions.
The Basic Constructions	Copying a line segment; copying an angle; bisecting a line segment; bisecting an angle; construction of perpendicular lines; construction of a parallel line; division of a line into equal parts; construction of regular polygons (square, hexagon, etc.).
Spirals	Equiangular spirals; the Archimedean spiral.
Advanced Constructions	Rotations of circles; the limaçon and the cardioid; the hierarchy of quadrilaterals; knot and interpenetrating polygons; the 24-division with all its diagonals; the King's Crown.
Area	Areas of rectangles, squares, and right triangles.

Math Main Lesson Blocks
1. Business Math (including percents, formulas, and graphing)
2. Geometry (geometric drawing)

Math Track Class meets twice per week.

Seventh Grade

Arithmetic (50%)

The World of Numbers	Mental math & math tricks; divisibility; roots.
Measurement	The metric system; review of the U.S. system.
Percents	Finding the base; strange percents; compound interest; calculating the percentage of increase or decrease.
Ratios	The three thoughts; the two forms; reciprocals of ratios ; proportion of the whole; similar figures; direct and inverse proportion.
Irrational Numbers	The ratio in a square; the ratio in a circle (π); repeating decimals; rational & irrational numbers; the square root algorithm (optional).
Other Topics	Puzzle problems with doubling; word problems (rates).

Algebra (20%)

Basic Ideas	Basic goals; the importance of form; an introductory puzzle; history; terminology.
Negative Numbers	A careful introduction; combining positive & negative numbers; rules for multiplication & division.
Expressions	Simplifying expressions.
Formulas	Gauss's summing formula; car rental formula; Galileo's law of falling bodies; Euclid's perfect number formula.
Equations	An equation as a puzzle; solving equations by *Guess and Check*; the *Golden Rule of Equations*; solving equations by balancing.
Algebraic Word Problems	An introduction to algebraic word problems.

Geometry (30%)

Area	The shear and stretch; areas of parallelograms, trapezoids, and non-right triangles.
Geometric Drawing	Geometric division; star patterns; triangle constructions (optional)
The Pentagon & The Golden Ratio	Construction and properties of the pentagon; the golden ratio; the golden rectangle & golden spiral; the golden triangle.
Angle Theorems & Proofs	Theorems arising from two parallel lines cut by a transversal; angles in a triangle add to 180°; angles in other polygons; angle puzzles; Theorem of Morley; Theorem of Thales.
The Pythagorean Theorem	Visual proofs; Pythagorean triples; calculating missing sides of triangles.
Other Topics	Perspective drawing, various other drawing exercises.

Math Main Lesson Blocks

1. Algebra (Intro to the Basics – not too much!)
2. Geometry (geometric drawing, areas, theorems up to the Pythagorean Theorem)

Math Track Class meets three times per week.

Eighth Grade

Arithmetic (45%)

Number Bases   Ancient number systems; expanded decimal notation; scientific notation; octal; base-five; base-sixteen (hexadecimal); base-two (binary); arithmetic in various bases; converting between binary and hexadecimal.

The World of Numbers   Square root algorithm; Pythagorean Theorem.

Percents & Growth   Four ways to find the base; increase/decrease problems; exponential growth; the exponential growth formula; the rule of 72.

Dimensional Analysis   The two methods; Converting between metric and U.S. units; converting units for rates; converting areas and volumes; density.

Proportions   Shortcuts for solving (moving along diagonals, cross-multiplying); solving word problems with proportions; rate problems.

Algebra (10%)

Expressions   The laws of exponents; fractions & negatives.

Equations   Order of operations; evaluating expressions; distributive property; equations with fractions; "strange solutions"; converting repeating decimals into fractions.

Computers (5%)

Computer Memory & ASCII code   Bits and bytes; decoding binary codes.

Computer Algorithms   Writing algorithms using English; the prime number algorithm; an algorithm for addition; an algorithm for long division, the square root algorithm.

Geometry (40%)

Mensuration   Baravalle's proof of the Pythagorean Theorem; area of a trapezoid; Heron's formula; the area of four types of triangles; area of a circle; portions of circles; volume & surface area of solids (box, prism, pyramid, cylinder, cone, sphere, octahedron, tetrahedron); Archimedes' ratio; tricks with dimensions.

Stereometry   Types of polyhedra; Platonic solids; the transformation of solids; orthogonal views; duality; Archimedean solids; the stretching process; the Archimedean duals; constructing paper model; close-packing; Euler's formula; imagination 3-D transformation exercises.

Loci   Curves generated from loci problems (a circle, two parallel lines, two concentric circles, a perpendicular bisector, two angle bisectors, parabola, ellipse, hyperbola); alternative definitions; conic sections; curves in movement, the Curves of Cassini.

Math Main Lesson Blocks

1. Number bases and Loci.
2. Geometry (mensuration and stereometry)

Math Track Class meets three times per week.

Sixth Grade

The year for strengthening skills

While there are new topics to be introduced in sixth grade math, much of the year is an important review, or a furthering of material introduced in earlier years. The challenge is to weave in the review in such a way that there is always something new. Each homework or practice sheet should include a fair amount of review problems. If your students enter seventh grade feeling that division, fractions, and decimals are all "easy", and they are excited about learning math, then you have succeeded.

A continual theme through the year is the sense of number and the interrelationship between division, fractions, decimals, and percents. Fractions play the central role. The key is that division, decimals, and percents can all be thought of as a fraction.

Another theme in sixth grade math is developing good work habits. I believe that weekly homework should be assigned and that it should be unthinkable that a student wouldn't complete it. Organization skills, including a good notebook, are very important.

The order of topics

The order in which topics are introduced in my workbook is as follows:

The four processes with fractions and decimals, long division (including repeating decimals), reducing fractions, casting out nines, short division, mixed numbers and improper fractions, exponents, converting decimals to/from fractions, estimating, square roots, divisibility, unit cost, U.S. measurement, formulas, metric, converting repeating decimals to fractions, factors and prime numbers, angle measurement, prime factorization, basic percents, mean/median/mode, pie charts, area and perimeter, percent increase and decrease, tax rate, discount, profit and loss, rate of pay, converting to/from percents, ratios, rate of speed, line graphs, foreign exchange rates, compound fractions.

Arithmetic

The World of Numbers

Mental Math

- See sections on *Mental Math* and *Multiplication Facts* in the *Introduction*.
- *Begin every class,* throughout the whole year, with either a speed sheet or mental math.

Math Tricks

- Cover the sixth grade math tricks. (**See Appendix B.**)
- Introduce one every other week and keep the tricks fresh by including them in mental math throughout the year.
- In general, the idea in sixth grade is not so much to explain why each math trick works, but instead to use them to build the students' calculating skills and to increase their confidence. These tricks will also develop their sense of wonder for numbers.

New multiplication facts to be memorized ("*" indicates optional):

13x2 = 26	14x2 = 28	15x2 = 30	16x2 = 32	18x2 = 36	25x2 = 50
13x3 = 39	14x3 = 42	15x3 = 45	16x3 = 48	*18x3 = 54	25x3 = 75
13x4 = 52	*14x4 = 56	15x4 = 60	16x4 = 64	*18x4 = 72	25x4= 100
*13x5 = 65	*14x5 = 70	15x5 = 75	*16x5 = 80	*18x5 = 90	25x5 = 125
13x13 = 169	14x14 = 196	15x15 = 225	16x16 = 256	18x18 = 324	25x6 = 150
					*25x8 = 200
					25x25 = 625

Casting Out Nines

- A must do! Lots of fun!
- Normally, we check a multiplication problem to see if it is right simply by redoing the problem. This is problematic for two reasons: it is time consuming, and we are likely to make the same mistake again.

- *Casting out nines* allows us to quickly check our answer after doing a multiplication problem.
  Example: The key is to realize that the *arrows represent summing the digits* (e.g., with 7296: 7+2+9+6=24):

$$
\begin{array}{l}
7296 \longrightarrow 24 \longrightarrow \quad 6 \\
\underline{\times\ 376} \longrightarrow 16 \longrightarrow \underline{\times\ 7} \\
43776 \qquad\qquad\qquad 42 \\
51072 \qquad\qquad\qquad\qquad\ \textcircled{6} \\
\underline{21888} \qquad\qquad\qquad \text{Correct!} \\
2743296 \longrightarrow 33 \longrightarrow \textcircled{6}
\end{array}
$$

  If the circled results aren't the same, then there is a mistake in the multiplication. A short cut for summing the digits is to *cast out* all groups of digits that add to *nine*, or multiples of nine. Thus, with the answer 2743296: the first two digits (27), the next three (432), and then the 9, are all *cast out*, leaving just the 6 as the result. With practice, this is very quick!

Exponents and Roots

- Introduce exponents and roots using only numbers and simple examples. Do *not* use variables.

  Example: $3^4 = 3\cdot3\cdot3\cdot3 = 81$ **Example:** $\left(\frac{2}{5}\right)^2 = \frac{4}{25}$ **Example:** $\sqrt{25} = 5$
  Example: $10^3 = 1000$ **Example:** $\sqrt{1000000} = 1000$
  Example: $2^5 = 32$ **Example:** $(4\frac{1}{2})^2 = \left(\frac{9}{2}\right)^2 = \frac{81}{4} = 20\frac{1}{4}$ **Example:** $\sqrt{12100} = 110$
  Example: $(0.02)^3 = 0.000008$ **Example:** $\sqrt{160000} = 400$

- Have the students calculate the *powers of two* as high as they can go. You may want to have them check their answer with every exponent increase of 10 or 20. (See **Appendix E,** *Powers of Two Table* for a listing of the powers of two up to 2^{100}.)
- The students should memorize the following powers:
  - $2^3 = 8$; $2^4 = 16$; $2^5 = 32$; $2^6 = 64$; $2^{10} = 1024$; $3^3 = 27$; $3^4 = 81$; $4^3 = 64$; $4^4 = 256$; $4^5 = 1024$; $5^3 = 125$; $5^4 = 625$
  - Optional ones: $2^7 = 128$; $2^8 = 256$; $2^9 = 512$; $3^5 = 243$; $3^6 = 729$; $6^3 = 216$; $7^3 = 343$; $8^3 = 512$; $9^3 = 729$

Divisibility Rules

- A number is evenly <u>divisible[1] by 2</u> only if it is even.
- A number is evenly <u>divisible by 3</u> only if the sum of the digits is divisible by 3. The nice thing here is that we can *cast out threes* or groups of digits adding to multiples of three (3, 6, 9, 12, etc.). For example, with 65387 we can immediately cast out the 6 and 3 because they are divisible by 3, and then we can cast out the 8 and 7 because they add to 15. This leaves us with just the 5, which is not divisible by 3, so *we conclude that 65387 is not evenly divisible by 3.*
- A number is evenly <u>divisible by 4</u> only if the last two digits are divisible by 4. For example, 6380716 is evenly divisible by 4, because it ends in 16, which is evenly divisible by 4.
- A number is evenly <u>divisible by 5</u> only if the number ends in a 5 or a 0.
- A number is evenly <u>divisible by 9</u> only if the sum of the digits is divisible by 9. Again we can *cast out nines* in order to check divisibility for 9 quickly. If we cast out nines and are left with nothing in the end, then the number is evenly divisible by nine. For example, for 71,284 we cast out the 7 and 2 and then cast out the 8 and 1 and we are left with just a 4, so the whole number is not evenly divisible by nine.
  On the other hand, with 2,381,697 we cast out the 8 and 1, the 6 and 3, the 2 and 7, and the 9, leaving us with nothing. Therefore, we can conclude that 2,381,697 is evenly divisible by nine.
- A number is evenly <u>divisible by 10</u> only if the number ends in a 0.

- *Practice using the divisibility rules to reduce large fractions.*
  Example: Reduce $\frac{132}{420}$

  Solution: We recognize that both the denominator and numerator are evenly divisible by 4 and 3. So after dividing both the denominator and numerator by 4 and 3 we get an answer of $\frac{11}{35}$.

  Example: Reduce $\frac{54}{126}$

  Solution: Dividing both the denominator and numerator by 2 and 9 gives an answer of $\frac{3}{7}$.

  Example: Reduce $\frac{14175}{14850}$

  Solution: Dividing both the denominator and numerator by 9 gives us $\frac{1575}{1650}$, then dividing by 5 gives $\frac{315}{330}$, then dividing by 5 again gives $\frac{63}{66}$, and then finally dividing by 3 gives our answer of $\frac{21}{22}$.

---

[1] "Evenly divisible" means it can be divided with no remainder.

Prime Factorization

- *Don't use factor trees.* While factor trees work, students often don't understand them, and are puzzled about what the final prime factorization is by looking at the tree.
- The best method is to keep breaking down any non-prime number into the product of two more numbers until there are only prime numbers left. The students need to realize that each step in the process is equal.

Example: Find the prime factorization of 700.

Solution: There are several routes to the answer. Below, we show two different ways to arrive at the same answer. Remember that each step represents a different way to express 700 as a product of numbers.

- $700 \to 7 \cdot 100 \to 7 \cdot 2 \cdot 50 \to 7 \cdot 2 \cdot 5 \cdot 10 \to 7 \cdot 2 \cdot 5 \cdot 5 \cdot 2 \to 2 \cdot 2 \cdot 5 \cdot 5 \cdot 7 \to \underline{2^2 \cdot 5^2 \cdot 7}$
- $700 \to 25 \cdot 28 \to 5 \cdot 5 \cdot 28 \to 5 \cdot 5 \cdot 14 \cdot 2 \to 5 \cdot 5 \cdot 7 \cdot 2 \cdot 2 \to 2 \cdot 2 \cdot 5 \cdot 5 \cdot 7 \to \underline{2^2 \cdot 5^2 \cdot 7}$

Example: Find the prime factorization of 208.   (Answer: $2^4 \cdot 13$)

Example: Find the prime factorization of 12375.   (Answer: $3^2 \cdot 5^3 \cdot 11$)

- (optional) *Least common multiples* (LCM) and *greatest common factors* (GCF).
  - Simple cases can easily be done in your head, such as:
    Example: Find the LCM and GCF of 12 and 8.
    Solution: The LCM is $\underline{24}$ and the GCF is $\underline{4}$.
  - For larger numbers, it is useful to use prime factorization in order to determine LCMs and GCFs. Build up to problems like:
    Example: Find the LCM and GCF of 29,040 and 207,900.
    Solution: The prime factorization for 29,040 is $2^4 \cdot 3 \cdot 5 \cdot 11^2$, and for 207,900 is $2^2 \cdot 3^3 \cdot 5^2 \cdot 7 \cdot 11$. The GCF is what is in common for both, therefore: $2^2 \cdot 3 \cdot 5 \cdot 11$, which is $\underline{660}$. The LCM includes everything from both (without duplicating), therefore: $2^4 \cdot 3^3 \cdot 5^2 \cdot 7 \cdot 11^2$, which is $\underline{9,147,600}$.
  - *Common denominators* for "ugly" fractions.
    Example: $\frac{5}{3024} + \frac{11}{576}$
    Solution: The prime factorization of 3024 is $2^4 \cdot 3^3 \cdot 7$ and the prime factorization of 576 is $2^6 \cdot 3^2$, therefore the common denominator (LCM) is $2^6 \cdot 3^3 \cdot 7$ (which is 12096). The first fraction must have its denominator and numerator multiplied by 2^2 (or 4), and the second fraction by $3 \cdot 7$ (or 21). This gives an answer of $\frac{5 \cdot 4}{12096} + \frac{11 \cdot 21}{12096} = \frac{251}{12096}$.

Division

Division and Fractions

- *Think of division as a fraction*
  - Reduce before dividing. (**See Appendix B,** *6th Grade Math Tricks.*)
    Example: $804 \div 44$
    Solution: $804 \div 44$ becomes $\frac{804}{44}$ and is then reduced to $\frac{201}{11}$. The division problem has been made easier. We now can divide 201 by 11, to get an answer of $\underline{18^3/_{11}}$.
    Example: $108 \div 48$ is reduced (by dividing top and bottom by 12) to $9 \div 4$, which is $2\frac{1}{4}$.
  - *Making the divisor easier.* Think Fractions! There are two ways to make the divisor easier:
    - Move the divisor's decimal point all the way to the right.
      Example: $30.17 \div 0.035$ becomes $30170 \div 35$ since we multiply numerator and denominator by 1000, or move the decimal point three places.
    - Chop off ending zeroes by moving the decimal point, which is initially invisible, to the left.
      Example: $173.6 \div 800$ becomes $1.736 \div 8$ since we divide numerator and denominator by 100, which is the same as moving the decimal point two places to the left.

Long Division

- *Vocabulary*
  - The *dividend* is the number that is being divided by the *divisor*. The *quotient* is the answer.

$$\begin{array}{r} 324 \leftarrow \text{Quotient} \\ \text{Divisor} \to 5\overline{)1620} \leftarrow \text{Dividend} \end{array}$$

- *Normal long division.* Practice lots of normal long division problems with divisors up to 4 digits.

- *Don't leave a remainder.* Students should leave their answers either as mixed numbers or as decimals. **Example:** The answer for $58 \div 5$ can be given either as $11^3/_5$ or as 11.6.

- *How do we know if a digit in the answer is too small?* If, at any point during the process, a remainder (before bringing down the next digit) is equal to or larger than the divisor, then you know that the previous digit in your answer was too small. Have students find this error:

$$
\begin{array}{r}
161 \\
47\overline{)7990} \\
-47 \\
\hline
329 \\
-282 \\
\hline
47 \\
-47 \\
\hline
0
\end{array}
$$

- *An explanation of why long division works*
  - Few people really understand why long division works. Giving the students an understanding of *why* it works, helps take the mystery out of it, and helps to develop their thinking.
  - The key to understanding long division is to realize that what we are really doing is figuring out *how many times the divisor can be taken out of the dividend.*
  - With long division, we are removing a multiple of the divisor from the dividend, looking at what is left, then removing more multiples of the divisor from that, and continuing until no more divisors can be taken out of what is left. Our answer is the sum of all the multiples that have been removed. Consider this **example:** $112182 \div 42$ (answer is 2671)

Normally our work looks like this:

$$
\begin{array}{r}
2671 \\
42\overline{)112182} \\
-84 \\
\hline
281 \\
-252 \\
\hline
298 \\
-294 \\
\hline
42 \\
-42 \\
\hline
0
\end{array}
$$

Fully-written, it looks like this:

$$
\begin{array}{r}
2000 + 600 + 70 + 1 = 2671 \\
42\overline{)112182} \\
-84000 \\
\hline
28182 \\
-25200 \\
\hline
2982 \\
-2940 \\
\hline
42 \\
-42 \\
\hline
0
\end{array}
$$

- Looking at our "fully-written" version, we can understand what long division really does. Remembering that what we are trying to figure out is how many 42's can be taken out of 112182, we start by taking out 2000 42's (= 84,000), which leaves us with 28182. We then remove 600 42's (= 25,200) from that, which gives us 2982 left over. From that we remove 70 42's (= 2940), resulting in just one 42 left over. Our final answer is the total number of 42's that have been removed, which, in this case is: 2000 + 600 + 70 + 1, or 2671.

- It is important for the students to understand that long division is just a shorter way of writing our "fully-written" method.

- It is also important to understand that while long division is restricted to working out the answer one digit at a time, and that each of those digits must be correct, that our "fully-written" method is not restricted in this way. For example, instead of removing 2000 42's, followed by 600 42's, followed by 70 42's and then finally one 42, we can (somewhat randomly) first remove 1500 42's, and, from what's left over, we could next remove 800 42's, and then 120 42's, and then 240 42's, and lastly 11 42's, and the result would be the same!

$$
\begin{array}{r}
1500 + 800 + 120 + 240 + 11 = 2671 \\
42\overline{)112182} \\
-63000 \\
\hline
49182 \\
-33600 \\
\hline
15582 \\
-5040 \\
\hline
10542 \\
-10080 \\
\hline
462 \\
-462 \\
\hline
0
\end{array}
$$

Sixth Grade

- *Making difficult division problems easier by rounding.* (Should be done in fifth grade.)
  - Students should be able to quickly estimate how many times the divisor goes into a remainder (at any point during the process) with reasonable accuracy.
  - It is very important for students to practice this. It increases their speed for doing long division, and develops a flexible sense of numbers.

A Key Example: 293346÷387

Solution: *It is important for the students to understand the following reasoning.*

They should immediately round the divisor to 400, and then they can ignore the ending zeroes. Therefore, the first question that they should be asking themselves with this problem is: *How many times does 4 go into 29?* instead of: How many times does 387 go into 2933? Since 4 goes into 29 seven times, we can make a fairly good guess that 387 goes into 2933 also seven times. We continue the long division problem in the normal way: writing the 7 above the house (as the first digit in our answer), then multiplying 7 times 387 to get 2709, and subtracting that from 2933, to get 224. Since 224 is less than 387 (our divisor), we know that 7 wasn't too small. Now we bring down the 4 and combine that with our remainder to get 2244. The problem now looks like this:

```
           7
    387 |293346
        -2709
        ------
         2244
```

Normally, people would now ask themselves: How many times does 387 go into 2244? but it is much easier to ask: *How many times does 4 go in 22?* The answer to this question is 5, which tells us that 387 probably goes into 2244 five times also. So we write the 5 down next to the 7 (as the next digit in our answer), multiply the 5 by 387 to get 1935, then subtract that from 2244 to get a remainder of 309, and bring down the 6. After all this, our problem now looks like this:

```
          75
    387 |293346
        -2709
        ------
         2244
        -1935
        ------
         3096
```

Once again we ask the easier question, not: How many times does 387 go into 3096, but rather, *How many times does 4 go into 31?* (Notice that we said 31 because 3096 rounds up to 3100.) Now, we ought to think that 4 goes into 31 seven times, but it is almost eight times. In fact, because we had initially rounded 387 to 400, then we should have a sense that our estimate of how many times 387 goes into 3096, could possibly be 8 instead of 7. But we can't be sure. If we first tried 7, and multiplied 7 times 387 to get 2709, and subtracted that from 3096 then we would get a remainder of 387, which tells us that we could have gotten one more 387 out of 3096 – in other words, 8 instead of 7. It turns out that 8 was our correct answer for the third digit is 8. The final result is shown below with an answer of 758.

```
         758
    387 |293346
        -2709
        ------
         2244
        -1935
        ------
         3096
        -3096
        ------
            0
```

<u>Short Division</u> for single digit divisors. (Should be introduced in third or fourth grade.)

Example: 58741÷7 (leave answer as a mixed number).

Step 1: 7 goes into 58 eight times with a remainder of 2

$$\begin{array}{r} 8 \\ 7\overline{)\,5\;8\;{}^2 7\;4\;1} \end{array}$$

Step 2: 7 goes into 27 three times with a remainder of 6.

$$\begin{array}{r} 8\;3 \\ 7\overline{)\,5\;8\;{}^2 7\;{}^6 4\;1} \end{array}$$

Step 3: 7 goes into 64 nine times with a remainder of 1.

$$\begin{array}{r} 8\;3\;9 \\ 7\overline{)\,5\;8\;{}^2 7\;{}^6 4\;{}^1 1} \end{array}$$

Step 4: 7 goes into 11 once with a remainder of 4. We then put this remainder over the divisor, thereby forming the fractional part of the mixed number.

$$\begin{array}{r} 8\;3\;9\;1\,{}^4/_7\;\leftarrow \text{answer} \\ 7\overline{)\,5\;8\;{}^2 7\;{}^6 4\;{}^1 1} \end{array}$$

<u>Checking Answers</u> by multiplying. Check answers also when the answer is a mixed number.

Example: Checking the answer to the above problem: $8391 \cdot 7 + 4 \rightarrow 58741$ correct!

Fractions

- Give a few fraction problems on every homework assignment throughout the sixth grade year. They need to get to the point that doing anything with fractions is easy.

Review from Fourth and Fifth Grade

- *Fractions aren't just pizza!*
  - See *Separation of Form and Number* in the introduction for the reason why an over-emphasis on the pizza image isn't good.
  - It's OK to show a couple "pizza problem" examples, but it needs to be pointed out that this is just one application in the real world for the concept of fractions. Be sure not to over-emphasize the pizza image, or to say "in order to understand fractions, we just need to picture a pizza".
- *Fractions are part of the whole.*
  - The denominator tells us how many parts the whole has been divided into, and the numerator tells us how many of those parts are present.
    Example: With $^5/_8$, we have divided the whole into 8 equal parts and we have 5 of those parts.
  - This helps to answer the following questions. It is helpful to give a few different examples to illustrate each one. For example, using $¾ = ^6/_8$, we can show how it can be applied to a group of 24 people, or to a sum of money (e.g., $24), or to a block of cheese (e.g., 24 ounces).
    - *Why* is $¾ = ^6/_8$? Eighths are half as large as fourths. So, it follows that $^6/_8$ represents twice as many parts that are half as large as $¾$, and if we take twice as many things that are half as large, then we have not changed the amount.
    - *Why* is $2¾ = {}^{11}/_4$? The two wholes (from $2¾$) can also be divided into fourths, thereby producing 8 fourths. Combining these 8 fourths with the 3 fourths (from $2¾$) gives us 11 fourths, or ${}^{11}/_4$.
    - *Why do we need a common denominator* to add or subtract fractions? Using $^2/_5 + ^3/_7$ as an example, we should point out that in the same way that we can't (directly) add together 2 dollars and 3 pesos, we also can't add together 2 fifths and 3 sevenths. And just as we could convert the dollars into pesos and then add that result to 3 pesos to get an answer, we can convert one fraction or (in this case) both fractions so that they will have the same size parts, and then we can add them. The common-sized part for $^2/_5 + ^3/_7$ is 35ths, so we change both fractions to these common-sized parts (denominators) and get ${}^{14}/_{35} + {}^{15}/_{35}$, giving us an answer of ${}^{29}/_{35}$.
    - *How can we think of doubling* $^3/_8$? We can either double the number of parts (the numerator), which gives us $^6/_8$ for an answer, or we can make the size of the parts (the denominator) twice as big - so instead of eighths we have fourths, and our answer is $¾$.
    - *How can we think of taking half of* $^4/_5$? We can either take half the number of parts, which gives us $^2/_5$ for an answer, or we can make the size of the parts twice as small - so instead of fifths we have tenths, and our answer is $^4/_{10}$.

- *Reducing fractions.*
  - Give reducing fractions as practice problems, such as:

    Example: Reduce $\frac{810}{4455}$

    Solution: We can see that the top and bottom are both divisible by 9. (**See** *Divisibility Rules*, above.) After dividing both the top and bottom by 9, we get $\frac{90}{495}$. Then we divide by 5 to get $\frac{18}{99}$. Lastly we divide by 9 to get a final answer of $\frac{2}{11}$.
  - Reducing fractions gets naturally mixed in with most fraction problems as it is expected that all answers with fractions should be in reduced form.

- *Fractions are division.*
  - The bar in a fraction is a division sign; therefore a fraction is an "undone" division problem.

    Example: $\frac{37}{3}$ is really the division problem $37 \div 3$, which is $12\frac{1}{3}$.
  - A fraction over a fraction is actually the same as a fraction divided by a fraction. The short cut is to take the denominator, flip it, and multiply by the numerator. Students need to see this frequently for it to sink in completely.

    Example: $\frac{5/8}{3/4}$ is the same as $\frac{5}{8} \div \frac{3}{4}$. This then becomes $\frac{5}{8} \cdot \frac{4}{3}$, giving a final answer of $\frac{5}{6}$.

- *"Of" means multiply.*

  Example: What is $^3/_7$ of 28?

  Solution: This is really $^3/_7$ times 28. Therefore we do $\frac{3}{7} \cdot \frac{28}{1} = \underline{12}$.

- *Mixed numbers.*
  - Practice *converting improper fractions into mixed numbers* and back.

    Example: What is $\frac{34}{5}$ as a mixed number? (Answer: $6\frac{4}{5}$)

    Example: What is $7\frac{2}{3}$ as an improper fraction? (Answer: $\frac{23}{3}$)
  - *Multiplying and dividing* mixed numbers: You need to first convert them to improper fractions.

    Example: $2\frac{4}{5} \cdot 3\frac{1}{3}$

    Solution: A common mistake is to multiply separately the 2 and 3 and then the $\frac{4}{5}$ and the $\frac{1}{3}$, giving a wrong answer of $6\frac{4}{15}$. Instead, we get the correct answer by first converting to improper fractions: $2\frac{4}{5} \cdot 3\frac{1}{3} \rightarrow \frac{14}{5} \cdot \frac{10}{3} \rightarrow$ cross canceling $\rightarrow \frac{14}{1} \cdot \frac{2}{3} \rightarrow \frac{28}{3} \rightarrow$ our answer is $\underline{9\frac{1}{3}}$.
  - *Adding and subtracting mixed numbers*: It's not necessary to convert them to improper fractions.

    Example: With $5\frac{2}{3} + 3\frac{1}{4}$, first add 5 and 3, then add $\frac{2}{3}$ and $\frac{1}{4}$, giving a result of $\underline{8^{11}/_{12}}$.
  - Mixed numbers are best for final answers (e.g., for word problems).

Comparing Fractions and Decimals

- Sometimes fractions are easier than decimals.

  Example: Calculate $85 \div 7$ both as a (repeating) decimal and as a mixed number.

  Solution: As a fraction, we get $12^1/_7$, and as a decimal, we get $\underline{12.\overline{142857}}$.

  Example: Calculate $450 \div 1.875$ (decimal) versus $450 \div {}^{15}/_8$ (fraction).

  Solution: The first is found by doing long division. The second is $\frac{450}{1} \cdot \frac{8}{15}$. Both give an answer of $\underline{240}$.

- With decimals it's easy to compare the size of two numbers. With fractions, it may not be so obvious.

  Example: Which is larger (and by how much): $\frac{13}{35}$ or $\frac{3}{8}$?

  Solution: We see that the two fractions have a common denominator of 280 (which is 35 times 8). $\frac{13}{35}$ then becomes $\frac{104}{280}$ and $\frac{3}{8}$ becomes $\frac{105}{280}$. Therefore we can say that $\frac{3}{8}$ is larger by $\frac{1}{280}$.

Compound Fractions

- Build up to problems like these:

Example: Simplify $\dfrac{3\frac{1}{2}-1\frac{2}{3}}{\frac{2\frac{1}{5}}{2\frac{7}{10}}}$

Solution: Converting to improper fractions makes the numerator $\frac{7}{2} - \frac{5}{3}$, which becomes $\frac{11}{6}$. The denominator is $\frac{12}{5} \div \frac{27}{10}$, which simplifies to $\frac{8}{9}$. We now have $\frac{11}{6}$ over $\frac{8}{9}$, which is also $\frac{11}{6} \div \frac{8}{9} \rightarrow \frac{11}{6} \cdot \frac{9}{8} \rightarrow \frac{33}{16} \rightarrow$ so the answer is $\underline{2\frac{1}{16}}$.

Example: Simplify $\dfrac{2\frac{1}{3} - \frac{\frac{1}{2}+\frac{1}{3}}{2} - \frac{1}{4}\cdot\frac{1}{3}}{\frac{1}{2-\frac{4}{5}} + 1}$

Solution: Starting with the middle of the numerator, we simplify $\frac{1}{2} + \frac{1}{3}$ to $\frac{5}{6}$. $\frac{5}{6}$ over 2 can be seen as $\frac{5}{6} \div \frac{2}{1}$, which is $\frac{5}{12}$. Simplifying the other parts of the numerator leads to the whole numerator becoming $\frac{7}{3} - \frac{5}{12} - \frac{1}{12}$, which simplifies to $\frac{22}{12}$, or $\frac{11}{6}$. Now working on the denominator, we simplify $2 - \frac{4}{5}$ to $\frac{6}{5}$. We now have 1 over $\frac{6}{5}$, which is the same as $\frac{1}{1} \div \frac{6}{5}$, which becomes $\frac{5}{6}$. The whole denominator is this number plus 1, which makes it $\frac{11}{6}$, which happens to be the same as the whole numerator, therefore leading to a final answer of $\underline{1}$.

Example: Simplify $\dfrac{2}{2 - \frac{2}{2-\frac{1}{2}}}$

Solution: In the small denominator we have $2 - \frac{1}{2}$, which is $\frac{3}{2}$. We now have 2 over $\frac{3}{2}$, which is $\frac{2}{1} \div \frac{3}{2}$, which becomes $\frac{4}{3}$. The whole denominator is now $2 - \frac{4}{3}$, which becomes $\frac{2}{3}$. The entire fraction is then 2 over $\frac{2}{3}$, which becomes $\frac{2}{1} \cdot \frac{3}{2}$, which gives a final answer of $\underline{3}$.

Example: Simplify $\dfrac{3}{3 - \frac{3}{3-\frac{1}{3}}}$

Solution: Following the same procedure as the problem above, we get an answer of $\underline{1\frac{3}{5}}$.

Example: Simplify $\dfrac{3}{3 - \frac{3}{3-\frac{3}{3-\frac{1}{3}}}}$

Solution: Plugging in the answer to the previous problem into this problem, we get 3 over $3 - 1\frac{3}{5}$. $3 - 1\frac{3}{5}$ simplifies to $1\frac{2}{5}$, which is $\frac{7}{5}$. The whole fraction is now 3 over $\frac{7}{5}$, which gives an answer of $\frac{15}{7}$ or $\underline{2\frac{1}{7}}$.

Decimals

Review from Fifth Grade

- *General concepts.*
  - *A decimal is a fraction* with a special denominator (10, 100, 1000, etc.)
    Example: Think of 0.37 as $\frac{37}{100}$ which is 37 parts, where each part is one-hundredth of the whole.
  - *Reading decimals*: 0.34 should be said as thirty-four-hundredths (NOT point three four). This reinforces the connection between decimals and fractions. In seventh and eighth grade, reading "point three four" is OK.
- *Arithmetic with decimals.*
  - *Do lots of practice using the four processes* with decimals.
  - Multiply and divide by 10, 100, 1000, etc. (**See Appendix B,** *6th Grade Math Tricks.*)
    - This must be done with ease.

Fraction to Decimal Conversions

- Convert fractions into decimals by dividing.
  - At first, only do examples that don't result in repeating decimals. Later give examples that result in repeating decimals (**see** *Repeating Decimals*, below). In each case, we divide the numerator by the denominator.
    Examples: $\frac{3}{8} \rightarrow 0.375$; $\frac{5}{16} \rightarrow 0.3125$; $\frac{31}{40} \rightarrow 0.775$

- *Memorize the following key fraction/decimal conversions:*
  Note: A line over decimal places means that those digits repeat. (i.e., $5.3\overline{72}$ means 5.3727272...)

½ = 0.5	$^1/_5 = 0.2$	$^1/_6 = 0.1\overline{6}$	$^1/_8 = 0.125$	$^1/_9 = 0.\overline{1}$
$^1/_3 = 0.\overline{3}$	$^2/_5 = 0.4$	$^5/_6 = 0.8\overline{3}$	$^3/_8 = 0.375$	$^2/_9 = 0.\overline{2}$
$^2/_3 = 0.\overline{6}$	$^3/_5 = 0.6$		$^5/_8 = 0.625$	$^4/_9 = 0.\overline{4}$
¼ = 0.25	$^4/_5 = 0.8$		$^7/_8 = 0.875$	$^5/_9 = 0.\overline{5}$
¾ = 0.75				$^7/_9 = 0.\overline{7}$
				$^8/_9 = 0.\overline{8}$

- *The trick for elevenths, and twentieths.*
  - The students don't need to memorize the following fraction to decimal conversions for the 11ths and the 20ths, but should be able to do it easily in their head.
  - *Elevenths*: Multiply the numerator by 9, and make that product repeat itself.
    - Give the students a few examples (e.g., $^3/_{11}$; $^7/_{11}$; $^8/_{11}$) and see if they can discover the trick for themselves!
    Example: Convert $^4/_{11}$ into a decimal.
    Solution: Instead of dividing 11 into 4, we can just multiply 4 times 9, giving a result of $0.\overline{36}$.
  - *Twentieths*: Multiply the numerator by 5, and place that after the decimal place, without repeating. The nifty short cut here is to "*think nickels*", because a nickel is worth $^1/_{20}$ of a dollar. For example, $^7/_{20}$ is thought of as 7 nickels, which is 35 cents, or 0.35 in dollars.
    Example: Convert $^{11}/_{20}$ into a decimal.
    Solution: We multiply 11 times 5, giving a result of 0.55.

Decimal to Fraction Conversions

- Simply make a fraction with 10, 100, 1000, etc. in the denominator and then reduce.
  Example: What is 0.075 as a fraction?
  Solution: This is $\frac{75}{1000}$ which reduces to $\frac{3}{40}$.

Repeating Decimals

- For additional ideas on repeating decimals **see Appendix C**, *Questions Regarding Repeating Decimals.*
- Emphasize that a division problem starts to repeat when a remainder is encountered for the second time.
- Even though any division problem will eventually repeat or end, you should make sure that the division problem is worked out ahead of time, so that the number of digits that repeat is manageable.
- (For the teacher only) *How to determine the number of digits that will appear under the repeat bar.*
  - It is useful to know this, so that when a division problem is given with an answer as a repeating decimal, you can know how difficult the problem is, based upon what the divisor is.
  - Recall that any division problem can be looked at as a fraction whereby we divide the numerator by the denominator. Assuming the fraction that we're given is already reduced, we can say that *the number of digits that will appear under the repeat bar depends only on what the denominator (divisor) is*.
  - The following list shows how many digits repeat (fall under the repeat bar) given various denominators:
    - The following denominators lead to decimals that end without repeating. (Notice that the prime factorization of each one consists only of powers of 2 and 5. **See 6th Grade Arithmetic**, *Other Topics: Prime Factorization.*):
      2, 4, 5, 8, 10, 16, 20, 25, 32, 40, 50, 64, 80, 100...
    - The following denominators lead to decimals that repeat every one digit. (Notice that the prime factorization of each one has one or two 3's, and any amount of 2's or 5's.):
      3, 6, 9, 12, 15, 18, 24, 30, 36, 45, 48, 60...
    - These denominators lead to decimals that repeat every two digits: 11, 22, 33, 44, 55, 66, 88, 99...
    - These denominators lead to decimals that repeat every three digits: 37, 74, 111...and 27, 54 (not 81)
    - These denominators lead to decimals that repeat every four digits: 101, 202, 303...and 1111, 2222..
    - These denominators lead to decimals that repeat every five digits: 41, 82, 123... and 271, 542...
    - These denominators lead to decimals that repeat every six digits: 7, 14, 21...and 13, 26, 39...
      also 143; 259; 297; 351; 407; 481.
    - These denominators lead to decimals that repeat every seven digits: 239, 478... and 4649, 9298...
    - These denominators lead to decimals that repeat every eight digits: 73, 146... and 137, 274...

- These denominators lead to decimals that repeat every nine digits: 81, 162... and 333667 (really!)

Example: $8 \div 37 \rightarrow 0.\overline{216}$
Example: $173 \div 808 \rightarrow 0.214\overline{1089}$
Example: $39 \div 64 \rightarrow 0.609375$ (doesn't repeat)

- Denominators that have just one digit repeated multiple times give an answer with the same number of digits under the repeat bar (except for sevens). For example, if we divide 273956 by 88888, then we know that the answer will have 5 digits under the repeat bar because with 88888 there is only one digit (an eight), and it repeats itself five times.
  - With these examples, we do long division and divide the numerator by the denominator:
    Example: $871 \div 1111 \rightarrow 0.\overline{7839}$
    Example: $179 \div 444 \rightarrow 0.40\overline{315}$

Division Problems with Repeating Decimals

- Do many of these.
- These can be done as straightforward division problems, or as problems that convert fractions into decimals.
- Notice how each one has a number of digits repeating that is consistent with the rules stated directly above.
  Example: $10 \div 13$ (or $^{10}/_{13}$)   (Answer: $0.\overline{769230}$)
  Example: $21 \div 88$ (or $^{21}/_{88}$)   (Answer: $0.238\overline{63}$)
  Example: $133 \div 54$ (or $^{133}/_{54}$)   (Answer: $2.4\overline{629}$)
  Example: $53 \div 81$ (or $^{53}/_{81}$)   (Answer: $0.\overline{654320987}$)

Converting Repeating Decimals to Fractions

- This topic stretches and develops the sixth grader's thinking in an age-appropriate way. It also helps the students to develop an appreciation of how numbers work.
- This topic is revisited in eighth grade, when the students learn how to use algebra to convert repeating decimals into fractions, and in tenth grade, when the students study repeating decimals as an infinite series.
- *Fractions with 9, 99, or 999, etc. in the denominator.* (**See Appendix B,** *6th Grade Math Tricks.*)
  - Give the students a few of these problems converting the fractions into repeating decimals, and they should be able to quickly see the pattern.
  - Practice many conversion problems in both directions (both by converting fractions into repeating decimals and repeating decimals into fractions) such as:

    Example: $\dfrac{7}{9}$ $\longleftrightarrow$ $0.\overline{7}$

    Example: $\dfrac{37}{99}$ $\longleftrightarrow$ $0.\overline{37}$

    Example: $\dfrac{13}{999}$ $\longleftrightarrow$ $0.\overline{013}$

    Example: $\dfrac{2503}{9999}$ $\longleftrightarrow$ $0.\overline{2503}$

- *Fractions with 90, 900, 990, 9900, 9990, etc. in the denominator.*
  - These are slight variations to the above problems.
  - To avoid unnecessary complications, make sure that the number of digits in the numerator is no more than the number of nines in the denominator.
  - The students should be able to discover for themselves that the number of nines in the denominator indicates the number of digits that will repeat in the answer, and the number of zeroes in the denominator indicates how many zeroes will be between the answer's decimal point and repeat bar.
  - Practice many conversion problems in both directions, such as:

    Example: $\dfrac{7}{90}$ $\longleftrightarrow$ $0.0\overline{7}$

    Example: $\dfrac{37}{990}$ $\longleftrightarrow$ $0.0\overline{37}$

    Example: $\dfrac{37}{9900}$ $\longleftrightarrow$ $0.00\overline{37}$

    Example: $\dfrac{19}{9990000}$ $\longleftrightarrow$ $0.0000\overline{019}$

- *General conversions of repeating decimals into fractions.*
  - This is fairly complicated and difficult for the students, but in the end, it is quite rewarding.
  - The idea is to determine the fractional equivalent of the repeating part and the non-repeating part separately, and then to add the results together for a final answer.

  Example: Convert $0.31\overline{6}$ into a fraction.

  Solution: Separating the two parts, we know that 0.31 is $\frac{31}{100}$ and that $0.00\overline{6}$ is $\frac{6}{900}$ as a fraction. $0.31\overline{6}$ can therefore be written as $\frac{31}{100} + \frac{6}{900}$. Getting common denominators and adding these two fractions gives us $\frac{285}{900}$ which reduces to a final answer of $\frac{19}{60}$.

  Example: Convert $0.147\overline{72}$ into a fraction.

  Solution: Separating the two parts, we know that 0.147 is $\frac{147}{1000}$ and that $0.000\overline{72}$ is $\frac{72}{99000}$ as a fraction (don't reduce it!). Getting common denominators and adding these two fractions gives us $\frac{14625}{99000}$ which reduces to a final answer of $\frac{13}{88}$.

  Example (challenge!): Convert $0.028\overline{4653}$ into a fraction.

  Solution: Separating the two parts, we know that 0.028 is $\frac{28}{1000}$ and that $0.000\overline{4653}$ is $\frac{4653}{9999000}$ as a fraction. Adding these two fractions gives us $\frac{284625}{9999000}$ which reduces (by dividing top and bottom by 25, then 5, then 9, and then 11) to a final answer of $\frac{23}{808}$.

Business Math Main Lesson
(Including Percents, Formulas, and Graphing)

A Few Thoughts on this Main Lesson

- *An Integrated Main Lesson.* If planned carefully, this three-week main lesson can include an introduction to percents, business math, formulas (algebra), and graphing.
- Business Math (Economics). In order to teach this main lesson, I recommend reading Ernst Schuberth's book, *The Mathematics Lessons for the Sixth Grade* (AWSNA Publications).
- What is listed here is too much to cover in one main lesson, and therefore much of the material on percents will need to be continued in the track class.

Keys to Success for Percents

- Emphasize that *a percent is a special fraction with 100 in the denominator.*
- Also emphasize that the big advantage of percents is that we can easily convert from a decimal into a percent by moving the decimal point over two places (e.g., $0.71 = 71\%$). This is because we are converting the decimal into a fraction that has 100 in the denominator, so we are essentially multiplying the numerator and denominator by 100, which moves the decimal point two places.
- *Keep it simple!* If you do too much with percents in sixth grade, the students will not be able to take it all in. The goal here is to lay the foundation which can then be built upon in the next two years.
- Practice lots of problems that can be done fairly easily in the head; avoid percent problems that require difficult calculations until seventh or eighth grade.
- Save *strange percents* (e.g., 200%, 12.53%, 0.04%) for seventh grade.
- Use formulas only well after the concepts have been introduced, allowing the students to first develop a good sense for percents.
- *Don't rely on pictures* (e.g., imagining a cylinder that is 80% full) in order to help the students "understand" percents.
  - See, also, *Separation of Form and Number* in the introduction.
- *Whenever students get stuck* they should remember that a **per**cent is simply the number of parts **per** one hundred (cent), and then retry doing the problem.
- Represent some answers to problems graphically (with a bar graph or pie chart).

Percent to Fraction Conversions
(to be calculated and then memorized)

$^1/_{100} = 1\%$ $^1/_{10} = 10\%$ $\frac{1}{2} = 50\%$ $^1/_5 = 20\%$ $^1/_6 = 16\frac{2}{3}\%$

$^1/_{50} = 2\%$ $^3/_{10} = 30\%$ $^2/_5 = 40\%$ $^5/_6 = 83\frac{1}{3}\%$

$^1/_{25} = 4\%$ $^7/_{10} = 70\%$ $\frac{1}{3} = 33\frac{1}{3}\%$ $^3/_5 = 60\%$

$^1/_{20} = 5\%$ $^9/_{10} = 90\%$ $\frac{2}{3} = 66\frac{2}{3}\%$ $^4/_5 = 80\%$ $^1/_8 = 12\frac{1}{2}\%$

     $^3/_8 = 37\frac{1}{2}\%$

$\frac{1}{4} = 25\%$ $^5/_8 = 62\frac{1}{2}\%$

$\frac{3}{4} = 75\%$ $^7/_8 = 87\frac{1}{2}\%$

Determining a Certain Percent of a Given Number

- I teach three different ways to do this. The students should use the easiest method, which varies depending on the problem.

1. *Looking at it as a division problem.* (Most important!)
   - This method of changing a percent problem into a division problem only works for these percents: 50% (we divide by 2); 33⅓% (we divide by 3); 25% (we divide by 4); 20% (we divide by 5); 10% (we divide by 10); 1% (we divide by 100)

   Example: What is 25% of 320?

   Solution: Recognizing that 25% is ¼, we rephrase the question as "What is ¼ of 320?", which is really $320 \div 4$, which gives us an answer of <u>80</u>.

2. *Converting to a fraction and multiplying.*

   Example: What is 80% of 350?

   Solution: Since 80% is $^4/_5$, we get $\frac{4}{5} \cdot \frac{350}{1}$ which is <u>280</u>.

3. *Converting to a decimal and multiplying.*

   Example: What is 31% of 62?

   Solution: $0.31 \times 62 \rightarrow$ <u>19.22</u>

   - Don't over-emphasize this process; students could end up blindly using it for all percent problems.
   - Especially make sure that students don't use this method for ones that can be done more easily using one of the two above methods, such as: What is 25% of 320?

Determining a Percentage

- Have the students practice lots of these.
- In order to determine a percentage, the students should *think of a fraction.*
- It is important for the students to learn all three of the following methods, as it helps to develop speed and mental agility. They should use the easiest method, which varies depending on the problem.

1. *The fraction is (or reduces to) something that they have memorized the percentage for.*

   Example: 240 is what percent of 400?

   Solution: $\frac{240}{400}$ reduces to $\frac{3}{5}$ which is <u>60%</u>. ($^3/_5 = 60\%$ should be memorized.)

2. *The fraction can easily have its denominator changed to 100.*

   Example: 7 is what percent of 25?

   Solution: We multiply the top and bottom of $\frac{7}{25}$ by 4, which gives us $\frac{28}{100}$ which is <u>28%</u>.

3. *The fraction is first converted into a decimal by dividing the numerator by the denominator.*
   - This method is *always* possible but often slower. Students should only use it when the previous two methods aren't feasible.

   Example: 270 is what percent of 2400?

   Solution: $\frac{270}{2400}$ reduces to $\frac{9}{80}$ and dividing 80 into 9, we get 0.1125, which is <u>11.25%</u>.

   Example: On a 75-question test, Fred answered 62 questions correctly. On a 70-question test, John answered 59 questions correctly. Who got a higher percentage correct?

   Solution: Fred got $\frac{62}{75}$ of the test correct, which is 82⅔% or $82.\overline{6}\%$ correct, and John got $\frac{59}{70}$ correct, which is $84^2/_7\%$ or $\approx 84.3\%$ correct. Therefore, John got a higher percentage correct.

Percent Increase and Decrease Problems

- *Increasing or decreasing a number by a certain percent.*
    - Start with very simple problems, and then build up to problems like these:
      Example: What is 430 increased by 20%?
      Solution: 20% of 430 is 430÷5, which is 86. We then increase 430 by 86 to get an answer of 516.
      Example: What is 60 decreased by 15%?
      Solution: Since 15% of 60 is 9, we decrease 60 by 9 to get an answer of 51.
- *Calculating the percentage of increase or decrease.* These types of problems (e.g., Going from 16 to 20 is what percentage increase?) should be saved for seventh grade, after the students have had some time to "digest" their introduction to percents in sixth grade.

Profit, Commission, and Tax

- Profit, commission, and tax are all percent increase problems. (See *Percent Increase and Decrease Problems*, above.)
  Example (Profit): If Bill makes chairs at cost of $36, including parts and labor, what must his selling price be if he wants to make a 30% profit?
  Solution: 30% of 36 is $10.80, which is his profit on each chair. So he should sell each chair for $36+$10.80, which is $46.80.

  Example (Commission): If a real estate agent makes a commission of 2% when he sells a house, then how much money does he earn if he sells a house for $348,000?
  Solution: 2% of $348,000 gives him a commission of $6960.

  Example (Tax): If a bicycle in a shop is marked at $260, then what must you pay if the tax rate is 7%?
  Solution: 7% of 260 is $18.20, which is the amount of tax. The total price is 260+18.20, which is $278.20.

Interest

- *Comparing simple interest and compound interest.*
    - Simple interest is *not* what is done with most bank accounts, therefore it should be taught from a historical perspective. For example, it could be pointed out that a long time ago moneylenders gave out loans on the basis of simple interest, because it made the calculations easier. At some point later, it was decided that simple interest wasn't fair, and therefore compound interest came into being.
      Example: To show the difference between simple and compound interest, imagine that John has a loan for $500 at 10% simple interest, and that Sue has a loan for $500 at 10% interest compounded annually. Each loan is for two years.
      With both Sue and John, they will owe $50 in interest after the first year. The difference comes in the second year. Because John's loan is simple interest, the interest for the second year is based only upon the amount of the initial loan – so he will owe $50 interest again for the second year. Sue's loan, on the other hand, is determined differently. Compounded interest means that the interest is calculated based upon the total current debt at that point, which is the initial loan *plus any interest accrued up to that point.* Therefore, the interest that Sue owes for the second year is calculated by taking 10% of $550 (which is 500 +50), which means that she owes $55 in interest for the second year.
      Therefore, at the end of the two years, John will owe $100 in interest, and Sue will owe $105 in interest.
- *Calculating simple interest.*
    - Students should first be able to do simple interest problems without the formula. Later they learn how to use the formula (see *Business Formulas*, below). This helps them to understand that the formula isn't just some mysterious thing; it expresses something that they already know, but in the *language of algebra.*
      Example: Kate agrees to loan $800 to Jeff at 5% simple interest. How much interest will Jeff need to pay to Kate after 4 years?
      Solution: The interest for a single year is 5% of $800, which is $40. After four years, Jeff will owe 4·40 = $160 in interest.
- *Calculating compound interest* should be delayed until seventh grade.

Discount and Loss

- Discount and loss problems are really percent decrease problems. (See *Percent Increase and Decrease Problems*, above.)

  Example: If a clothing store is offering a sale of 35% off all its marked prices, then what is the new discounted price of a jacket that was originally marked at $119?

  Solution: 35% of 119 is a discount of 41.65, giving a new price of 119−41.65, which is $77.35.

Rate of Pay

Note: "per" means "for each", and in a word problem it is a division symbol.

Example: How long does it take Sue to earn $2000 if she is paid $12.50/hr, and she works 25 hrs/week?

Solution: We divide 2000 by 12.5 to find that it takes 160 hours to earn $2000. To get the number of weeks, we see that 25 goes into 160 six times with 10 hours left over. Therefore our answer is that in order for Sue to earn $2000 she must work 6 weeks and 10 hours.

Example: What is the hourly rate of pay for someone that has an annual salary of $75,000 per year, given a 40-hour workweek and two weeks of vacation annually?

Solution: Working 50 weeks per year and 40 hours per week means that they work a total of 2000 hours per year. Dividing 2000 into 75000 gives an hourly wage of $37.50 per hour.

Example: If Morgan gets paid $4.50 per hour for babysitting, then how much does he earn babysitting for 3 hours and 20 minutes?

Solution: 20 minutes is ⅓ of an hour, so we do: $4.50·3⅓, which is $4.5·\frac{10}{3}$ and gives an answer of $15.

The Unitary Method and Unit Cost.

- These are good problems for the students to practice frequently, and to get good at.
- This is used for determining the cost of items sold at a certain cost per unit.

  Example: If 7 pens cost $3.64, then how much do 12 pens cost?

  Solution: The "unitary method" requires us to first calculate the unit cost. With this example we divide 3.64 by 7, giving us a unit cost of $0.52 per pen. 12 pens then cost 12 x 0.52, which is $6.24.

  Example: If 2½-pounds of cheese costs $10.98, then what is its unit cost per pound, and per ounce?

  Solution: The cost per pound is 10.98÷2.5, which is $4.39/lb. The cost per ounce is thus divided by 16, which is about 27.5¢/oz.

Temperature Conversion Formulas $\qquad C = \frac{5}{9}(F - 32) \qquad F = \frac{9}{5}C + 32$

- This serves (done in track class) as an introduction to formulas before the *Business Math* main lesson.
- I don't explain why these formulas work – they are perhaps a bit "magical", giving the students a sense of the power of formulas. This changes during the business math main lesson, when the business formulas (see *business formulas*, below) show that formulas express something we are already familiar with.

C°	F°
35	95
30	86
25	77
20	68
15	59
10	50
5	41
0	32

- It helps to relate the two temperature scales by thinking of a thermometer that has both Fahrenheit and Celsius. At the freezing point of water we see that 32°F = 0°C. From there, every increase of 5°C is exactly equal to an increase of 9°F, as can be seen on the thermometer on the right. This also sheds light on where the above formulas come from.
- Avoid problems that deal with negative numbers (e.g., 10 degrees below zero) until seventh grade.

  Example: 30°C is what in Fahrenheit?

  Solution: Putting 30 into C in the second formula, we get $F = \frac{9}{5}(30) + 32$, which gives an answer of 86°F.

Business Formulas

- Formulas serve as an introduction to the concept of a variable, and give the students a brief glimpse into the thinking behind algebra.
- Before introducing each business formula, the students should first be able to easily do each problem without using a formula. This helps them to understand that the formula isn't just some mysterious thing; it expresses something that they already know, but in the *language of algebra*. Otherwise, the students will just use the formulas blindly, without a real understanding of what they are doing.
  - *Rate of pay* $\$ = R \cdot T$ where $\$$ is the amount of pay, R is rate of pay, T is time
  - *Simple interest* $I = P \cdot R \cdot T$ where I is the amount of interest owed, T is the number of years, P is the principle (or size of loan), and R is percent tax rate expressed as a decimal or fraction.

    Example: Using the same example as above (see *Calculating Simple Interest*, above): Kate agrees to loan $800 to Jeff at 5% simple interest. How much interest will Jeff need to pay to Kate after 4 years?
    Solution: P = 800; R = 5%, which is 0.05 as a decimal; T = 4. Therefore I = 800·0.05·4 = $160.
  - *Price after Tax* $F = B + B \cdot R$ where F is final price, B is base price, and R is percent tax rate expressed as a decimal or fraction.

    Example: How much do you have to pay for a shirt marked at $28 if there is 4% tax?
    Solution: The base price (B) is 28, and the tax rate (R) is 0.04. Therefore, we do:
    F = 28 + 28·0.04, which means that the final price is $29.12.
  - *Discount Price* $F = B - B \cdot R$ where F is final price, B is base price, and R is discount rate expressed as a decimal or fraction.

    Example: What is the new price of a bike that was originally marked at $320, if it is on sale at a 30% discount?
    Solution: The base price (B) is 320, and the discount rate (R) is 0.3. Therefore, we do:
    F = 320 − 320·0.3, which means that the final price (before tax) is $224.
- Perhaps cover some other business related formulas, as well.

Graphing

- It is best not to spend too much time on graphing, since much of it is rather intuitive. Do only a few exercises, but make sure that they are done effectively. Examples of graphs from current newspapers and magazines can be helpful.
- *Pie charts.* See my sixth grade workbook for a few good examples.
- *Line graphs.* See my sixth grade workbook for a few good examples.
- *A good page for a main lesson book*: Have the students make a pie chart that shows how their time is spent during the day.
  - To the nearest ¼ hour, each student should record how their time is spent during the day. The day should be divided into around eight activities (e.g., eating, sleeping, studying, in school, etc.).
  - Convert the times into percentages out of 24 hours.
  - Determine the number of degrees that each activity will take out of 360° in the pie chart.
  - Make the pie chart using a protractor. Label each section with the activity and its percentage.

Other Topics

US Standard Tools

- This topic may be best to include as a review of the US measurement system.
- Give examples using tape measure, bolt sizing, etc.
- Fractional measurement ($\frac{3}{4}$, $\frac{13}{16}$, $\frac{5}{8}$, etc.)

    Example: If one drill bit has a diameter of $\frac{3}{8}$ and another is $\frac{11}{32}$, then which one is bigger, and by how much is it bigger?

    Solution: We first get a common denominator of 32, so that $\frac{3}{8}$ becomes $\frac{12}{32}$, giving us an answer that $\frac{3}{8}$ is bigger than $\frac{11}{32}$ by $\frac{1}{32}$.

    Example: If one board is exactly 3' 4$\frac{5}{8}$" long, and another board is 5' 2¼" long then how much longer is the second board?

    Solution: One way to do this is to convert to inches. 3' 4$\frac{5}{8}$" becomes 40$\frac{5}{8}$, and 5' 2¼" becomes 62¼. 62¼ $-$ 40$\frac{5}{8}$ $\rightarrow$ 62$\frac{2}{8}$ $-$ 40$\frac{5}{8}$ now borrow a 1 $\rightarrow$ 61$\frac{10}{8}$ $-$ 40$\frac{5}{8}$ $\rightarrow$ 21$\frac{5}{8}$" or 1' 9$\frac{5}{8}$" longer.

    Example: If the width of a saw blade is $\frac{1}{8}$" and we cut a board that is 9' 8¼" long into 7 pieces of equal length, then how long will each piece be?

    Solution: In order to end up with 7 pieces, we need to make six cuts in the board. These cuts account for $\frac{6}{8}$, or ¾" of board length. Subtracting ¾" from 9' 8¼" gives us 9' 7½", which is 115½". Dividing this by 7 gives us seven boards each with a length of 16½", which is 1' 4½".

Metric System

- Ideally, the metric system should be introduced as part of a main lesson in fifth grade.
- In sixth grade, the metric system should be reviewed fairly briefly, or, if it wasn't covered in fifth grade, it can be briefly introduced. Much more is done with the metric system in seventh grade.
- *Definitions.* Give *imaginative definitions only.* NO calculations! These definitions need time to digest before doing calculations in seventh grade.
    - A *meter* is the approximate height of a 4-year-old. It is a bit longer than a yard.
    - A *centimeter* is the approximate length of a fly. There are 100 centimeters in a meter.
    - A *millimeter* is the approximate diameter of a poppy seed. There are 10 millimeters in a centimeter, and 1000 millimeters in a meter.
    - A *kilometer* is a bit more than half a mile. Measure a kilometer from the school to some landmark to give the children a sense of the length of a kilometer. There are 1000 meters in a kilometer.
    - A *liter* is the volume of water in a large water bottle. It is a bit more than a quart.
    - A *milliliter* is the approximate volume of a large drop of water. It is the result of dividing a liter into 1000 parts.
    - A *kilogram* is the weight of a large block of cheese. It is a bit more than 2 pounds. It is also the exact weight of a liter of water.
    - A *gram* is the weight of a large pill. It is also the weight of a "nibble" of cheese – the result of taking a thousandth of a one-kilogram block of cheese.
    - A *milligram* is the weight of a tiny spec that you get if you take a large pill or a nibble of cheese that weighs 1 gram and divide it into 1000 pieces. It is perhaps a "nibble" of cheese for a ant!
- *Developing a sense for metric.*
    - *Length.* Estimate the length of things (e.g., the room, pencil, someone's height), and then use a ruler or tape measure to check how good your guesses were.
    - *Volume.* Estimate the volume of things (e.g., cup, bucket, etc.) and then check your answer by measuring (e.g., using a graduated cylinder or a metric measuring cup).
    - *Weight.* Estimate the weight of things (e.g., person, pencil, rock, etc.) and then check your answer with a scale.

Word Problems

- See comments on *Word Problems* in the introduction.
- *General word problems.* Give word problems that practice a variety of things from the topics listed above, while trying to have them develop their intuitive sense of when it is necessary to multiply and when to divide.
  Example: 120 minutes is how many seconds? (Answer: 120·60 = 7200 seconds)
  Example: 210 minutes is how many hours? (Answer: 210÷60 = 3½ hours)
- *Rate of speed.*
  - In sixth grade, only give a brief introduction that uses simple problems. Much more is done with rate of speed problems in seventh grade.
  - Introduce this topic first by only doing problems that find the distance given a certain speed and an amount of time. After they have really grasped these types of problems, then you may introduce problems that find the speed or the time.
  - It may help some students to draw diagrams for some of these problems.

  Example: How far does Hank bike in 5½ hours if he averages 18 mph?
  Solution #1: Given that he goes 18 miles every hour, we can say that after 5 hours he goes 90 miles, and in the next half hour he goes another 9 miles, for a total of <u>99 miles</u>.
  Solution #2: We realize that we need to multiply 18 by 5½, which gives us our answer of <u>99 miles</u>.

  Example: What is the average speed of a plane that goes 2800 miles in four hours?
  Solution: Speed is given in miles per hour (mph), so we ask ourselves how many miles the plane goes every (one) hour. Since it goes 2800 miles in 4 hours, it makes sense to say that it goes ¼ as far in 1 hour. So we divide 2800 by 4 to get an answer of <u>700 mph</u>.

  Example: How long does it take a train to go 350 miles if it is traveling 70 mph?
  Solution: Given that the train is going 70 miles every hour, we can picture the train going 140 miles in two hours, and then 210 miles after three hours. It then hopefully becomes clear that we must divide 350 by 70, giving an answer of <u>5 hours</u>.

- *Word Problems in Business Math.* (**See** *Business Math*, above.)

- *A Key Strategy*: Change "ugly" numbers into something easier.
  - Ugly numbers can turn an otherwise simple problem into confusion for many students, so much so that they might not have the slightest idea even of what operation (e.g., multiply, divide, etc.) to perform. The strategy is to change the ugly numbers into something much simpler and then to do the problem with the easier numbers. We can then ask ourselves, "What calculation did we perform for the easier problem?", and then apply the same process to the original problem.

  Example: How far does Hank bike in 5 hours and 15 minutes if he averages 13.2 mph?
  Solution: We change the problem to something with much easier numbers, such as: "How far does Betty bike in 3 hours if she averages 20 mph?" Many students can readily determine that the answer to this easier problem is 60 miles. They should then ask themselves, "What did I do with the easier problem – did I multiply or divide?" They can see that they multiplied with the easier problem, and therefore it follows that they must also multiply with the original problem. Therefore, the answer is 5 hours 15 minutes times 13.2 mph, and since 15 minutes is 0.25 hours, the calculation that we actually do is 5.25·13.2, which gives us an answer of <u>69.3 miles</u>.

Ratios

- *The Basic Idea.*
  - Ratios and fractions are very similar, but there are important differences. In general, we can say that a ratio compares the size of two quantities or numbers.
  - If we say that the ratio of water to flour in a recipe is 5:4, we read this as "five to four", and it means that *for every five units (e.g., cups) of water there are 4 units of flour.*
- In sixth grade, only do a brief introduction to ratios with simple examples that use whole number form. Much more detail will come over the next two years.
  Example: What is the ratio of boys to girls in a class with 15 boys and 12 girls?
  Solution: The ratio of 15:12 is reduced to <u>5:4</u>.

  Example: What is the ratio of the heights of two buildings if one is 36 feet tall and the other is 24 feet tall?
  Solution: The ratio of 36:24 is reduced to <u>3:2</u>.

Statistics

- This topic should be covered briefly.
- *Averaging*.
  - The <u>Arithmetic Mean</u> is what we normally think of when we think of "average". We calculate the arithmetic mean by adding up all the scores and then dividing by the number of scores.
  - The <u>Median</u> is the score that is in the middle, which is also the 50th percentile. We simply put all the scores in order (i.e., from smallest to largest), and then the median is the score that falls exactly in the middle. Half the scores are higher than (or equal to) the median, and half the scores are lower than (or equal to) the median. If there is an even number of scores, then the median is halfway between the two middle scores.
  - The <u>Mode</u> is the score that occurs most frequently. It is possible to have more than one mode.

    Example: Find the mean, median, and mode of the ages of a group of ten people with these ages:
    18, 12, 72, 25, 13, 12, 16, 13, 12, 14.

    Solution: The mean is the sum of all the ages (207) divided by 10, which is <u>20.7</u>. The median is the middle score, so we list the ages in order as 12, 12, 12, 13, 13, 14, 16, 18, 25, 72. Since there are an even number of scores, there are two scores (13 and 14) that fall at the middle of this order, making the median halfway between the two, which is <u>13.5</u>. The mode is the most common score, which is <u>12</u>.

    Question: In 2000, the mean income for Americans was $31,000 and the median income was $22,000. (The mode income is the minimum wage.) Why is the mean income in the U.S. greater than the median income?

    Answer: The mean income is greater because a small segment of the population is very wealthy and "throws off the curve". For example, if a small village has only ten people, and nine of them earn $10 per hour and the tenth makes $1000 per hour, then the mean income would be $109 per hour and the median income would be $10 per hour.
    For this reason, the median income is generally considered to be a better indicator of what the average person is earning.

Significant Digits (or significant figures)

- The number of significant digits for a number is equal to the number of digits in the number, without the ending and beginning zeroes.
  Example: 2,300,000 has two significant digits. 0.000408 has three significant digits.
- Often times when doing calculations in science and math, we cut off the answer after a certain number of digits, especially when using decimals. One reason for this is that the initial given number is often only accurate to a couple of significant digits, and so it doesn't make sense to say that our final answer is accurate to more significant digits.
  Example: If Sue ran 3.25 km in 12 minutes 32 seconds, then what was her average speed (in meters per second)?
  Solution: 12 minutes 32 seconds is 752 seconds, and this number, as well as the distance, both have three significant digits. Therefore our answer should be rounded to three significant digits. The average speed is 3250m÷752sec ≈ 4.321808511 m/s, which gets rounded to <u>4.32 m/s</u>.

Currency Exchange Rates

- I usually do these problems at the end of the year in my track class, if time allows. These are good problems because they challenge the students and help to develop their thinking in a way that is appropriate for sixth grade. They also get the students to work on division and multiplication, and give them a glimpse of how financial institutions make money through trading.
- To get the latest exchange rates, visit the website www.x-rates.com. You can also call Citibank's automated exchange rate line at 1-800-756-7050. National Westminster Bank (in London, England) has its exchange rates posted at www.natwest.com/corporate/international.

Note: The below example is probably too complicated to present to a class of sixth grade students. I include it here in order to help the teacher understand how exchange rates are actually done. In particular, the idea that selling dollars for 1.39 *dollars per pound* is the same as selling dollars for 0.719 *pounds per dollar*, is rather confusing. (See the explanation, below.) I simplify things somewhat for the students, and only give exchange rates in terms of a price per unit of foreign currency (e.g., *Dollars per pound* for a bank located in the U.S., or *pounds per dollar* for a bank located in England). See my sixth grade workbook for good examples of problems that I give to my students.

Example (for the teacher only): National Westminster Bank in London posts its exchange rate for the dollar as: *selling dollars* for 1.39 dollars per pound (£), and *buying dollars* for 1.54 dollars per pound. (These were the rates on 12/21/01.) In New York on the same day, Citibank's exchange rate for the pound was listed as: *selling pounds* for 1.56 dollars per pound, and *buying pounds* for 1.37 dollars per pound.

Explanation: First, we must realize what the rates mean. At first glance, it seems that the London bank is selling for less (1.39) than they are buying (1.54), and that it must be losing money. This becomes a bit less confusing once we realize that it is arbitrary whether their rates are listed in terms of dollars per pound or pounds per dollar. In other words, the London bank could have just as well listed their rates as: *selling dollars* for 0.719 pounds per dollar (which is 1÷1.39), and *buying dollars* for 0.649 pounds per dollar (1÷1.54).

For example, if the bank is buying $20 dollars from an American tourist in London, then it could do the calculation as 20·0.649, instead of what it actually does, which is 20÷1.54. The result is the same either way (ignoring any negligible difference due to rounding), and the tourist would walk away with £12.98.

Secondly, we should keep in mind that the words "selling" and "buying" specify whether the bank is buying or selling the *foreign* currency. Of course, with every currency exchange, the bank is buying one currency and selling the other. Therefore, the *selling dollars* rate for the London bank (1.39 $/£) is basically the same as the *buying pounds* rate for the New York bank, because in both cases, the bank is selling dollars *and* buying pounds at the moment the money is exchanged between the bank's teller and the customer.

Problems: Assuming no extra costs (e.g., commission, tax, etc.), then:
- (a) At National Westminster Bank, how many pounds will you get for $500?
- (b) At Citibank, how many pounds will you get for $500?
- (c) At National Westminster Bank, how many dollars will you get for £80?
- (d) At Citibank, how many dollars do you need to give in order to receive £200?
- (e) What is National Westminster Bank's profit if one person changes $1000 into pounds and then another person purchases this $1000?

Approach: For each problem, we must first answer two questions:
- (1) Is the bank *buying* or *selling* the foreign currency?
- (2) Should we *multiply* or *divide* by the given rate?

Answers (to each of the above problems):
- (a) The bank is *buying* dollars. We *divide* 500 by 1.54 for an answer of £324.68.
- (b) The bank is *selling* pounds. We *divide* 500 by 1.56 for an answer of £320.51.
- (c) The bank is *selling* dollars. We *multiply* 80 by 1.39 for an answer of $111.20.
- (d) The bank is *selling* pounds. We *multiply* 200 by 1.56 for an answer of $312.00.
- (e) First the bank *buys* $1000 for £649.35 (1000÷1.54), and then they *sell* the $1000 for £717.42 (1000÷1.39). They have made a profit of £68.07.

Sixth Grade Geometry

- This is a great main lesson block to start the year with. It can nicely share a main lesson with math review.
- *Recommended Reading.* Julia Diggins' book, *String Straightedge and Shadow*, gives a great, readable summary of the history and thinking of Greek geometry.

The Basics

Basic Geometry Terminology

- *Don't have the students write down or memorize definitions.* Familiarity is the idea here.
- Give examples for each of these: *Point, line, line segment, plane, polygon, parallel, perpendicular.*
- *Supplementary angles* are angles that together form a straight line equaling 180°.
- Two lines that are *perpendicular* form 4 *right angles*.
- *Vertical angles* are opposite angles formed when two lines intersect. Vertical angles are always equal.

Angle Measure

- With a circle, an angle that has its rotation from its center going completely around is 360°.
- A hexagon is specially related to the circle because a compass set to the radius of the circle goes around the circle *exactly* six times. This allows for the hexagon to be divided into six equilateral triangles.
- Develop a good feeling for angle measurement. Students should be able to look at an angle and give a good estimate of how many degrees it is.
- Have a student stand, point directly forward, and then jump up and spin to see how many degrees they can turn in the air.
  Example: What does a 360° turn mean? A 720° turn? A 270° turn? A 540° turn?
- *Using a Protractor.* Do constructions given specific angle measures in order to practice using a protractor.
  Example: Construct a triangle that has two angles equal to 98° and 34°, and then find the measure of the third angle. (Answer: 48° is what they should get, but a degree or two off is acceptable. This is because the number of degrees in a triangle is 180°, which is learned in seventh grade.)

Polygon Terminology

- The *perimeter* is the distance around the outside of a figure.
- An *equilateral* figure has sides that are all congruent (equal).
- An *equiangular* figure has angles that are all congruent.
- A *regular* figure is both equilateral and equiangular.
- Two *congruent* figures are identical in shape and size.
- Two *similar* figures have the exact same shape, but they are different in size – one is an enlargement of the other.

| 1 | 2 | 3 | 4 | 5 | 6 | 7 | 8 | 9 | 10 | 11 |

- *Types of triangles*
  1. An *equilateral triangle* has three congruent sides and three congruent (60°) angles. It is *regular*.
  2. A *right triangle* has one 90° angle.
  3. An *isosceles triangle* has two congruent sides and two congruent angles.
  4. An *obtuse triangle* has one angle greater than 90°.
  5. An *acute triangle* has all its angles less than 90°.
  * A *scalene triangle* has three sides all of different length. (Shown in drawings #2, #4 and #5.)
- *Types of quadrilaterals* (4-sided polygons)
  6. A *square* has four right angles and all its sides are congruent. It is *regular*.
  7. A *rectangle* has four right angles, and its opposite sides are congruent. It is *equiangular*.
  8. A *parallelogram* has opposite angles congruent, and opposite sides are both parallel and congruent.
  9. A *rhombus* (i.e., diamond) is *equilateral*, and opposite angles are congruent.
  10. A *trapezoid* has one pair of parallel sides.
  11. A *kite* has two pairs of adjacent sides that are congruent.
- *Introduce polygons with more than four sides*: Pentagon (5), Hexagon (6), Heptagon (7); Octagon (8), Nonagon (9), Decagon (10), Dodecagon (12).

Circle Terminology

- Radius, diameter, circumference.
- An *arc* is a portion of the circumference of a circle.
- A *chord* is a line segment that connects two points on a circle (line B in the drawing).
- A *secant* is a line that passes through a circle (line D in drawing)
- Two geometrical objects are *tangent* if they just touch one another at one point without actually crossing. (Line C is tangent to the circle in the drawing.)

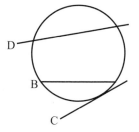

The Three Dimensions

- This is just a brief introduction. Be careful not to make this too abstract.

What is one-dimensional?

- Lines and curves are one-dimensional.
- If you are hiking on a trail, then you are moving one-dimensionally (even if you are going around curves and up mountains) because you can only go forward or backward along the trail.
- One-dimensional objects have only length, and we measure their distance (feet, meters, etc.).

What is two-dimensional?

- Surfaces and flat figures are two-dimensional (e.g., a meadow, a hexagon, the surface of the earth).
- If you are sailing on the open seas, or walking in a field, you are moving two-dimensionally, because you can move forward/backward and left/right.
- Two-dimensional objects have both length and width, and we measure their area (square feet, square meters, square miles, acres, etc.).

What is three-dimensional?

- Most everything in the physical world is three-dimensional (e.g., a sphere, a box, a person, the earth).
- If a bird is flying through the air, or a fish is swimming through the sea, it moves three-dimensionally, because it can move forward/backward, left/right, and up/down.
- Three-dimensional objects have length, width, and height (or depth) and we measure their volume (cubic feet, cubic meters, cubic miles, gallons, etc.).

Geometric Drawing

Tips for doing Geometric Drawings

- Geometric drawings require great care and precision.
- High quality compasses and sharp pencils are essential.
- Any coloring or shading-in needs to be done thoughtfully, so that it emphasizes, rather than distracts from, the key features of the form.
- Mostly, the students should learn to do each drawing by watching the teacher do the constructions on the board. Doing it in this way is a good exercise for the students in following instructions (and good practice for the teacher in giving clear instructions too!).

The Basic Constructions

- It is very important for the students to develop competence in doing these basic constructions.
  Note:
  - While there may be multiple ways to accomplish a construction, only one is offered for each case below.
  - The drawings below are only intended to help the teacher learn each construction while reading the instructions. These drawings are smaller, lacking in color, and generally significantly different from what the students should do. The students' work in their main lesson books should be beautifully done, *without labeling points with letters*, and should include color and shading in. The teacher needs to be clear about their expectations.

Copying a Line Segment

Instructions (for the teacher only): *The intention is to copy line segment AB onto line CD.* Make sure that CD is longer than AB. Set the compass's width equal to AB. Put the needle of the compass on C, and mark an arc that passes through line CD at point E. CE is now equal in length to AB.

Copying an Angle

Instructions (for the teacher only): *The intention is to copy angle ABC onto line DE.* Set the compass at a width that is a bit less than the shortest of the line segments AB, BC, and DE. Using this width of the compass, draw an arc with the needle at B that passes through both AB (at X) and BC (at W), and then draw an arc with the needle at D that passes through DE at Y. Place the needle at W and adjust the compass so that it reaches to X, and then draw a short arc through X. Keeping this width of the compass, draw an arc, with the needle at Y, that crosses through the previously drawn arc at point Z. Angle ZDY is now equal to angle ABC.

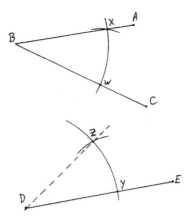

Bisecting[1] a Line Segment (and construction of the perpendicular bisector)

Instructions (for the teacher only): *The intention is to bisect the line segment AB, and to draw a perpendicular bisector through it.* Set the compass width so that it is a bit more than half the length of AB. Using this compass width, draw two arcs, one with the needle at A and the other with the needle at B, so that they cross one another in two places – at points C and D. CD is the perpendicular bisector of AB, and M is the midpoint of AB.
Note: This same technique is used to bisect an arc.

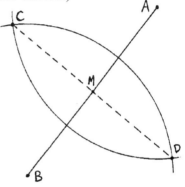

Bisecting an Angle

Instructions (for the teacher only): *The intention is to bisect angle ABC.* Set the compass width a bit less than the shorter of AB and BC. Draw an arc, with the needle at B, that passes through AB at D, and passes through BC at E. Now draw two arcs, both with the same compass width, with the needle at D and then at E, so that the two arcs cross inside angle ABC at point F. The line BF is the desired bisector of the angle ABC. Notice that this will still work if the two arcs are made to intersect "outside" (in this case, to the left of) the angle.

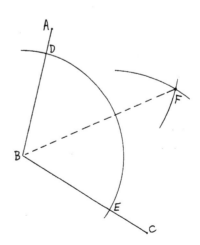

---

[1] Bisecting means cutting something into two equal pieces.

Constructing a Perpendicular Line through a Point on that Line

Instructions (for the teacher only): *The intention is to construct a line perpendicular to AB that passes through X, which is a point on AB.* First, draw two arcs, each one using the same compass width and with the needle at X – one arc passing through AX at C and the other passing through XB at D. Now lengthen the compass somewhat and draw two long arcs – one with the needle at C and the other with the needle at D, such that they cross each other at points E and F. Line EF is the desired line; it passes through X and is perpendicular to AB.

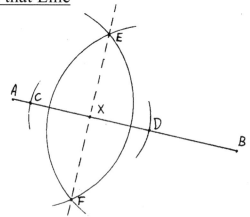

Constructing a Perpendicular Line through a Point *Not* on that Line

Instructions (for the teacher only): *The intention is to construct a line perpendicular to AB that passes through X, which is NOT on AB.* First, set the compass width a bit longer than the distance that X is from line AB and then draw an arc, with the needle at X, that passes through AB in two points, C and D. Now draw two long arcs, both using the same compass width, one with the needle at C and the other with the needle at D. They should cross each other at X and at another point E, which is on the other side of AB from X. Line EX is the desired line – it passes through X and is perpendicular to AB.

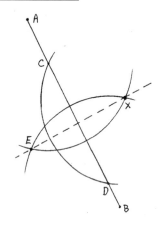

Constructing a Parallel Line

Instructions (for the teacher only): *The intention is to construct a line that is parallel to AB and that passes through X, which is not on AB.* Draw line AX significantly beyond X. Set the compass width so that it is a bit shorter than AX, and draw an arc, with the needle at A, that passes through both AB at D and AX at C. Using that same compass width, draw an arc, with the needle at X, that passes through both the extended line AX (at E) and the line (not yet drawn) that passes through X and is parallel to AB. Now, adjusting the compass width, draw a short arc, with the needle at C, that passes through D, and then using the same compass width, draw an arc, with the needle at E that crosses, at point F, the arc that was drawn earlier that passed through E. The line XF is the desired line – it passes through X and is parallel to AB.

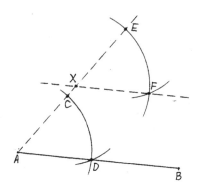

Dividing a Line Segment into Equal Parts

Instructions (for the teacher only): *The intention is to divide AB into N equal parts.* (In the drawing, AB is divided into 5 parts, so N is 5.) Choose a point C such that AC is somewhat longer than AB and angle BAC is approximately 45° (but this angle could be anything). Using a compass width that is about one-Nth as long as AB, draw short arcs that cross AC with equally long steps, first with the needle at A, crossing AC at L, then with the needle at L and crossing AC at M, then with the needle at M and crossing AC at N, etc., until N steps along AC are produced. We now have N equal steps along AC such that segments AL, LM, MN, and so on, are all equal. From the last point (P) where an arc crosses AC, draw a line to B. This is line PB. Now draw lines from each of the other points on AC so that they are each parallel to line PB, and cross line AB. We have now divided AB into N equal segments.

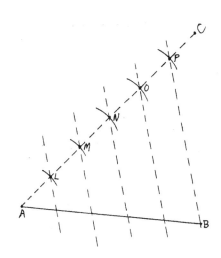

Constructing an Equilateral Triangle, Given One Side

Instructions (for the teacher only): *The intention is to construct an equilateral triangle that has each side equal in length to AB.* Set the compass width equal to AB. Place the compass needle first on point A and draw an arc upward, then do the same with the compass needle on point B. The apex of the triangle (point C) is where these two arcs intersect. Finish the triangle by connecting points A and C, and connecting points B and C.

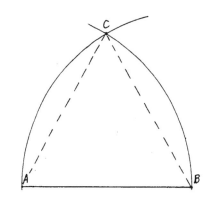

Constructing a Square, Given One Side

Instructions (for the teacher only): *The intention is to construct a square that has each side equal in length to AB.* Extend AB past A to N, and then mark point M on AB such that the length of NA is equal to the length of AM. Adjust the compass so that it is somewhat wider than AB and draw two arcs – one with the needle at N, and the other with the needle at M, so that they intersect vertically above A, at point C. Line AC is now perpendicular to AB. Set the compass width equal to AB and draw an arc, with the needle at A, so that it crosses line AC at point D. Using the same compass width, draw two more arcs: one that is horizontally to the right of D, with the needle at D, and a second arc that is above B, with the needle at B. These two arcs cross at point E. Finish the square by connecting the four points ABED.

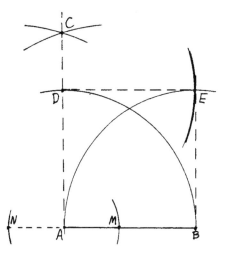

Constructing a Hexagon, Inside a Given Circle

Instructions (for the teacher only): *The intention is to construct a regular hexagon inside the given circle.* Draw diameter AB passing through the center of the circle, X. Then set the width of the compass equal to the radius of the circle, and draw one arc with the needle at B, which crosses the circle at points C and D, and another arc, with the needle at A, which crosses the circle at points E and F. The desired hexagon is AFDBCE.

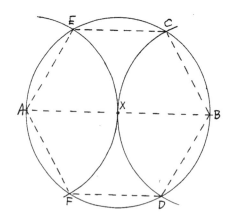

Constructing a Square, Inside a Given Circle

Instructions (for the teacher only): *The intention is to construct a square inside the given circle.* Draw diameter AB passing through the center of the circle, X. Construct the line that is perpendicular to AB passing through X and crossing the circle at E and F. The desired square is AFBE.

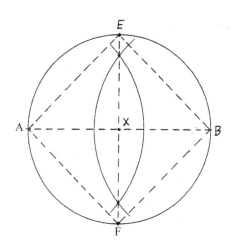

Constructing a Triangle, Inside a Given Circle

Instructions (for the teacher only): *The intention is to construct an equilateral triangle inside the given circle.* Draw diameter AB passing through the center of the circle. Set the compass width equal to the radius of the circle, and draw an arc, with the needle at A, that passes through the circle in two places, labeled C and D. The desired triangle is BCD.

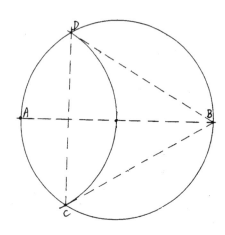

Constructing an Octagon, Inside a Given Circle

Instructions (for the teacher only): *The intention is to construct a regular octagon inside the given circle.* Start by constructing the square ABCD inside the circle, as described above. We now only need to bisect two of the right angles formed by AC and BD. To do this, set the compass width equal to the radius of the circle and draw two short arcs, with the needle at B and then at D, that are vertically above the needle. Next, draw a long arc, with the needle at C, that passes through the center of the circle, and then intersects the two short arcs (just drawn) at points X and Y. Draw lines XM and YM, and extend them so that each one intersects the circle in two places. We now have the 8 equally spaced points along the circle that are needed to draw the octagon.

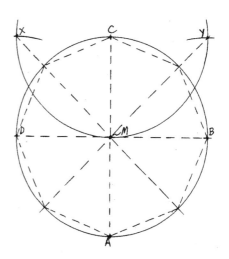

The 12-Division of the Circle (Constructing a Dodecagon)

Instructions (for the teacher only): *The intention is to construct a dodecagon (12-gon) inside the given circle.* Locate the 6 points (A, B, C, D, E, F) of the hexagon inside the given circle (with center M) as described above. Now, set the width of the compass to a bit less than the diameter of the circle. We only need to bisect 3 out of the 6 central angles (e.g., angle AMB) in order to locate the 6 additional points needed for the dodecagon. We do this by drawing two arcs – one with the needle at B and the other with the needle at C – by having the compass reach over the center of the circle. These two arcs cross each other at point Y. Then, with the same compass width, draw two shorter arcs – one with the needle at A and the other with the needle at D – that cross the two previously drawn arcs at X and Z, respectively. We can now locate six new points on the circle by extending XM, YM, and ZM to form diameters of the circle so that they each cross the circle in two places. This gives us the 12 points on the circle that are needed to draw the dodecagon.

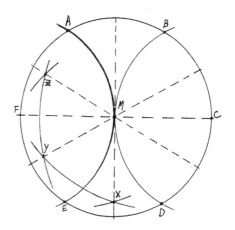

The 24-Division of the Circle (Constructing a 24-gon)

Instructions (for the teacher only): *The intention is to construct a 24-gon inside the given circle.* We start here with the 12-division of the circle as described just above. Using that same method, we set the width of the compass to a bit less than the diameter of the circle and draw arcs, with the needle at each one of the 12 points on the circle, where the compass reaches over the center of the circle. It is only necessary to draw arcs from 7 of the 12 points on the circle, but in the drawing shown here I have done all 12 arcs. This gives us added accuracy for drawing the 6 diameters of the circle, since we now have three points with which to draw each diameter, rather than just the required two points. These 6 diameters give us 12 more points on the circle. We now have the 24 points along the circle that are needed to draw the 24-gon.

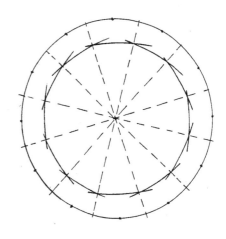

Spirals

The central idea here (as with most of this main lesson block) is to learn about these forms through the experience of drawing, and *not to analyze them.* In sixth grade, students can make observations about the forms of the spirals (e.g., How does an equiangular spiral look different from an Archimedean spiral?). In tenth grade, we investigate the mathematical properties behind these differences that we observed in sixth grade.

The Equiangular Spiral (also known as a *logarithmic spiral*)

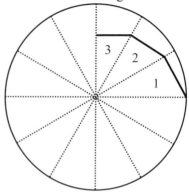

Construction (from the 12 division of a circle):

- *Construct 12 points* on the circumference of a circle (**see** *Constructing a Dodecagon*, above). Erase all construction lines.
- *Lightly draw 6 diameters* by connecting all opposite points.
- *Start the spiral* by lightly drawing a line segment from one of the 12 points on the circle that is perpendicular to a neighboring radius (use a right-angled drawing triangle in order to save time). From that point lightly draw another line segment that is again perpendicular to the next radius. Continue lightly drawing line segments in this manner thereby creating a spiral in toward the center of the circle. (See drawing at right.) Finish by darkly drawing a smoothly curved spiral over the light line segments.

The Beginning of the
Equiangular Spiral Construction

- *Interesting questions:*

  Question: Why is this called an *equiangular spiral*?
  Answer: This spiral can be seen as a series of progressively smaller, *equiangular* (similar) right triangles.

  Question: How can these triangles be seen to be in movement?
  Answer: Each triangle moves into the position of the next triangle by rotating it about the center of the spiral (e.g., triangle #1 moves to triangle #2, and triangle #2 moves to triangle #3). As each triangle is rotated, it is shrunk down enough so that it "fits" into the next position.

  Question: Can we produce a spiral by using types of triangles other than right triangles?
  Answer: Yes, (almost) any triangle will work, as long as the triangles are all similar and they are rotated about the center of the circle and shrunk down as needed.

  Question: How many triangles does it take before the spiral reaches the center?
  Answer: Infinitely many.

  Question: Does the spiral actually ever reach the center?
  Answer: That depends on how you look at it. This interesting question is addressed in tenth grade.

- It is good to have different students start out with a different number of points on the circle (6, 8, or 24) so that the resulting spirals can be compared.
- Good examples of equiangular spirals that appear in nature are rams' horns, sunflowers, and nautilus shells.

Geometric Progressions and the Equiangular Spiral (For the teacher only)

- A *geometric progression* is a type of growth (or shrinking). In tenth grade, geometric growth is analyzed mathematically, and it is shown that each step in the sequence is a certain percentage larger than the previous step (e.g., with 200, 220, 242, 266.2…each step is a 10% increase of the previous). Other names for this mathematical behavior are *geometric growth, exponential growth,* or *constant percentage growth.* An example of this is a bank account with monthly compounded interest – it increases each month by the same percentage. On the other hand, an *arithmetical progression* is where each number in the progression is increased by the same amount (e.g., 4,7,10,13,16…). None of this is mentioned in sixth grade. The students simply make drawings that show geometric progressions, and then make observations about those drawings.

Other Ways to Construct an Equiangular Spiral

- *Formed with inscribed regular polygons.* (**See Appendix A,** *Equiangular Spirals,* for drawings.)
  - *Nested Octagons.* Start by carefully drawing an octagon in a circle (**see** *Constructing an Octagon,* above). Connect the midpoints of each side thereby forming another smaller octagon. Continue in this manner, drawing one octagon inside another as far as possible. It is amazing how beautifully the students can shade in this drawing. Look at the drawing in Appendix A, or for an extraordinary example of how to shade in nested octagons, look at the cover of this book!
  - Do three more drawings starting with a hexagon, a square, and a triangle. Notice how the spirals from the different drawings approach the center at different rates.

- *Joining the quarter-points of the sides of the squares.* (**See Appendix A,** *Equiangular Spirals.*)
  Draw a large square, and as you go around the perimeter of the square in one direction, mark points at one-quarter the length along each side. Connect these four new points in order to create a new, slightly smaller square. Continue making new, smaller squares in this manner, so that the squares are all rotating in one direction as they get smaller. Shade in spirals as shown in the drawing in Appendix A.

The Spiral of Archimedes

Construction: Draw a line across and slightly below the middle of the page, and mark equal distances (perhaps ¼ inch) out from the center along that line. Using the midpoint of that line as the center, lightly draw circles with radii that get progressively longer (e.g., ¼ inch, ½ inch, ¾ inch, etc.) by using the distances that have just been marked on the line. Now, mark 12 evenly spaced points around the perimeter of the largest circle, and then lightly draw six diameters by joining the six pairs of opposite points. Finally, carefully draw the Archimedean spiral by starting from one of the 12 outside points and move inward, such that each step goes to the point of intersection of the next smaller circle and the neighboring radius.

Notice that how quickly the spiral comes in to the center of the circle is determined by the spacing of the circles and the number of circles. Therefore, using the 12-division of the circle (as suggested above), and spacing the circles ¼ inch apart, will result in a spiral that goes around exactly 2 full times before reaching the center *if there are 24 circles*. This would require the outside-most circle to have a radius of 6 inches, which may be too big to fit on the paper. Drawing only 18 circles would result in a spiral going around 1½ times. Another option, which was used for the original of the drawing below, is to draw 36 circles that are ¹/₈ inch apart, resulting in a spiral that goes around exactly 3 times, and has a radius of 3½ inches.

- Make observations about how the Archimedean spiral is different from an equiangular spiral, including the most important difference: the Archimedean spiral clearly reaches the center, and the equiangular spiral needs an infinite number of rotations about the center before it reaches the center.

Note: The drawing below has been reduced in size.

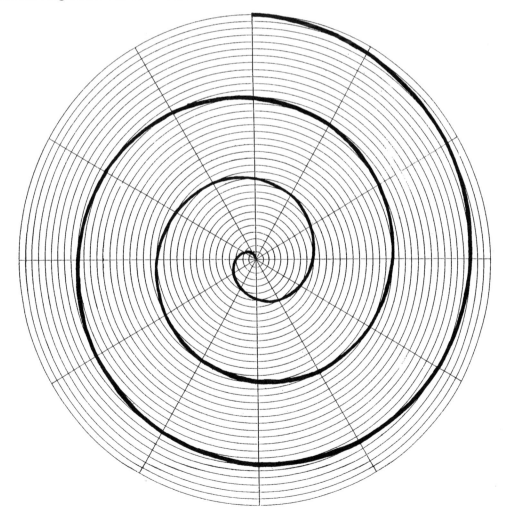

Advanced Constructions

Rotations of Circles (**See Appendix A** for drawing.)

- Notice with the page titled *Rotations of Circles* in Appendix A that the three drawings on the left are exactly the same as the drawings on the right, but the drawings on the right have been shaded-in.

Construction: Look at the drawing in Appendix A. With each of the drawings on the left side, you start with a 24-division of a circle (shown as a dotted circle in the drawing). Erase the construction lines, but keep the 24 points. Then use each of these 24 points as the center to draw a circle. The difference between the three types of drawings is that the top drawing has its 24 circles with a much larger radius than the original circle, the middle drawing has its 24 circles with radii that are equal to the original circle, and the bottom drawing has its 24 circles with radii equal to half the original circle.

The Limaçon and the Cardioid (**See Appendix A** for drawing.)

- This drawing can be used to demonstrate how a curve can metamorphose.

Construction: Have the students start with a circle in the center of the paper that has a radius of approximately 5cm. Using a compass (or a protractor), do a 24-division of the circle, and then mark the 24 points on the circle with a pen. Erase everything except for the 24 points. Now each student is assigned a special point, called the cusp. Some students' cusp should be outside the circle (anywhere from 1 to 5cm above the top of the circle); others should be inside the circle (anywhere from 1 to 3 cm below the top of the circle); a couple of students should have their cusp on the top of the circle; and one student should have a cusp at the center of the circle. The students create their limaçon by placing their compass needle, in turn, on each one of the 24 points of the circle, and, for each one, they adjust their compass in order to draw a circle that goes through the cusp. The resulting curve is a limaçon, and should be carefully traced with a colored pencil. The various results should then be displayed at the front of the classroom so that the students can observe how the limaçon becomes transformed as the cusp moves from the center of the construction circle toward the edge of the circle, and then to the outside of the circle. (**See Appendix A**, *The Metamorphosis of a Limaçon*, for drawing.)

- A cardioid is the special case of a limaçon when the cusp is located on the construction circle. In the drawing in Appendix A, the cardioid (meaning "heart-shaped") is the drawing on the lower right.
- A cardioid can also be generated by tracing a fixed point on a circle as it rolls around another circle of equal radius. There is a children's art toy, called a spirograph, which I used as a child that does something similar to this.

The Hierarchy of Quadrilaterals (**See Appendix A** for drawing.)

- This drawing is a wonderful example of how order can emerge from chaos.

Construction: Draw a large irregular (random) quadrilateral. Connect the midpoints to form a parallelogram. Bisect the parallelogram angles to get a rectangle. Bisect these angles to get a square.

Knots and Interpenetrating Polygons (**See Appendix A** for drawing.)

- With these drawings, it may be best to simply let the students see an example drawing and have them figure out how to do it. Then have them come up with different knots and interpenetrations of their own.

The 24-Division with all its Diagonals (**See Appendix A** for drawing.)

- This drawing is very simple in concept, but requires much care and time.
- You should see rings of circles expanding outward from the center and fading.

The King's Crown (**See Appendix A** for drawing.)

- This drawing starts again with the 24-division of the circle, and includes most of the diagonals from only two of the 24 points. Students love to color this drawing in a variety of ways.

Area

- Students should be able to picture square units (square inches, square feet, etc.).
- *What does it mean* to say that a room has an area of 600 square feet? Students should be able to picture that a room 20' by 30' (or another room 12' by 50') would be covered by a total of 600 one-foot by one-foot squares.
- Don't introduce the shorthand way of writing square feet (ft^2) until seventh or eighth grade, since students often think of this as an exponent for the number (e.g., making 7 ft^2 incorrectly into 49ft).
- Mention area in metric (square centimeters, square meters, etc.) also.
- *Do areas of squares, rectangles, and right triangles only*. Have the students do drawings to show that the areas "work". Include rectangles that have fractional dimensions.

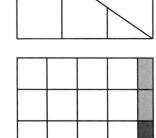

Example: What is the area of a right triangle that has a base of 3 feet and a length of 2 feet?

Solution: The area is half that of the rectangle it sits in. We can also see how the pieces of squares can be put together to form whole squares. Therefore the area equals ½·3·2, which is exactly 3 square feet.

Example: What is the area of a rectangle that is 4½ inches by 3⅓ inches? Construct an accurate drawing that demonstrates this.

Solution: We can quickly see that we have 12 complete squares. Then the 2 half-squares can be added to form one square, as can the 3 third-squares. We are left with 1 half square, 1 third square, and 1 sixth-square (½·⅓), all of which nicely combine to form one whole square. The total area is therefore exactly 15 square inches.

Example: What is the area of a rectangle that is 2⅔ inches by 3¼ inches? Construct an accurate drawing that demonstrates this.

Solution: We can quickly see that we have 6 full square inches (6·1=6). Then the 3 two-third-squares can be added together to form 2 square inches (3·⅔=2). The 2 quarter-squares combine to form a half square inch (2·¼=½), and the remaining rectangle (⅔ by ¼) has an area of ¹/₆ of a square inch (⅔·¼=¹/₆). Now we add the parts to get 6+2+½+¹/₆ = 8⁴/₆ = 8⅔ square inches.

Seventh Grade

The importance of seventh grade

Seventh grade is an important year academically. This the year when the students start to develop abstract thinking (through algebra, physics, essay writing, etc.), and when study habits are developed. Getting homework done regularly (even in small amounts), and keeping a well-organized notebook, are both very important. It is relatively common for a student to enter seventh grade weak in math, but then to "wake-up" during seventh grade, and, in the end, to enter high school quite strong in math.

The order of topics

My seventh grade workbook (contact Jamie York Press for ordering) allows the students to practice their skills with most of the topics listed here, with a few exceptions (e.g., puzzle problems). The order of the units in my workbook is:

1. Arithmetic review
2. Measurement
3. Ratios Part I
4. Percents
5. Ratios Part II
6. Rates
7. Geometry
8. Square Root Algorithm (optional)
9. Algebra (for the *algebra* main lesson)

Arithmetic

Review Sixth Grade

- Especially review fractions, decimals, and division (**see 6th grade Arithmetic**).
- Integrate review into new material, as feasible.

The World of Numbers

Math Tricks

- Review *sixth grade math tricks* (**see Appendix B**).
- Do the *seventh grade math tricks* (**see Appendix B**). Introduce perhaps one new trick each week, and work on practicing new ones with old ones during mental math. (**See Introduction,** *Mental Math.*)

Divisibility Rules

- Review sixth grade *Divisibility Rules*, and then do these as well:
    - A number is evenly <u>divisible by 6</u> only if it is divisible by both 2 and 3.
      Example: 577,368 is evenly divisible by 6 because it is divisible by both 2 and 3 .
    - A number is evenly <u>divisible by 8</u> only if the last 3 digits are divisible by 8. This is because it will evenly divide into any number of thousands.
      Example: 8,736,104 is *not* evenly divisible by 8 because the last three digits aren't divisible by 8.
    - A number is evenly <u>divisible by 12</u> only if it is divisible by both 4 and 3.
      Example: 57,481,932 is evenly divisible by 12 because it is divisible by both 4 and 3.
    - A number is evenly <u>divisible by 11</u> only if the difference of the sums of every other digit is evenly divisible by 11.
      Example: With 6,273,905, we get one sum by adding the digits 6, 7, 9, and 5 to get 27. The other sum comes from adding the digits 2, 3, and 0, which gives 5. The difference of the two sums is 27−5, which is 22. And since 22 is evenly divisible by 11, then we can say that the original number 6273905 is also evenly divisible by 11.
      Example: With 378,543 both sums are equal to 15, making the difference equal to zero. Since zero is evenly divisible by 11, then we can say that 378543 is also evenly divisible by 11.
      Example: With 68,479, the two sums are 19 and 15, which have a difference of 4. Therefore, we conclude that 68479 is not evenly divisible by 11.

Roots

- Review sixth grade square roots.
- Do also cube roots, fourth roots, etc., such as:

    Example: $\sqrt[3]{125} = 5$ (because $5 \cdot 5 \cdot 5 = 125$)

    Example: $\sqrt[4]{81} = 3$ (because $3 \cdot 3 \cdot 3 \cdot 3 = 81$)

    Example: $\sqrt[3]{1000} = 10$

    Example: $\sqrt[10]{1024} = 2$

Measurement

Review

- Metric system from sixth grade. Especially review visualizing how big each metric unit is. (**See 6th Grade,** *metric system.*)
- The US standard measurement system. This includes: length (miles, feet, etc.), weight (ounces, pounds, tons, etc.), and volume (fluid ounces, cups, pints, etc.).

The Metric System

- Spend a good amount of time on this unit, so that the students become very confident operating in the metric system.

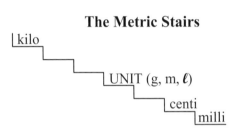

The Metric Stairs

- *The metric stairs.* Early on in the unit, I give the students the *metric stairs*, which can help the students figure out how many places the decimal point should be moved for a given conversion problem. The idea is that every step up or down the stairs results in a move of one position of the decimal point.

    Example: 5700cm is equal to how many km (kilometers)?

    Solution: Rather than have the students memorize any particular procedure (like moving up the stairs means moving the decimal point to the left), I try to have the students understand the following reasoning.

    We are going from centi up to kilo, which is 5 steps on the metric stairs. This means that we need to move the decimal point 5 places. The only question now is whether to take 5700 and move the decimal point to the right or to the left. So the possible answers are 0.057km (after moving the decimal point to the left) or 570,000,000km (after moving the decimal point to the right). The students should picture all these distances. Is 5700cm the same as 0.057km or the same as 570,000,000km? It should be obvious after a bit of thought that 570,000,000km, which is actually far greater than the distance to the sun, is not reasonable. Therefore, the only reasonable answer is that 5700cm is equal to 0.057km.

- Emphasize to the students that they should always check their answer to see if it is reasonable. For instance, with the above example, if they moved the decimal point the wrong way, they should realize that 5700cm is not even close to being equal to 570,000,000km.

Practice doing lots of conversions that remain in a given system, such as:

 Example: How many inches are in 6 yards? (Answer: 6 yards = 18 feet = 216 inches)
 Example: How many quarts are in 200 fluid ounces? (Answer: 200 fl.oz. = 25 cups = 12½ pt = 6¼ qt)
 Example: How many kilograms are in 18 grams? (Answer: 0.018kg)
 Example: How many milligrams are in 23.6 kilograms? (Answer: 23,600,000mg)

Converting between Systems – Don't!

- Wait until eighth grade to do conversions between the metric and the U.S. system (e.g., "How many feet are in 13 kilometers?").

Percents

<u>Review</u> sixth grade percents and business math and cover any material that was not covered in sixth grade.

<u>Finding the Base</u> (usually the larger number)

- The "Base" is the number that we are taking the percentage of – usually it is the larger number.
  Example: With the statement "3500 is 70% of 5000", the base is 5000.
  Example: With the statement "800 decreased by 25% is 600", the base is 800.
  Example: With the statement "60 increased by 8% is 64.8", the base is 60 (which is *not* the larger number).
- Also see **8th Grade Percents**, *Four Ways to Find the Base.*
- Finding the base for an increase/decrease problem is delayed until eighth grade.
- *Easier ones.* Sometimes finding the base (larger number) is quite easy.

  Example: 36 is 25% of what number?
  Solution: Since 36 is ¼ of the number we are looking for, we can say that the number must be 4 times greater than 36, which gives us an answer of <u>144</u>.

- *Thinking of inverses.* Up until now, we have usually been required to find the percentage of a larger number. Now we are going the other way around. In essence, we are doing inverse operations.
  - This method is only introduced here in seventh grade. Much more is done in eighth grade.
  Example: Here, we will play with the fact that 38 equals 8% of 475. We can either be given 475 and be asked to find 38, or be given 38 and be asked to find 475. Specifically, the two questions are:

  Question A (finding the smaller number): *What is 8% of 475?* (This is the normal percent question.)
  Solution #1 (using decimals) **for A:** We do 475·0.08 to get an answer of 38.
  Solution #2 (using fractions) **for A:** We do $\frac{8}{100}$·475 to get an answer of 38.

  Question B (finding the larger number): *38 is 8% of what number?* (This is the inverse of Question A.)
  Solution #1 (using decimals) **for B:** We do 38÷0.08 to get an answer of 475. (This is the inverse of solution #1 given above – we *divide* by 0.8 instead of *multiplying* by 0.8.)
  Solution #2 (using fractions) **for B:** We do $\frac{100}{8}$·38 to get an answer of 475. (This is the inverse of solution #2 given above – we multiply by $\frac{100}{8}$ the reciprocal, instead of multiplying by $\frac{8}{100}$.)

- *Trickier ones.* It is good to practice each of the above two types of solutions for finding the base. (Another method, which uses more advanced algebra, is introduced in eighth grade. See 8th Grade Percents, *Four Ways to Find the Base.*)

  Example: 12 is 80% of what number?

  Solution #1 (using decimals): Using the fact that 80% is 0.8, we can say that since 12 is 0.8 times the number we are looking for, then the inverse thought is: *the number is 12 divided by 0.8.* Therefore, our answer is 12÷0.8, which is <u>15</u>.

  Solution #2 (using fractions): Using the fact that 80% is ⁴/₅, we can say that since 12 is ⁴/₅ of the number we are looking for, then the inverse thought is: *the number must be ⁵/₄ of 12.* Answer: ⁵/₄·12 = <u>15</u>.

  Example: 60 is 90% of what number?
  Common Error: Often people reason that since 60 is 90% of the number that we are looking for, then that number (call it X) must be 10% more than 60. Since 10% of 60 is 6, we would get an answer of 60+6 = 66. The fault with this reasoning is that while 60 is 10% less than X, X is *not* 10% more than 60. Along those same lines, 75 is 25% more than 60, but 60 is only 20% less than 75! This idea is further investigated in eighth grade.
  Correct Solution: Using the method from solution #2 shown above, we see that 90% is ⁹/₁₀. Therefore we multiply 60 by ¹⁰/₉ (the reciprocal of ⁹/₁₀). Alternatively, using the method from solution #1, we divide 60 by 0.9. Either way, the answer works out to <u>66⅔</u>.

<u>Strange Percents</u>

  Example: What is 3¼% of 3000?   (Answer: 0.0325·3000= 97.5)
  Example: What is 12.52% of 60?   (Answer: 0.1252·60 = 7.512)
  Example: What is 0.06% of 2100?   (Answer: 0.0006·2100 = 1.26)
  Example: What is 250% of 18?   (Answer: 2.5·18 = 45)

Compound Interest

- Review sixth grade interest (**See 6ᵗʰ Grade Arithmetic**, *Interest*), including the "John and Sue" example.
- Only do interest compounded annually.
- Don't use the formula $P = P_0(1 + r)^t$ until eighth grade.
- Give an example that demonstrates the difference between simple and compound interest.
    Example: Calculate the balance after 5 years of two accounts, each one with a beginning investment of $600 and 10% interest; the only difference being that one account has simple interest and the other has interest compounded annually.
    Solution: *Simple interest:* Each year earns the same interest, which is $60. So after 5 years $300 has been earned, and the ending balance is $900.
    Compound interest: The interest earned in the first year is $60, giving a balance of $660. The second year earns $66 interest and ends with a balance of $726. The third year earns $72.60 interest and ends with a balance of $798.60. The fourth year earns $79.86 of interest and ends with a balance of $878.46. The fifth year earns $87.85 (rounded) of interest and ends with a balance of $966.31.

Calculating the Percentage of Increase or Decrease

- When calculating the percentage of increase or decrease, we think of it as the fraction:

$$\% \text{ increase} = \frac{\text{amount of increase}}{\text{starting point}} \qquad \% \text{ decrease} = \frac{\text{amount of decrease}}{\text{starting point}}$$

- Make sure that the students can understand why this idea is true:
    75 is 25% more than 60, but 60 is 20% less than 75.

- In order to calculate the percentage of increase (or decrease), the students should answer these three questions:
    1. What is the amount of increase (or decrease)?
    2. What is the starting point (i.e., the number that we started at)?
    3. The amount of increase (or decrease) is what percentage of the original amount?

Example: What percentage increase is it going from 350 to 420?
Solution: Answering the above three questions, we get: (1) The amount of increase is 70. (2) We started at 350. (3) We ask: 70 is what percentage of 350? The answer to this is the fraction $\frac{70}{350}$ which reduces to $\frac{1}{5}$, which is 20%. Our final answer is that going from 350 to 420 is a 20% increase.

Example: What percentage decrease is it going from 320 down to 208?
Solution: Answering the above three questions, we get: (1) The amount of decrease is 112. (2) We started at 320. (3) We ask: 112 is what percentage of 320? The answer to this is the fraction $\frac{112}{320}$ which reduces to $\frac{7}{20}$, which is 35%. Our answer is that going from 320 down to 208 is a 35% decrease.

Example: If a bike shop purchases a bike wholesale at $300 and then sells it retail for $372, then what percent profit do they make?
Solution: Answering the above three questions, we get: (1) The amount of increase is $72. (2) We started at $300. (3) We ask: 72 is what percent of 300? The answer is 24%.

Example: If a shirt that is on sale was originally $24 and is now marked at $20.40, what is the discount given as a percent?
Solution: Answering the above three questions, we get: (1) The amount of decrease is $3.60. (2) We started at $24. (3) We ask: $3.60 is what percent of $24? This we picture as $\frac{3.60}{24}$. We can then divide 24 into 3.6, which gives us 0.15. Alternatively, we can convert $\frac{3.6}{24}$ into $\frac{36}{240}$ which then reduces to $\frac{3}{20}$ and multiplying the top and bottom by 5 gives us $\frac{15}{100}$. Either way, we get 15%.

Example: What is 200 increased by 10%, then decreased by 10%?
Solution: It is *not* 200! Instead, 200 increased by 10% is 220, and 220 decreased by 10% is 220 minus 22, which is 198.

Example: *Challenge Problem!*

(a) John bought a new SUV for $39,000 and then sold it for $20,000 two years later. What percent loss is this?

(b) Over those two years, what was the total operating cost and the cost per mile given that he spent $1500 per year on insurance, $450 annually on repairs and maintenance, an average of $220 monthly for interest payments, $850 annually for other costs (parking, tolls, tax, etc.) and drove it 12,000 miles per year? (Use 15 miles/gallon for gas mileage, and $1.30/gallon for the cost of gas.)

(c) Given the answer from part b, how much did it cost him, in total, when he drove to Denver and back on a shopping trip covering a total of 120 miles?

(d) What percent of the total operating cost was gas? (Rounded to three significant digits.)

Solutions: (a) The amount of decrease is $19,000, and from $39,000 it is approximately a <u>48.7% loss</u>.

(b) The total amount of gas used is 24,000 miles÷15 miles per gallon, which is 1600 gallons, and at $1.30/gallon 1600 gallons costs $2080. Combined with $19,000 depreciation costs (drop in the price of the car), $3000 for insurance, $900 for repairs, $5280 for interest, and $1700 for other costs, gives us a <u>total cost for the two years of $31,960</u>. Lastly, we divide this cost by 24,000 miles and conclude that it cost John <u>$1.33 per mile</u> to drive his SUV.

(c) The 120-mile trip costs 1.33·120, which is <u>$159.60</u>.

(d) Since the total cost of driving was $31,960, the cost of gas ($2080) was <u>6.51%</u>.

Ratios

- Ratios are a central theme for the year.
- This unit needs to be done before the geometry main lesson, and before the physics main lesson.

<u>Review</u> sixth grade ratios.

Key Ideas

- *The amount doesn't matter; the essence of ratio is the relationship between the two amounts.*
- *Ratios have no units.*
  - The ratio of two people's heights is the same whether measured in the metric or US system.

  Example: John's height is 7 feet 4 inches, which is 224cm. Sam's height is 4 feet 7 inches, which is 140cm. Find the ratio of their heights, using both measurement systems.

  Solution: First, using their heights as given in feet and inches, we convert to inches, which gives us 88" and 55". This is a ratio of <u>8:5</u>. Now redoing the problem by using their heights given in centimeters, we reduce the ratio 224:140, by dividing by 8, to the ratio <u>8:5</u>. These ratios are the same, thereby showing that no matter how we measure their heights, the ratio of their heights is the same.

  - Likewise, if the ratio of Mary's to Jane's salary is 5:4, it means that for every 5 dollars that Mary makes that Jane makes 4 dollars. Notice that if Mary and Jane instead were paid in an equivalent amount of a different currency (e.g., Pesos) then the numbers associated with their individual salaries would be changed, but the ratios of their salaries with respect to each other would still be 5:4.

- *Ratios of more than two things.* Ratios can be used to compare three or more numbers.

  Example: If there are 12, 15, 15, and 20 students, respectively, in four classes, then we can say that the ratio of the four classes is 12:15:15:18, which reduces to 3:5:5:6.

The Three Thoughts of a Ratio (in whole number form)

- These *three thoughts*, associated with any ratio given in whole number form, get to the essence of the meaning of a ratio.

  Example: What does the ratio J:K = 4:3 mean?

  Solution: One way to think of this is: *the ratio of Jim's money to Kevin's money is four to three.* (Alternatively, we can think of it as a ratio of Jim's height to Kevin's height.) Immediately, we should be able to see that Jim has more money than Kevin. We can then list the three thoughts associated with this ratio as:

  - 4K = 3J (4 times Kevin's money is equal to three times Jim's money.)
  - $K = \frac{3}{4}J$ (Kevin has ¾ as much as Jim.)
  - $J = \frac{4}{3}K$ (Jim has $^4/_3$ as much as Kevin.)

Example: If the ratio of Jim's money to Kevin's money is 4:3, then what does Jim have if Kevin has $270?

Solution: Looking at the above example, the third thought ($J = \frac{4}{3}K$) is the most helpful. This tells us that Jim's money is $\frac{4}{3}$ of Kevin's. So we do $\frac{4}{3}$ times 270 to get a final answer of <u>$360</u>.

Example: If the ratio of Mary's height to Nancy's height is 5:7, then how tall is Mary if Nancy is 5'4"?

Solution: The three thoughts associated with this ratio are:

- $5N = 7M$ (5 times Nancy's height is equal to 7 times Mary's height.)
- $M = \frac{5}{7}N$ (Mary's height is $\frac{5}{7}$ of Nancy's height.)
- $N = \frac{7}{5}M$ (Nancy's height is $\frac{7}{5}$ of Mary's height.)

Of the above three thoughts, the second one is the most useful. This tells us that Mary's height is $\frac{5}{7}$ of Nancy's height. Our answer is therefore $\frac{5}{7}$ of 64 (since Nancy is 64 inches tall), which works out to approximately 45.7 inches, which is about 45¾ inches, or <u>3'9¾"</u>.

The Two Forms for a Ratio

- Any ratio can be expressed either as two whole numbers, or as a decimal. A good deal of time will need to be spent on this, so that the students can work equally well with either form, and so that they can convert one form into the other.
- *Whole number form.* This form is what was introduced in sixth grade, and is expressed in terms of two whole numbers. It is best to make sure that the answer is reduced, just as we would reduce a fraction. For example, a ratio of 15:12 reduces to 5:4.
- *Decimal form.* This form is expressed in such a way that the first number is a decimal, and the second number is *always* equal to one. The ratio 5:4 is equivalent to 1.25:1 in decimal form.

    Example: If there are 560 cars and 320 bikes in a certain town, then what is the ratio of cars to bikes?

    Solution: The answer can be expressed in either form:

    Whole Number Form (done by reducing the fraction $\frac{560}{320}$ to $\frac{7}{4}$)   C:B = 7:4

    Decimal Form (done by dividing 560 by 320 <u>or</u> by dividing 7 by 4)   C:B = 1.75:1

    Example: Convert the ratio 19:4 (which is in whole number form) into decimal form.

    Solution: We divide 4 into 19 to get 4.75, and therefore our answer is <u>4.75:1</u>.

    Example: Convert the ratio 2.4:1 (which is in decimal form) into whole number form.

    Solution: Our goal is make the ratio into two whole numbers. We can do this most easily by multiplying both 2.4 and 1 by 10, thereby giving us a ratio of 24:10, which then reduces to <u>12:5</u>.

- *The Two Thoughts of a Ratio* (in decimal form).
    - These *two thoughts*, associated with any ratio given in decimal form, get to the essence of the meaning of a ratio.

    Example: What does the ratio J:K = 1.2:1 mean?

    Solution: We can tell by looking at the ratio that J is slightly bigger than K. No matter if J and K represent heights, or money, or anything else, the two thoughts are:
    - $J = 1.2 \cdot K$ (J is 1.2 times bigger than K)
    - $K = J \div 1.2$ (K is 1.2 times smaller than J)

Reciprocals of Ratios

- Finding the reciprocal of a ratio that is expressed as a fraction is simple - just reverse the ratio.

    Example: If a rectangle has a base of 16, and a height of 10, then we can say that the ratio of the base to the height is B:H = 8:5, or we could say that the ratio of the height to the base (which is the reciprocal of the first ratio) is H:B = 5:8. Quite simple!

- Finding the reciprocal of a ratio that is expressed as a decimal is trickier.

    Example: Again, using a rectangle that is 16 by 10, we can divide 16 by 10 to get a ratio of B:H = 1.6:1. The reciprocal of this ratio is found by dividing 10 by 16, which gives us the ratio H:B = 0.625:1.

Example: Find the reciprocal of the ratio A:B = 1.8:1.

Solution #1: We think of it as the fraction $\frac{1.8}{1}$ and then flip it to get $\frac{1}{1.8}$. Lastly, we convert this to a decimal by dividing 1.8 into 1, giving an answer of B:A = $0.\overline{5}$:1.

Solution #2: We first change the ratio to whole number form 18:10, then reduce to 9:5. The reciprocal of this is 5:9, and then finally changing $^5/_9$ into a decimal gives us a final answer of B:A = $0.\overline{5}$:1.

Proportion of the Whole

- If the whole of something is divided into two parts, we can consider not only the ratio of these two parts, but we can also determine what *proportion* each part is of the whole, and use this to solve problems.

    Example: Mrs. Smith's class has 21 students, and the ratio of girls to boys is 3:4. How many in the class are boys, and how many are girls?

    Solution: Since 3 out of every 7 students are girls, we can say that $^3/_7$ of the *whole* class is girls. Likewise, we can say that $^4/_7$ of the *whole* class is boys. So to get the number of girls we take $^3/_7$ of 21, which gives us 9 girls. Similarly, the number of boys is $^4/_7$ of 21, which gives us 12 boys.

    Example: If a gallon of milk is completely poured into two pitchers in a ratio of 5:3, then how much is in each pitcher?

    Solution: The ratio tells us that $^5/_8$ of the *whole* gallon is in one pitcher, and $^3/_8$ is in the other. Since a gallon is 128 fluid ounces, we get $^5/_8$ of 128 = 80 fl.oz. in one pitcher, and $^3/_8$ of 128 = 48 fl.oz. in the other.

    Example: How can $540 be split between three people in a ratio of 2:3:4?

    Solution: The ratio tells us that the three people get $^2/_9$, $^3/_9$, and $^4/_9$, respectively, of the *whole* $540, which results in $120, $180, and $240.

Similar Figures

- *What can we say about similar figures?*
    - Similar figures have the same shape. We can make one into the other by putting it into a photocopier (perhaps imaginatively) and enlarging or shrinking it.
    - All the angles in similar figures are the same.
    - The lengths of the sides of similar figures are in equal ratios.
- *Solve problems* that find a missing side from two similar rectangles, or two similar triangles.
    - Do these problems *without using algebra* (algebra is used to solve proportions in eighth grade).
    - Start with easy problems, like the following:

        Example: What is the length of a rectangle if its height is 8 inches, and it is similar to a rectangle that measures 6 inches by 3 inches? (Assume that the length is greater than the height.)

        Solution: With the second rectangle, we can see that the length is twice the width. Since the rectangles are similar, we can say that the first rectangle's length is also twice its height. Therefore, the answer is that the length is 16 inches.

    - The problems are then made more complicated by having answers that turn out to be fractions, but the logic is exactly the same.

        Example: What is the length of a rectangle if its height is 7 inches, and it is similar to a rectangle that measures 5" by 4"?

        Solution: Here, we are looking for the length of the first rectangle, so we look at the second rectangle and ask: "the length is how much of the height?". We see that the length is $^5/_4$ of the height. Therefore the length of the first rectangle must also be $^5/_4$ of its height (which is 7), leading us to an answer of $^5/_4 \cdot {}^7/_1$, which is $^{35}/_4$, or 8¾.

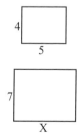

- *Shadow problems.*
  - By using similar triangles, find the height of something tall, by measuring the length of its shadow, and the height of something short (e.g., a ski pole), and the length of its shadow.

  Example: Find the height of a tree if the length of its shadow is 75 feet, and a ski pole held vertically next to the tree is 4 feet tall and has a shadow 5½ feet tall.

  Solution: It is helpful to first draw two triangles, where the vertical and horizontal sides represent the height and shadow length of the two objects. The key is to realize that the two triangles are similar, and therefore that the ratio of the two sides is the same with both of the triangles. Since the ratio of the sides of the triangle created by the ski pole is 4:5½, which (multiplying both by two) simplifies to 8:11, we know that the ratio of the sides of the triangle created by the tree must be the same. Since the height of the ski pole is $^8/_{11}$ of its length, the height of the tree must be $^8/_{11}$ of the length of its shadow. Therefore its height is $^8/_{11}$ times 75, which is $^{600}/_{11}$, or approximately <u>54.5 feet</u>.

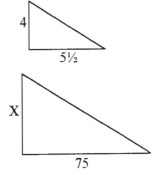

Direct and Inverse Proportions

- *Speed, time, and distance.*
  - *Speed and time are inversely proportional.*

    Example: If Jeff biked to school Monday in 20 minutes, then how long did it take Tuesday to bike to school if he went $^4/_5$ as fast?

    Solution: Since speed and time are *inversely proportional*, we can say that biking $^4/_5$ as fast means that it took $^5/_4$ (we take the reciprocal of $^4/_5$) as long. Therefore, the answer is $^5/_4$ times 20, which is <u>25 minutes</u>.

  - *Speed and distance are directly proportional.*

    Example: If Cathy went on a 56-mile bike ride on Wednesday. How far did she go on Thursday if she rode for the same amount of time but went $^7/_8$ as fast?

    Solution: Since speed and distance are *directly proportional*, we can say that biking $^7/_8$ as fast means that she goes $^7/_8$ as far (using the same fraction). The answer is then $^7/_8$ of 56, which is <u>49 miles</u>.

- *String length and frequency* (from seventh grade Physics).
  - *The ratio of two string lengths is the reciprocal of the ratio of their frequency.* In mathematics, we say that *the string length and the frequency are inversely proportional.* This means that if one thing goes up (e.g., if the length of the string gets longer), then the other (e.g., the frequency) must go down. This is consistent with our experience of string instruments - a longer string makes a lower pitch (frequency).

    Example: If a C string (90cm long) on a cello has a frequency of 256Hz, and you press your finger at the 60cm mark (which is a G - the *fifth note* above C), then what is the frequency of the resulting note? (Note that Hz stands for "hertz" and means vibrations per second.)

    Solution: The ratio of the string lengths of the two notes is G:C = 60:90 = 2:3, which means that the length of the string for the G note is ⅔ as long as the length of the string for the C note. Now we know from the above stated rule that the ratio of their frequencies will be the reciprocal of the ratio of the string lengths. Specifically, the ratio of the frequencies of the two notes must therefore be G:C = 3:2 (which is the reciprocal of 2:3). Therefore the G note has a frequency that is $^3/_2$ of the frequency of the C note. $256 \cdot ^3/_2 = $ <u>384Hz</u>.

- *The law of the lever* (from seventh grade Mechanics).
  - To balance a seesaw, *the ratio of the weights is the reciprocal of the ratio of the distances to the center of the fulcrum* (the balance point). For example, if the ratio of the weights of the left side to the right side is L:R = 3:2 then the ratio of the distances to the fulcrum is L:R = 2:3. This can be expressed as:

    The weights of two objects on a seesaw are inversely proportional to their distances away from the fulcrum. As a formula, this is: $W_L : W_R = D_R : D_L$ <u>or</u> $W_L \cdot D_L = W_R \cdot D_R$ (W is weight, H is height)

  - Experientially, if two children are trying to balance a seesaw, and the heavier one weighs $^3/_2$ as much as the lighter one, then the heavier one must sit ⅔ as far from the fulcrum as the lighter one.

    Example: If a boy, who weighs 25 kg, is sitting 1.8 meters away from the fulcrum of a seesaw, how far from the fulcrum must a girl, who weighs 20 kg, sit in order that the seesaw is balanced?

    Solution: The girl is $^4/_5$ of the boy's weight, so she must sit $^5/_4$ as far away. $^5/_4 \cdot 1.8 = $ <u>2.25m</u>.

A New Type of Number: Irrational Numbers

The Ratio in a Square (of its diagonal to its side)

- *Guessing the ratio.* Start by drawing a square on the board and ask the students to guess what the ratio of the diagonal to the side of the square might be. Certainly, they should be able to see that it is less than 2:1 (i.e., the diagonal is less than twice the length of the side). They might guess that it is 3:2 or 5:3. The best (very lucky!) guess would be 7:5.

- *The Great Pythagorean Crisis.*

  One of the central tenets of the School of Pythagoras was that God had made the world so that it was imbued with harmony and perfection. Perfect ratios were a key theme. For example, in music, they knew that the ratio of two notes an octave apart was 2:1, and that if the notes were a fifth apart, then the ratio was 3:2. (See *Direct and Inverse Proportions*, above.)

  Similarly, they believed that any two lengths were *commensurable*, meaning that they could be expressed as an exact ratio in whole number form. For example, with a rectangle that measures 2½" by 4¼", the ratio of the length to the width can be expressed as 17:10, which means that 17 times the width is *exactly* equal to 10 times the length.

  Yet the square – one of the most fundamental geometrical forms – did not yield such a simple ratio. No one could determine *exactly* what the ratio of the diagonal to the side of a square was. Then, after much effort to find this elusive ratio, someone within the School *proved* that no such ratio could possibly exist – that no matter how big the two numbers in the ratio were, there was no way to *exactly* express the ratio in whole number form.

  This discovery was so horrifying to them that it was forbidden to leak the secret outside of their school. As one version of the story goes, one person did leak it, and this transgression was found out and that person was drowned!

  This marked the discovery of a new type of number, which was so disturbing that it is known still today as an *irrational number*. (See *Irrational Numbers*, below.)

- A further study of the Pythagorean School and the "irrational crisis" is done in tenth grade.

- *The Four Ratios of a Square.* Given that X is the length of the side of a square and D is the length of its diagonal, we can express the ratio of these two lengths in one of four ways:
  - D:X ≈ 7:5
  - X:D ≈ 5:7
  - D:X ≈ 1.414:1
  - X:D ≈ 0.707:1   (0.707 comes from dividing 1.414 into 1, and also happens to be half as big.)

- *Practice calculating the diagonal or the side.*

  Example: Find the length of the side of a square that has a diagonal of 21cm.

  Solution: Using the above ratios we can get the answer by doing any of the following: X ≈ 21÷1.414, <u>or</u> X ≈ 21·0.707, <u>or</u> X ≈ 21÷$\frac{7}{5}$ <u>or</u> (the easiest method) X ≈ 21·$\frac{5}{7}$. Each answer is close to <u>15cm</u>.

π – The Ratio in a Circle (of its circumference to its diameter)

- π is the ratio of the circumference to the diameter of <u>any</u> circle.   C:D = π:1

- Have the students precisely measure various circles and calculate this ratio (in decimal form). They should measure a fairly large circle in order to minimize error and get better results. If they have done this well (and without anyone telling them a value for π) then they should get 3 point something – perhaps 3.08, or 3.12, or 3.19.

- *The impossibility of measuring.* It is interesting to have a class discussion about why the answers to the above experiment weren't all the same. It seems puzzling, since we know that all circles are similar and should therefore have the same ratio of circumference to diameter. The reason for the variation in our answers is that it is impossible to measure anything perfectly. Ultimately, there is no such thing as a perfect circle, *except in our minds.* Therefore, with the most accurate machines and tools, making the best circles possible, and measuring the diameters and circumferences with the greatest accuracy, we can get better values for this ratio, but they still won't be perfect.

- *Archimedes method for calculating π.*

  It should be briefly mentioned that Archimedes was the first one to invent a method for calculating π with as much accuracy as desired. *His method had nothing to do with measurement – Archimedes' circle was only in his mind, and he figured out how to calculate π through thinking alone.* While his method could be continued indefinitely, the calculations were very tedious. He went as far as being able to conclude that π is between $3^{10}/_{71}$ and $3^{10}/_{70}$, which, in terms of decimals, is the equivalent of saying that π is between 3.1408. and 3.1429. (Further study of Archimedes' method is done in tenth grade.)

Since Archimedes, there have been several people that have calculated π to greater accuracy using his method. Today, computers are programmed using similar methods to calculate π to several billion decimal places. But they still can never get an exact value for π, because it is an *irrational number* − it will never end and never repeat.

- *Decimal approximations for π.*

    Just as it is impossible to *exactly* express the ratio in a square (diagonal:side), so, too, is it impossible to *exactly* express the ratio of the circumference to the diameter of a circle (π) – it is *irrational!* It can be expressed approximately as a decimal, but it will never repeat or end. (**See Appendix B**, *π to 5000 Decimal Places,* to get more decimal places for π.) Here it is to 60 decimal places:

    π ≈ 3.141592653589793238462643383279502884197169399375105820974944...

- *Fractional approximations for π* (in order of least to most accuracy):

    $\dfrac{22}{7}$, $\dfrac{355}{113}$, $\dfrac{52163}{16604}$, $\dfrac{104348}{33215}$, $\dfrac{833719}{265381}$, $\dfrac{5419351}{1725033}$, $\dfrac{80143857}{25510582}$

- *The Four Ratios of π* (as opposed to thinking of π as only 3.14).
    - C:D ≈ 3.14:1
    - D:C ≈ 0.318:1   (0.318 comes from dividing 3.14 into 1)
    - C:D ≈ 22:7
    - D:C ≈ 7:22

- *Practice calculating the circumference or diameter.*
    - Save calculating the area of a circle ($A = π \cdot r^2$) for eighth grade.
    - Avoid using the formula $C = π \cdot D$ until eighth grade.
    - In seventh grade, all answers should be given as approximate decimals or fractions. In eighth grade, answers can be given in terms of π (e.g., 8π).
    - To calculate a circumference or diameter, the students should use one of the four ratios given above. Although any of the four ratios can be used for any given problem, often one of them will be the easiest, and this will vary depending upon the problem. Using different methods will produce answers that are slightly different, because they are all based on approximate, but different, values for π. The students should become adept at using each ratio; this helps to develop flexibility in their thinking.

Example: What is the circumference of a circle that has a diameter of 14m?
Solution: Here, we notice that 14 is divisible by 7, so it is easiest to use the ratio C:D ≈ 22:7, which tells us that $C ≈ \frac{22}{7} \cdot D$, and since D = 14, we do $\frac{22}{7} \cdot \frac{14}{1}$, giving us an answer of <u>44m</u>. (Notice that this is easier than doing this the typical way of multiplying 14 by 3.14.)
Example: What is the diameter of a circle that has a circumference of 330m?
Solution: With this problem, the ratio D:C ≈ 7:22 is the easiest one to use, since it is the diameter that we are trying to find and we notice that 330 and 22 are both divisible by 11. This ratio tells us that $D ≈ \frac{7}{22} \cdot C$, and since C = 330, we do $\frac{7}{22} \cdot \frac{330}{1}$, which, after cross canceling by 11, gives us $\frac{7}{2} \cdot \frac{30}{1}$, and a final answer of <u>105m</u>. (Notice that this is much easier than dividing 330 by 3.14.)
Example: What is the diameter of a circle that has a circumference of 20m?
Solution: Here, it is easiest to use the ratio D:C ≈ 0.318:1, since it is the diameter that we are trying to find. This ratio tells us that D ≈ 0.318 · C, and since C = 20 we do 0.318 · 20, which gives us an answer of <u>6.36m</u>. (Note that this is *much* easier than the typical way of dividing 20 by 3.14. Be sure to emphasize this!)
Example: What is the circumference of a circle that has a diameter of 8m?
Solution: Here, I would tend to use the typical method of multiplying 3.14 by 8, which is using the ratio C:D ≈ 3.14:1, and gives us an answer of <u>25.12m</u>. If we had used the fractional approximation for π (C:D ≈ 22:7), we would have gotten an answer of $^{22}/_7 \cdot 8 = \underline{25^1/_7}$ in. The students will ask which answer is correct, and it is important for them to understand that both are acceptable, but neither answer is *exactly* correct because we cannot say *exactly* what the value for π is. We can only approximate π, and therefore *our answers can only be approximations.*

Repeating Decimals

- What are the possibilities when we convert a fraction into a decimal by dividing the numerator by the denominator? We know that in order to get an exact answer we need to keep going until the remainder repeats or becomes zero. How long do we need to go until a division problem will repeat or end? Will it necessarily ever repeat or end? Why? **See Appendix C**, *Questions regarding Repeating Decimals*, for answers and explanations to these questions and more.

- *The two laws of repeating decimals.*
  - Every fraction (with whole numbers in the numerator and denominator) is exactly equal to a decimal that either repeats or ends. In other words, if we divide the numerator by the denominator, it will eventually repeat or end.
  - When a fraction is converted into a decimal, the most number of digits that can possibly appear under the repeat bar is one less than the number in the denominator. For example, $^5/_7$ is equal to $0.\overline{714285}$, which has 6 digits (one less than the denominator) under the repeat bar.

Irrational Numbers

- A *Rational Number* is any fraction with whole numbers in both the numerator and denominator. Given the above *Laws of Repeating Decimals*, we can also say that a rational number is a repeating or ending decimal.
- Have the students use the Guess and Check method in order to calculate decimal values for $\sqrt{5.29}$ and $\sqrt{30}$ (**See Appendix C**, *The Square Root Algorithm, Method #1*). They should discover that $\sqrt{5.29}$ is exactly equal to 2.3, but that they can't get an exact value for $\sqrt{30}$. ($\sqrt{30} \approx 5.4772255750516611345696978280802...$)
- Ask the questions: "*How far do we need to go until we are finished calculating $\sqrt{30}$?*" and "*What is the exact value of $\sqrt{30}$?*" The answer to these questions is that there is no exact decimal value for $\sqrt{30}$ and we can *never* finish it no matter how far we go!
- Irrational numbers are studied in detail in ninth and tenth grade, but here in seventh grade, the following points should be emphasized:
  - An *irrational number* is a number that cannot be expressed *exactly* as a decimal, or as a fraction.
  - An irrational number is an unending, non-repeating decimal.
  - A square root that doesn't work out evenly (e.g., $\sqrt{30}$) is one type of irrational number.
  - A calculator gives an approximation of the value of any irrational number, like $\sqrt{30}$, as would a computer that could calculate its value to one million decimal places.

(Optional) The Square Root Algorithm

Comments for the Teacher

- This unit, if done at all, needs to be done towards the end of the year.
- This unit is <u>very</u> challenging for both the students and the teacher, but very rewarding, if done well.
- An algorithm (a word derived from al-Khwarizmi's name) is a step-by-step procedure that you follow in order to do something. The word "algorithm" is associated today mostly with computers. A computer program is an algorithm.
- The *square root algorithm* is something that used to be taught in schools before the invention of the calculator. It allows someone to calculate the square root of a number to as many decimals as desired (e.g., $\sqrt{43} \approx 6.557$) in a manner similar to long division. Simply follow the proper procedure, and you'll get the answer – even if you don't understand how it works.
- The goal here is not only to teach the students how to calculate square roots, but, more importantly, *to bring the students to an understanding of why the square root algorithm works.*
- Much of the content here is taken from Ernst Schuberth's book *Introduction of Advanced Arithmetical Operations in Seventh Grade at Waldorf Schools*. I believe that teaching the square root algorithm, as Schuberth suggests, meets the seventh grader perfectly – with their thinking awakening, a sense of wonder for number, and a desire to do something really challenging.
- **See Appendix C** for a detailed lesson plan outline for teaching the square root algorithm.

Word Problems

- Don't do algebraic word problems except, perhaps, for a couple during the algebra main lesson (**see 7th Grade Algebra,** *Algebraic Word Problems*).
- *Non-algebraic word problems.* Do longer, more complex word problems than previous years, but be sure not to make them too difficult, thereby causing the students to get frustrated.

Measurement Word Problems

Example: Given 50 people and 6 gallons of juice, how much juice (in fluid ounces) is there per person?

Solution: 6 gallons is 768 fluid ounces. Dividing 768 by 50, we get <u>15.36 fluid ounces per person</u>.

Rate Problems

- Review *rate of pay* and *rate of speed* problems from sixth grade.
- In seventh grade, a good deal of time should be spent on *rate of speed* problems.
- Give problems that help develop their intuitive sense of when to multiply and when to divide.

  Example: Beth cycled down the hill from her house to school covering 5.4 miles in 11 minutes. What was her average rate of speed in miles per hour?

  Solution: Since average speed is total miles divided by total hours, we need to think of the time in hours, which here is $^{11}/_{60}$ of an hour. The speed is therefore $5.4 \div (^{11}/_{60})$, which works out to <u>$29^5/_{11}$ mph</u>.

  Example: If a train leaves Hillsdale at 7:53am and averages 75 miles per hour, at what time does it arrive at Greenville, 240 miles away?

  Solution: The travel time is $240 \div 75 = 3.2$ hours, which is $3^1/_5$ hours. One-fifth of an hour ($^1/_5 \cdot 60$) is 12 minutes, so the total travel time is 3 hours 12 minutes, which puts the train at Greenville at <u>11:05am</u>.

- *Average rate of speed* equals total distance divided by total time. $\quad \text{Average Speed} = \frac{\text{Total Distance}}{\text{Total Time}}$

  Example: If Jill bikes 5 miles to her friend's house at a rate of 20 mph, and then returns at a rate of 10 mph, then what was her average rate of speed for the whole trip?

  Solution: This is tricky!! Most people think that the average speed must be halfway between 10 and 20, which is 15 mph. That's incorrect because she spent more time going 10 mph than going 20 mph; the average rate for the whole trip must be less than 15 mph. To calculate the average speed we figure that it took her ¼ hour to get to her friend's house, and ½ hour to get back. Average rate of speed is *total distance* divided by *total time*, so we get $10 \div \frac{3}{4}$, which is $^{40}/_3$, or <u>$13\frac{1}{3}$ mph</u>.

- (Optional) *Compound rate problems.* (Problems that involve two moving objects.)
  - These problems are very challenging for the students, but very rewarding if taught well.

  Example: Jane leaves home at 10:15 jogging at 8 mph. If Sue leaves the same house at 10:35 on her bike at 18 mph, when, and how far from home, will she catch up to Jane?

  Solution: We start by figuring out how far ahead Jane is at the moment that Sue leaves. We get this distance by multiplying the rate (8 mph) times the time (20 minutes, or ⅓ of an hour), giving us $^8/_3$, which is 2⅔. We now know that *Jane is 2⅔ miles ahead at the moment that Sue leaves.*

  The real key to solving this problem is realizing that once Sue starts out, the gap between them (initially 2⅔ miles) is closing in at a rate of 10 mph (the difference of their speeds). So the real question becomes "At a rate of 10 mph, how long does it take this gap of 2⅔ miles to close in?" The answer to this is found by dividing 2⅔ by 10, giving a result of $^4/_{15}$ of an hour, which is 16 minutes. Therefore Sue catches up to Jane after 16 minutes, or at <u>10:51</u>. To determine how far from home they meet, we calculate how far Sue went, which is done by multiplying her rate (18 mph) times her elapsed time ($^4/_{15}$ of an hour), resulting in an answer of <u>4.8 miles from home</u>.

  Example: A train leaves Bigtown toward Smallville (545 miles away) at 1:20pm going 70 mph. At 1:50pm another train leaves Smallville heading for Bigtown at 50 mph. At what time, and how far from Bigtown, do they pass one another?

  Solution: We first calculate that when the second train leaves, the first train is 35 miles along the way, so at that moment the trains are 510 miles apart. They are approaching each other at a rate of 120 mph (the sum of the two speeds). We then calculate that the initial gap of 510 miles (which is closing at 120 mph) completely closes (when the trains meet) in $510 \div 120 = 4\frac{1}{4}$ hours. The trains therefore meet at <u>6:05</u>. The second train has thus traveled 212.5 miles ($4\frac{1}{4} \cdot 50$), and they therefore meet <u>332.5 miles</u> away from Bigtown.

  Another very clever way to do this problem is by using ratios. Once the second train has started (and the trains are 510 miles apart), it can be said that because the ratio of their speeds is 5:7, then the faster train must cover $^7/_{12}$ of the 510 miles, and the slower train must cover $^5/_{12}$ of it. The rest follows fairly easily and yields the same answer that we found above.

Seventh Grade Algebra

Basic Goals

Even though the subject matter may not be that different, the Waldorf approach to teaching algebra is quite different to that found in the mainstream. What makes the Waldorf approach to algebra so unique - and very powerful − is this seventh grade algebra main lesson. The crucial foundation of algebra (up to solving basic equations) is presented here in one main lesson and then no more algebra is done until eighth grade, thereby giving the children time to "digest" the material before we build on it. In the mainstream, the basic foundation is introduced, and then there is usually no pause before introducing new topics.

Keep in mind that our goal is to have our students enter high school feeling confident about their ability to do algebra, even if this main lesson is basically all of the algebra that they ever see in middle school. *Don't cover too much material during this main lesson.* It is vital that *every* student completes this main lesson feeling very confident in his/her ability to do algebra, and that this foundation for future years of algebra study is solid.

With all this in mind, it is possible to accomplish your basic goals in a brief two-week main lesson. If time is especially short, I have even taught one three-week main lesson that combines algebra with geometry. If this is done, the "heady" topic of algebra is nicely complemented with the drawing aspect of the geometry lesson. (**See Introduction,** *Algebra.*)

The Importance of Form

It is crucial for students to develop good work habits. Since this is their first experience with algebra, form and organization are actually more important than getting the problem correct. All the steps for the solution to each problem need to be written down neatly. Above all, the students must be able to follow their own work. Developing good habits now will really pay off in the years to come.

History of Algebra

- The roots of algebra go back to the Greeks, but it was the Arabs who developed the basis of algebra between 650 and 850ad.
- In the early 800's, the Abbasid Empire, perhaps the largest empire in the world at that time, was under the rule of the caliph (king) Al-Ma'mun (809-833) who was very interested in mathematics and astronomy. He collected many of the classic works from the Greeks, Jews, Hindus, and other cultures from around the world. He then established his school, *The House of Wisdom* in Baghdad, and invited the greatest scholars in his empire to join it.
- Mohammad ibn Musa al-Khwarizmi was one of the mathematicians who joined the House of Wisdom. He came from the city of Khiva in Amudarya, which was just south of the Aral Sea in what is now Uzbekistan.
- Al-Khwarizmi wrote a book around 825 called *Hisab al-jabr wal-muqabala*, which roughly translated means "the science of equations". Little, if anything, from the book was original. What made the book so great was that it was a collection of all the algebra known at that time (especially from Greece and India), and it was written in a way that people could fairly easily understand. It was translated into Latin 300 years later and it made a big impact on the mathematicians of Europe. Today, we call al-Khwarizmi *the father of algebra*.
- The book had none of the algebra notation that we take for granted today. It was written out in words, in paragraph form, like any ordinary book. Problems and their step-by-step solutions were "talked" about in normal written language. Most of our basic modern mathematical notation wasn't developed until the 1400's and 1500's. For instance, writing "+" to mean adding two numbers was first used in Germany in 1489. Negative numbers were not even accepted (e.g., as solutions to equations) until the 1600's.
- Algebra has developed into a powerful universal language that allows people to communicate complex mathematical thoughts in a simple and concise form.

Terminology

- *Equations* have an equal sign and are solved.
- *Expressions* have no equal sign and are *simplified* or *evaluated*, but not solved.
- With the equation $5X - 6 = 2X + 12$
    - X is a *variable*.
    - There are four *terms*: +5X, -6, +2X, +12.
    - 5 and 2 are both *coefficients*.
    - −6 and +12 are both *constants* because they are not attached to any variable.

Formulas

Review formulas from sixth grade.

- *Review temperature conversion formulas from sixth grade.* $C = \frac{5}{9}(F - 32)$ $F = \frac{9}{5}C + 32$

  - Now problems can be given that result in negative numbers.

  Example: 13°F is what in Celsius?
  Solution: By putting 13 into F in the first formula, we get
  $C = \frac{5}{9}(13 - 32)$. This then becomes
  $C = \frac{5}{9}(-19)$, or $C = \frac{5}{9} \cdot \frac{-19}{1}$ giving an answer of $\underline{-10\frac{5}{9}}$ °C.

Gauss's Formula for summing a sequence of numbers

$$S = \frac{N}{2} \cdot (F+L) \quad \underline{or} \quad S = N \cdot \frac{F+L}{2}$$
S is the total sum, N is the number of numbers,
F is the first number, L is the last number.

- Tell the story of Carl Friedrich Gauss (1777-1855). He was one of the greatest mathematicians ever. When Carl was 9 or 10 years old, his teacher (Herr Büttner, in a poor school in Braunschweig, Germany) gave the class the assignment to sum all the numbers from 1 to 100 (i.e. 1+2+3+4+5+...+100) in order to keep the students busy. Carl did the problem in his head almost immediately, wrote the answer on his slate, handed it in, and then sat with his hands folded while the rest of the students worked diligently and the teacher looked at him scornfully. When the teacher finally went through the stack of slates, Carl was the only one to have the correct answer: 5050. Carl realized that he could add the numbers in pairs: 1+100, and then 2+99, and then 3+98, etc. He saw that this sequence really consisted of 50 pairs of numbers, each pair adding to 101. He then simply multiplied 50 times 101 to get 5050.

- Gauss's formula (above) helps us to quickly calculate the sum of a sequence of numbers. (A *sequence* is a list of numbers that increase by the same amount each step.)
  Example: Find the sum of the sequence 13, 17, 21...53.
  Solution: We need to add   13 + 17 + 21 +...+ 53.   Instead of adding up this list one number at a time, we

  use the formula, and get: $S = 11 \cdot \frac{13+53}{2} \rightarrow S = 11 \cdot \frac{66}{2} \rightarrow S = 11 \cdot 33$ which is $\underline{363}$.

Note: It is a bit tricky figuring out what N (the number of numbers in the sequence) is. We can do this most easily by writing down all the numbers in the list until we get to 53, and we then count to see that it is the 11th number in the sequence. We could also follow this reasoning: because the *third* number (21) is *two* steps of four above the first number (13). We can determine which position 53 is in the list by asking initially: how many steps of four is 53 above 13. We see that 53 is 40 greater than 13, so we can say that 53 is *ten* steps of *four* greater than 13, which makes it the 11th number in the sequence, just as the third number (21) was *two* steps of four above 13.

Cost of Renting a Car

Example: Nifty Car Rental charges \$35 per day and 9¢ per mile. What would be the cost (before tax) for a car that is rented for one week and driven a total of 550 miles?

Solution: The formula here is: $C = 35 \cdot D + 0.09 \cdot M$
where C is the cost, D is the number days, and M is the number of miles.
Putting 7 into D, and 550 into M, we get:
$C = 35 \cdot 7 + 0.09 \cdot 550 \rightarrow C = 245 + 49.5$ giving us a final answer of $\underline{\$294.50}$.

Galileo's Law of Falling Bodies $D = 16 \cdot T^2$

- D is the distance in feet, and T is the time in seconds.
- The formula gives the distance traveled by a dropped object (assuming no air resistance).
  Example: A rock is dropped out of a plane. How far does it fall after 10 seconds?
  Solution: We put 10 into the formula, and get $D = 16 \cdot 10^2$. We must first square 10 (which is 100), then multiply by 16 to get a final answer of $\underline{1600 \text{ feet}}$.

Euclid's Perfect Number Formula $\quad P = (2^{(N-1)}) \cdot (2^N - 1)$

- Review perfect numbers from fifth or sixth grade.
- N is a whole number. Beginning with $N = 2$, this formula produces all the even perfect numbers (P), with the condition that $(2^N - 1)$ *must be a prime number.*
- *Using Euclid's formula*
  - Show that the formula generates 6 and 28 as the first two perfect numbers (which we knew from sixth grade).
      Using with $N = 2$, we get $(2^{(2-1)}) \cdot (2^2 - 1)$, which is $2^1 \cdot 3$, giving us an answer of <u>6</u>.
      Using $N = 3$, we get $(2^{(3-1)}) \cdot (2^3 - 1)$, which is $2^2 \cdot 7$, giving us an answer of <u>28</u>.
  - Have the students determine the next few perfect numbers. They should be able to come up with the third, fourth, and fifth perfect numbers fairly easily, but finding the sixth and seventh ones is somewhat challenging. (**See Appendix B,** *Euclid's Formula for Perfect Numbers.*)
  - The difficulty is determining, for a given value of N, whether $(2^N - 1)$ is *definitely* prime, which would mean that it produces a perfect number. It is helpful to give the students the following hint: *It happens to be, that for all values of N less than 20, that the values of $(2^N - 1)$ that aren't prime have either 3,5, or 7 as factors.* The only exception to this is for N=11 where $(2^N - 1) = 2047$, which isn't prime. Its only factors are 23 and 89 (e.g., $23 \cdot 89 = 2047$).
  - The first 7 perfect numbers are[1]:
      6;   28;   496;   8128;   33,550,336;   8,589,869,056;   137,438,691,328.
  - For More Details, **See Appendix B** *Euclid's Formula for Perfect Numbers.*

Positive and Negative Numbers

A Careful Introduction

- *Be Careful how Negative Numbers are Introduced.* Negative numbers should be introduced in terms of *pure number.*
- *Don't rely on pictures or a number line* in order to help the students "understand" negative numbers.
  - A number line, or even a picture of a mountain and valley below sea level (e.g., Death Valley and Mt. Whitney), misguides the students into thinking that negative numbers can be represented physically. The essence of negative numbers, however, is freed from physical space.
  - See *Separation of Form and Number* in the introduction for the reason why an over-emphasis on such a picture isn't good.
- *Introduce the concept of negative numbers* by asking "Is it possible to have less than nothing, or less than zero?" The answer is: yes. Money is one example.

Combining Positive & Negative Numbers

- *A new perspective.* $18 - 3$ is now looked at as *combining* positive 18 with negative 3, instead of subtracting 3 from 18. The result, of course, is 15 either way you look at it.
- Compare *combining* positive and negative numbers to how a checking account works.
  - A positive number means that we are making a deposit into our checking account.
  - A negative number means that we are writing a check, and therefore subtracting from our checking account.
    Example: Simplify $13 - 20 + 3 - 12 - 5$.
    Solution: This is looked at as first depositing $13, then writing a check for $20, then making a deposit for $3, then writing a check for $12, and, lastly, writing another check for $5. The final balance is $21 overdrawn, which is <u>−21</u>.
- Back-to-back signs.
  Example: $8 - -5$ becomes $8 + +5$ (Taking away a negative is the same as adding a positive), which is <u>13</u>.
  Example: These are all the same: $8 - +5$; $8 + -5$; $8 - 5$ (The answer is <u>3</u>.)

---

[1] Note that "1" is not considered to be a perfect number for the same reason that it isn't considered to be a prime number: it is the basis of all numbers. "1" can't be said to have any "genuine" factors because to get to "1" we didn't have to multiply by anything.

Multiplication Rules
Pos·Pos → Pos   (I know something.)
Neg·Pos → Neg   (I don't know anything.)
Pos·Neg → Neg   (I know nothing.)
Neg·Neg → Pos   (I don't know nothing.)

Division Rules
Pos÷Pos → Pos
Neg÷Pos → Neg
Pos÷Neg → Neg
Neg÷Neg → Pos

Practice
- Do lots of practice with positive and negative numbers using all four processes.
  Examples: Find each: (a) $-5+13$ (b) $-4\cdot7$ (c) $-12--19$ (d) $-48\div-6$
  Solutions: (a) 8   (b) -28 (c) 7   (d) 8

Expressions

Simplifying Expressions
- *Law of Any Order*: You can change the order of the terms that are being added or subtracted. This is more commonly known as the *commutative property of addition*, such as:
  Example: Simplify $4 - 3 - 11 + 12 - 14$
  Solution: We can group the negatives together and the positives together, by changing the order, to get: $4 + 12 - 3 - 11 - 14$. Now we combine the two positives to get 16 and combine the three negatives to get -28. So our expression is now: $16 - 28$, which gives a final answer of $\underline{-12}$.

- *Combining like terms.*
  Example: Simplify $3k - 16f + 7 + 5k - 21$
  Solution: We combine the two "k" terms and the +7 and –21 to get the answer $\underline{8k - 16f - 14}$.

- *Fractions and decimals* as coefficients and constants.
  Example: Simplify $\frac{2}{5}X - \frac{1}{2} - \frac{1}{3}X + \frac{2}{3}$
  Solution: Combining $\frac{2}{5}X$ and $-\frac{1}{3}X$ results in $\frac{1}{15}X$. And $-\frac{1}{2}$ combined with $\frac{2}{3}$ is $\frac{1}{6}$. Therefore, our answer is $\underline{\frac{1}{15}X + \frac{1}{6}}$.

Use an arrow to show the progression of steps with equations when working from left to right.
Example: Solve $5x - 2 = 3x + 8$
Solution: It is best to show the work so that the steps are under one another. But if it is necessary to work from left to right, then an arrow can be used to show the progression from one step to another:
$$5x - 2 = 3x + 8 \;\rightarrow\; 5x - 3x = 8 + 2 \;\rightarrow\; 2x = 10 \;\rightarrow\; \underline{x = 5}$$
Incorrect: Do not connect the steps with more equal signs because it is harder to read, such as:
$$5x - 2 = 3x + 8 = 5x - 3x = 8 + 2 = 2x = 10 = x = 5 \quad \text{(Don't do this!)}$$

Equations

An Equation is a Puzzle
The goal is to find a value (or values) that we can put into the equation in order to make the equation work, or balance. If we plug the solution into the equation, then both sides of the equation will have the same value, thereby showing that the solution works.

An Introductory Puzzle
- The following puzzle is a nice way to introduce the idea of an equation.
  We use a scale to represent the equation $3x + 9 = 5x + 2$. First, we place 9 equal weights and 3 bags on the left side of the scale, where each bag is hiding the solution ($3\frac{1}{2}$ weights) inside it. We also place 2 weights and 5 bags (with each bag again hiding $3\frac{1}{2}$ weights) on the right side of the scale. The scale should balance. Each bag represents the *variable* (or *unknown*). The students should be told that all the bags have the same number of weights inside them and that the goal is to solve the puzzle: How many weights are in each bag? Soon the students should come to realize that they can remove two weights from each side of the scale, and that they can remove three bags from each side. The scale remains balanced with 2 bags on one side and 7 weights on the other. They can then figure out that each bag must contain half of 7, or $3\frac{1}{2}$

weights. Make sure that all the students really understand each step that was done in order to solve the puzzle. Review it thoroughly the next day, and then show the equivalent puzzle being solved as an equation, like this:

$$3x + 9 = 5x + 2$$
$$\underline{ -2 = -2}$$
$$3x + 7 = 5x$$
$$\underline{-3x -3x}$$
$$7 = 2x$$
$$\underline{\div 2 \div 2}$$
$$\boxed{3\tfrac{1}{2} = x}$$

Solving by Guess and Check (Trial and Error)

- The idea with this method is to guess what the solution is and then check to see if it works.
- This method is obviously not very efficient, and would almost surely fail if the solution to the equation happened to be a fraction (e.g., $^{13}/_{21}$).

Example: Solve for x: $3x + 8 = 8x - 2$

Solution: We simply try plugging in different values for X, and see if it balances the equations. If we put in 5 for x, we get 23 on the left side of the equation, and 38 on the right side. Therefore, 5 is not a solution to the equation. After a while, and with a bit of luck, we finally guess the correct answer, which is X=2. We see that it works, because when we put in 2 for X we get 14 on both sides of the equation.

The Golden Rule of Equations

"What is done to one side of the equation must also be done to the other."

- It is crucial for the students to understand and remember this.

Solving Equations by Balancing

- Solve simple equations by showing that the same is done to both sides, step-by-step (balancing).
- *This is the most important concept of the entire main lesson.* Every student should come to a thorough understanding of the below example.

Example: Solve for x: $3x - 23 - 7x = 11 + 8x + 2$

Solution:
$$3x - 23 - 7x = 11 + 8x + 2$$
$$-4x - 23 = 8x + 13$$
$$\underline{+4x +4x}$$
$$-23 = 12x + 13$$
$$\underline{-13 -13}$$
$$-36 = 12x$$
$$\underline{\div 12 \div 12}$$
$$\boxed{-3 = x}$$

- Solve equations that have *fractional solutions*, such as:

Example: $7x + 4 = 10$. (Answer: $x = {}^{6}/_{7}$)

- Work up to equations with *fractional coefficients and constants*. (This can be delayed until eighth grade.)

Example: $\frac{2}{3}X + \frac{7}{8} - X = \frac{3}{4} - \frac{3}{5}X$

Solution:
$$\frac{2}{3}X + \frac{7}{8} - X = \frac{3}{4} - \frac{3}{5}X$$

$$\frac{2}{3}X + \frac{7}{8} - \frac{3}{3}X = \frac{3}{4} - \frac{3}{5}X$$

$$-\frac{1}{3}X + \frac{7}{8} = \frac{3}{4} - \frac{3}{5}X$$

$$\underline{+\frac{3}{5}X \qquad\qquad +\frac{3}{5}X}$$

$$\frac{4}{15}X + \frac{7}{8} = \frac{3}{4} \qquad \text{(because } -\frac{1}{3}X + \frac{3}{5}X \text{ is } \frac{4}{15}X\text{)}$$

$$\underline{-\frac{7}{8} \qquad -\frac{7}{8}}$$

$$\frac{4}{15}X = -\frac{1}{8} \qquad \text{(because } \frac{3}{4} - \frac{7}{8} \text{ is } -\frac{1}{8}\text{)}$$

$$\underline{\div\frac{4}{15} \qquad \div\frac{4}{15}}$$

$$1X = -\frac{1}{8} \cdot \frac{15}{4}$$

Answer: $\boxed{X = -\frac{15}{32}}$

Algebraic Word Problems

Key Ideas

- Word problems are *not* a major theme of the main lesson. Don't overdo it! The idea is to show the students that algebra is a powerful tool that can be used to solve problems or puzzles. Be careful not to lose any of the students here. It may be fine to do no algebraic word problems during this main lesson block.

- With an algebraic word problem, we must translate an English statement into an algebraic equation.

- Mathematical thoughts can be expressed more clearly and concisely in algebra than in English.

    Example: The English sentence: "Two less than a number is ten more than two times that number", is translated into the equation: "$X - 2 = 2X + 10$".

- Algebra is a *universal language*. No matter where you are in the world, algebra is the language for communicating mathematical ideas.

- Perhaps it is best to only do one very clear problem, which is then put into their main lesson book.

    Example: 4 less than 5 times a number is 14 more than two times that same number. What is that number?
    Solution: Remembering that "is" means "=", we translate this perplexing sentence into the equation: $5X - 4 = 2X + 14$, which we can easily solve to get an answer of X=6.

Seventh Grade Geometry

Area

- Review *Area* from sixth grade.

The Shear and Stretch

- This is a "visual proof" of the formula for the area of a parallelogram and of a non-right triangle (see below).
- There are three different variations of the Shear and Stretch that Euclid proves as theorems in his book *The Elements*. They are:
  - If two parallelograms lie between the same two parallel lines, and their bases have the same length, then their areas are equal. (See drawing below.)
  - If two triangles lie between the same two parallel lines, and their bases have the same length, then their areas are equal. (See drawing below.)
  - If a triangle and a parallelogram lie between the same two parallel lines and have the same length base, then the area of the triangle is half the area of the parallelogram. (Drawing not shown.)

- The central idea is to imagine slicing the parallelogram (or triangle) into infinitely many thin strips, and then sliding its top along the upper parallel line, thereby stretching it out. In this way, we can transform any parallelogram into a rectangle of equal area, or transform any non-right triangle into a right triangle.
- In order to visualize the height, the students should imagine dropping a ball from the top. The height is how far the ball drops before hitting the ground. In this way, we can see that the heights remain the same. And since the height and base have not changed, the area of the figure does not change either as the figure is stretched.
- Show that this also works if the parallel lines run vertically or at a slant (in preparation for Baravalle's proof of the Pythagorean Theorem in eighth grade).

Area of a Parallelogram

- We only need to know the length of the base and the height.
- The area is the *Base* times the *Height*, which is: **A = B·H**.
  Example: Find the area of the parallelogram on the right.
  Solution: It is best for the students to picture the parallelogram "righting" itself by having its top sliding over until it becomes a rectangle. We can see that the length of the side (4 in) doesn't matter. The area is: $3 \cdot 6 = \underline{18in^2}$

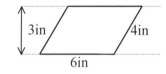

Area of a Non-Right Triangle

- We only need to know the length of the base and the height.
- The area is *half* the *Base* times *Height*, which is: **A = ½B·H**.
  Example: Find the area of the triangle on the right.
  Solution: Again, we picture the apex of the triangle sliding parallel to the base until it becomes a right triangle, then we can see that the area is equal to: $\frac{1}{2} \cdot 3 \cdot 4 = \underline{6 \ cm^2}$

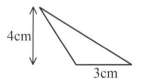

Geometric Drawing

- Review sixth grade Geometric Drawing and Basic Constructions.
- *More than just Pretty Pictures.* In sixth grade, the geometry main lesson allows the students to dive into the artistic realm with their geometric drawings. I believe that the emphasis with seventh grade geometry should be less on the artistic and more on accuracy and thought content. The material presented should be a good balance between the thinking realm and the artistic. This main lesson is best done toward the end of the year.

Triangle Constructions (optional)

The instructions given here for each drawing are intended for the teacher only. Mostly, the students should learn to do each drawing by watching the teacher do it on the board.

- **SSS (side-side-side):** *Constructing a triangle given three line segments.*
  Instructions (for the teacher only): We are given three line segments (a, b, c), and our objective is to construct a triangle that has its sides equal to the length of these three segments. Start by drawing a horizontal line segment that is somewhat longer than segment c. Using a compass, copy the length of c onto this line segment (**see 6ᵗʰ grade Geometry,** *Copying a Line Segment*). This is now the base of our triangle. Set the width of the compass equal to the length of segment a, and by placing the compass needle on the right end of the base of the triangle (point B), draw a short arc close to where the apex of the triangle will end up. Now set the width of the compass equal to the length of segment b, place the compass needle on the left end of the base of the triangle (point A), and draw an arc that passes through the arc previously drawn. These two arcs pass through the third point (the apex, or point C) of the triangle. Check, by using your compass, to see if the three sides of the triangle ABC are indeed equal in length to the original three given line segments.

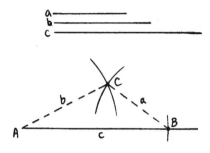

  Note: This construction will not work if the longest given line segment is equal to, or longer than, the sum of the other two given line segments.

- **SAS (side-angle-side):** *Constructing a triangle given two sides and an in-between angle.*
  Instructions (for the teacher only): We are given two line segments (a and c) and an angle (B), and our objective is to construct a triangle that has two of its sides equal in length to these two given sides, and that has the angle that is *in-between* these two sides equal to the given angle. Start by drawing a horizontal line segment that is somewhat longer than segment c. Using a compass, copy the length of c onto this line segment (**see 6ᵗʰ grade Geometry,** *Copying a Line Segment*). This is now the base of our triangle. Now copy angle B so that its vertex falls on the left side of the base of the triangle. In the drawing here, this is shown as the two arcs intersecting at point Q. (**See 6ᵗʰ grade Geometry,** *Copying an Angle.*) Draw a line segment from point B through and beyond point Q, making sure that it is longer than the

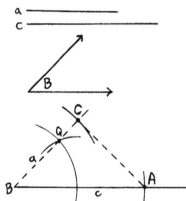

  line segment a (the original given line segment). Now copy line segment a onto the line segment BQ, so that the length from B to C is equal to the given line segment a. Lastly, draw a line connecting points A and C. Triangle ABC is the desired triangle.
  Note: This construction will work for any angle and any two line segments.

- **ASA (angle-side-angle):** *Constructing a triangle given two angles and an in-between side.*
  Instructions (for the teacher only): We are given one line segment (c) and two angles (A and B). Our objective is to construct a triangle that has a side equal in length to the given side (c), and that has the two angles that are adjacent to that side and equal to the two given angles (A and B). This construction is very similar to the SAS construction done above. Start by using the same steps given with the SAS construction to draw side c with angle A constructed onto its left end. Then copy the second angle (B) onto the other end of side c. The drawing here shows that points R and Q are used to copy angles A and B to the triangle. We then extend the lines AR and BQ until they intersect at point C, which is the third point of the triangle. We finish by drawing a line that connects points A and C, and then a line that connects points B and C. Triangle ABC is the desired triangle.

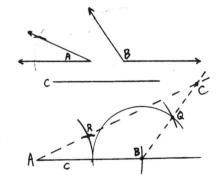

  Note: This drawing will not work if the two angles combine to 180° or more.

Seventh Grade

- *SSA (side-side-angle). Constructing a triangle given two sides and a non-in-between angle.*
  Instructions (for the teacher only): As with the SAS construction, we are given two sides and an angle. This drawing is, however, much more complicated. Of the two given line segments, one (b) is intended to be adjacent to the triangle's given angle (A), and the other line segment (a) is then attached to the other end of side b. Since the angle in-between these two sides is not given, we can imagine that there is a hinge between sides a and b that swings open or closed until it finds the proper moment when the desired triangle is found. The actual construction is not very complicated. As with the SAS construction, we simply copy line segment b onto the base of the triangle (with endpoints A and C), and then copy angle A (by finding point Q) so that angle A lies on the right side of side b. Now extend AQ well beyond Q.

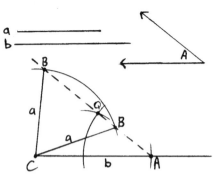

Then set the compass to the length of given segment a, and by placing the compass needle at point C, draw an arc. Depending on the sizes of the given angle and sides, this arc may end up crossing the extended line AQ in one or two places, or not at all. In the drawing shown, the arc crosses line AQ in two places. This means that for this drawing there are two possible shapes for the desired triangle ABC, since B could be in either of two places (as shown in the drawing).

Note: In general, there are 6 possibilities for this SSA construction, depending on the sizes of the two sides and the given angle:

1. The angle is acute, and side a (the "swinging" side) is shorter than side b and crosses the line AQ in two places. This results in two possible triangles as the solution. (This case is shown in the above drawing.)
2. The angle is acute, and side a is shorter than side b but barely reaches the line AQ, thereby forming a right angle. The result is one right triangle as a solution.
3. The angle is acute, and side a is shorter than side b, and is not long enough to reach line AQ. The result is an impossible triangle; there is no solution.
4. The angle is acute, and side a is longer than side b, therefore crossing line AQ in just one place, and resulting in one solution.
5. The angle is either right or obtuse, and side a is longer than side b. This results in exactly one solution.
6. The angle is either right or obtuse, and side a is shorter than side b. This triangle is impossible because side a cannot reach the line AQ; there is no solution.

- *(optional) AAS (angle-angle-side): A triangle given two angles and a non-in-between side.*
  Instructions: (for the teacher only): This is the most complicated construction. We are given two of the three angles in a triangle and a side that is not in-between them. We start by copying line segment a to the base of the triangle, and angle B adjacent to it, as we did with the SAS construction. We then label the endpoints of this base as C and B. Next, we extend the other side of angle B (in the drawing, this is segment BQ) well beyond Q and label its endpoint as point M. Then, we copy angle A to point M (by finding point R). We now need to construct the third side of the triangle, which passes through point C and is parallel to MR. We do this by first extending segments BC and MR to meet at point E. Now, copy angle CEF to DCT. (We could have instead copied angle CEM to angle BCA.) We have now located point A and have therefore determined the third side (AC) of the desired triangle ABC.

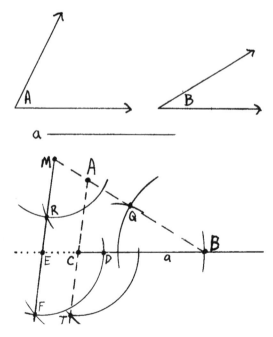

62

Euclidean Constructions - The Greek "Geometric Game" (optional)

- *The three rules of the game.*
  1. A *straightedge* can only be used to draw a line through two chosen points.
  2. A *compass* can only be used to draw a circle (or a part of a circle) with a chosen point as its center and a determined distance (the width of the compass) as its radius.
  3. Other than a compass and straightedge, no other tools (e.g., a ruler, a protractor, drawing triangle, etc.) may be used.

- *Why compass and straightedge only?* According to the Greeks, all geometric constructions were to be done using only two tools: a compass and a straightedge (without any marks for the purpose of measurement). Marked rulers, protractors, and right-angled drawing triangles were not allowed. For the Greeks, this was a challenging mental game. The objective was to come up with theoretically perfect methods to do certain constructions using only these two tools. Some constructions turn out to be very simple, such as bisecting an angle, or putting a hexagon in a circle. Some constructions were fairly complicated, such as constructing a pentagon, or constructing a square that is equal in area to a given polygon. Some construction puzzles were never solved by the Greeks, such as the construction of a 7-gon, the construction of a 17-gon, and the trisection of an angle. Some two thousand years later, a few of the solutions (e.g., the 17-gon) were discovered, but most were proved to be impossible (e.g., the 7-gon, and the trisection of an angle).

- *Recommended Reading.* Julia Diggins' book, *String Straightedge and Shadow*, gives a great, readable summary of the history and thinking of Greek geometry.

Various Methods for doing Constructions (optional)

- There are four types of methods for doing constructions:
  1. *Euclidean constructions with compass and straightedge.* These are the theoretically exact, Euclid-approved constructions (i.e., the "game" described above) that are done in sixth and seventh grade. The students should come to an understanding that *in practice* no construction can be absolutely perfect. A perfect square, for instance, has four sides that are *exactly* equal, and its angles are all *exactly* 90°. Nobody can construct a *perfect* square. On the other hand, *in theory*, we can *imagine* in our minds a construction that is absolutely perfect.

  2. *Measurement constructions.* These constructions allow the use of a protractor, a drawing triangle, or a ruler (as opposed to just a straightedge), and can be, *in practice*, quite accurate, but because you can never measure anything with *perfect* accuracy, they are not *theoretically perfect*, and therefore would have been frowned upon by Euclid.
     Example: Most people construct a square using a drawing triangle (or protractor) and a ruler.

  3. *The guess and check method.* Here we use a compass (or perhaps something else) as a tool for *guessing* how big a length should be, see how much error results, and then adjust the compass and redo the construction. We keep *guessing, checking, and adjusting* until we get satisfactory results. This method is not theoretically perfect (and not Euclid-approved), but can be in practice as close to perfect as we would like. Any regular polygon can be done quite accurately and quickly this way.
     Example: To construct a 15-gon inside a circle, we first guess what the length of a side of the 15-gon will be, and set the compass width equal to that. Mark a point on the circle, place the compass needle on that point, and then make a cross on the circle. We now have two of the 15 required points on the circle. Using that same compass width, step around the circle marking one point at a time. If the results are good, then the 15th step should come out right at the original point on the circle. If the results aren't satisfactory, then simply adjust the compass slightly and try it again. Usually the third guess produces very accurate results.

  4. *Approximate constructions.* These constructions are done mostly for Euclidean impossible constructions, and are useful because they are a specific method that can, in practice, quickly produce very accurate constructions. They are not theoretically perfect, but they have little error.
     Example: Many different approximate constructions are known for cases that are impossible by Euclidean means. One such case is the construction of a regular 7-gon inside a given circle, which uses the fact that the length of the side of the 7-gon (A in the left figure) is *almost* equal to the length of the inscribed hexagon's short radius (B in the right figure). This has, in theory, only 0.2% error!

Geometric Division

- This is a good way to practice some of the skills learned in sixth grade, and in the process some very beautiful drawings can be created.
- We can best do geometric division with a polygon that has a large number of sides (n), where n is not a prime number. 12-gons, 15-gons, 20-gons, and 24-gons all produce good results.

- *Geometric division of a 12-gon.*
  Construction: Start by drawing 6 circles and then mark the 12 points of the 12-gon around each circle (**See 6th Grade Geometry,** *Constructing a Dodecagon*). With the first circle, draw lines that connect consecutive points. This is division by 1, since each step moves one point over. In the next circle (division by 2), draw lines that connect every other point, which produces (look carefully!) two overlapping hexagons. In the next circle, draw lines that connect every third point. This is division by 3, and it produces three squares. In the next circle (division by 4), we connect every fourth point, which results in four triangles.

  In the next circle (division by 5), we get a 12-pointed star. Here, we end up going around the circle completely 5 times before we finally return to the point where we started. To prove this to yourself, place your finger on the top-most point of the star (labeled "÷5"), and then trace with your finger following along the lines until you get back to where you started. Finally, division by 6 produces just six diagonals of the circle. For an added challenge, ask the class what happens if we divide by 7, 8, 9, 10 and 11. **Answer:** The drawings are the same! Division by 7 is the same as division by 5; division by 8 is the same as division by 4, etc.

- *Geometric division of a 15-gon.*
  Construction: Start by drawing 6 circles of equal size, and then mark off the 15 points around each circle by using the *guess and check method* as described above. Then draw the different forms resulting from each division by following the same general procedure as outlined above in *Geometric Division of a 12-gon.*
  - Notice that division by 2, by 4, and by 7 all produce different 15-pointed stars.
  - The surprise with this construction is that a 15-gon is geometrically divisible by 6 (producing 3 pentagrams), even though the number 15 is not evenly divisible by 6. This is because 6 and 15 have a common factor of 3.

Star Patterns with Geometric Division (**See Appendix A,** for drawings)

- Looking at the drawings in Appendix A, we can see that the top drawing of each column is a certain geometric division of the 12-gon. The three star patterns, which are drawn under each one, result from taking the top drawing and then carefully erasing parts of the lines.

The Pentagon and the Golden Ratio (or Golden Section)

Constructing the Pentagon (with nested pentagons and pentagrams)

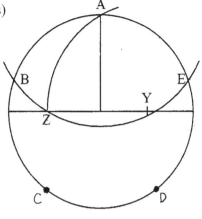

- Draw a circle, and a diameter of that circle. Find the midpoint, Y, of the radius (Y is ¼ way along the diameter). Draw the perpendicular bisector of the diameter, which intersects the circle at point A. Placing the needle of the compass at Y, draw an arc through A to point Z on the diameter. The distance from A to Z is precisely the length of the sides of the desired pentagon. Place the needle of the compass at A, and draw an arc through Z that intersects the circle at points B and E. Points A, B, and E are three of the points of the pentagon. Now, keeping the compass at the same width, place the needle at B and draw an arc that crosses the circle at C. Similarly, place the needle at E, and draw an arc that crosses the circle at D. The sides of the pentagon are now drawn by connecting, in order, the points A, B, C, D, and E. With your compass, check to see that the five sides have equal length. Create as many nested pentagrams and pentagons as desired by drawing the diagonals of the pentagons. (See drawing at bottom of page.)

Places where the Pentagon Appears

- *The human being.* A person's head, hands, and feet form the five points of a pentagon.
- *Cutting an apple.* If you cut an apple horizontally such that the knife cuts through the "equator" of the apple, then the core is seen as a pentagon.
- *Flowers.* Several flowers have five petals.
- *Sea life.* Starfish and sea urchins have five tentacles.
- *A paper knot.* If a half-hitch (a simple knot) is tied in a rope, then a pentagon is formed. This can be seen most clearly by taking a strip of ordinary paper (perhaps 1" by 11"), and carefully tying a simple half hitch in it and flattening it out. A pentagon, with a pentagram inside it, can then be seen if it is held up to a light.

A Paper Knot

The Geometrical Properties of the *nested pentagon and pentagram* drawing

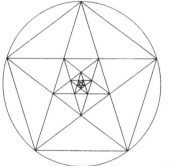

- Of all the triangles to be found in this drawing, there are only two shapes. Every triangle is either similar to the tall isosceles triangle, or similar to the wide (obtuse-angled) isosceles triangle.
- Point out similar rhombuses, and trapezoids[1].
- Each angle of the pentagon is trisected (divided into three equal angles) by the pentagram that sits inside it.
  Question: Given that the angle in the pentagon is trisected, what are all the angles inside each of the two types of isosceles triangles?
  Answer: There are five overlapping tall isosceles triangles inside the largest pentagon. Given that the angle of the pentagon is trisected, we can see that the base angle of one of these triangles is bisected by the apex of another one of these triangles. Therefore the base angle is twice the apex angle. By using the fact that the angles inside a triangle add to 180°, and setting the apex angle to X, and the base angle to 2X, we get: X + 2X + 2X = 180. Solving this gives us X = 36°, and that the base angles (2X) are 72°. It follows that the wide isosceles triangle has its base angles equal to 36° and its apex angle is 108°. Notice that this also shows that the angle inside a regular pentagon is 108°.

[1] A *rhombus* is a quadrilateral (four-sided figure) that has all sides equal. It looks like a "pushed-over" square. A *trapezoid* is a quadrilateral where one pair of opposite sides is parallel.

The Golden Ratio Φ

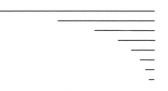

- Look at the drawing of the *nested pentagons and pentagrams* above. There are many line segments of differing lengths within this drawing. Carefully copy all line segments of different length so that they lie above one another in order of longest to shortest (see drawing at right). There are two amazing properties that can be stated regarding these line segments:
    1. The length of any line segment is equal to the sum of the lengths of the previous two shorter segments.
    2. Each line segment is approximately 61.8% longer than the previous one. Alternatively, we can say that *each line is about 1.618 times as big as the previous one.* This number (approximately 1.618) is known as the *golden ratio*, or Φ.
- Mathematically, we say that the ratio of the lengths of the diagonal to the side of a pentagon is Φ:1.
- Φ (written as "phi" and rhymes with "my") is, as with π, an irrational number (**see 7th Grade Arithmetic,** *Irrational Numbers*). Expressed as a decimal, it never repeats or ends, and is approximately equal to 1.61803398874989485...
    - Amazingly, if we square this number (with its infinitely many decimal digits) we get the exact same number, but starting instead with a 2 (i.e., **2**.618033...). And if we take the reciprocal (i.e., divide it into 1), then we get the exact same number, but starting with a 0 (i.e., **0**.618033...).
- The successive bones in a human hand are approximately in a ratio of Φ:1.

The Fibonacci Sequence

1, 1, 2, 3, 5, 8, 13, 21, 34, 55, 89, 144, 233…

- In 1225, Leonardo de Pisa (best known as Fibonacci) came up with his famous sequence.
- To get the sequence, you start with two 1's, and then each term is simply the sum of the previous two terms.
- There are many amazing properties associated with this sequence. One surprising property is that the further you move along the sequence, the closer the ratio (e.g., in whole number form) gets to Φ (approximately 1.618033). For example, $233 \div 144 \approx 1.618056$. Furthermore, the same thing happens even if you modify the sequence by starting with two different numbers. For example, start with 4 and 7. Once again, the further you go, the closer the ratio gets to Φ. Try it!

The Golden Rectangle

- **One Method for Constructing** a golden rectangle is to use the length of the side of a pentagon as the rectangle's height, and to use the length of that same pentagon's diagonal as the rectangle's base.
- With the golden rectangle, the ratio of the length to the width is Φ:1 (which is also the ratio of the diagonal to the side of a pentagon).
- This is the only shape for a rectangle where you can cut off a square (ABCD), and the remaining smaller rectangle (BEFC) will be similar to the original rectangle (AEFD).
- **Alternate Construction:** Construct a square. Mark the corners clockwise from top left A,B,C,D. Extend lines AB, and DC to the right. Using a compass, construct the midpoint (x) of AB, and the midpoint (y) of DC. Place the needle at x, and draw an arc so that it passes through point C and intersects the extended part of the line AB to the right of B at point E. Draw another arc with the needle at y, so that it passes through point B and intersects the extended part of the line DC to the right of C at point F. AEFD is a golden rectangle, and so is BEFC.

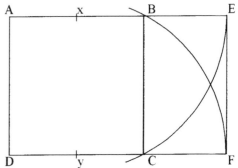

- *Historical Importance.*
    - The Golden Rectangle was considered the most aesthetically pleasing proportions for a rectangle.
    - The Parthenon was built using golden rectangles.
    - If we take a golden rectangle, split it along its diagonal, and join the two resulting right triangles along their middle-sized sides, then we get the shape of the isosceles triangle that was used to build the Great Pyramid. (See drawing at right.)

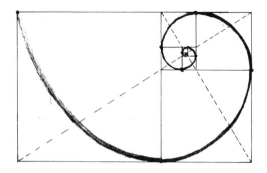

- *The Rectangle of Whirling Squares* (<u>The Golden Spiral</u>).
  Construction: Construct a large golden rectangle and then
  draw a line that divides the rectangle into a square and
  a smaller golden rectangle. Draw a diagonal across the
  original (larger) rectangle, and a diagonal across the
  smaller rectangle, so that they intersect. Draw a line
  dividing the smaller rectangle into a square and another
  golden rectangle, and divide that rectangle, and every
  succeeding one in the same manner, so that the squares
  spiral in toward the intersection of the two diagonals.
  The students should draw the spiral freehand as shown
  in the drawing at the right.

(Optional) <u>The Golden Triangle and its Spiral</u>

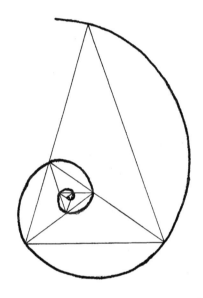

Construction: Start with the tall acute triangle that appears
in the *nested pentagon drawing,* as described above.
(Alternatively, you can construct the same triangle by
using a protractor to make the apex angle equal to 36°
and the two base angles equal to 72°.) Draw a line that
bisects the base angle on the right side, thereby creating
two smaller triangles, one of which is similar to the
original. As was done with the Rectangle of Whirling
Squares, keep dividing the smaller triangle into two
triangles, so that the smaller triangles spiral in toward a
point.

Angle Theorems and Proofs

<u>Review</u> these three ideas from sixth grade (without giving proofs).
- The sum of angles forming a straight line equals 180°.
- The sum of angles forming a full rotation equals 360°.
- Vertical angles are congruent.

Theorems arising from Two Parallel Lines Cut by a Transversal

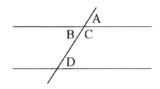

- *A Transversal* is a line that crosses two parallel lines.
- *Corresponding angles are congruent* (equal).
  - Corresponding angles are two angles in similar locations at different intersections, when two parallel lines are cut by a transversal. Angles A and D are corresponding angles in the drawing on the right – they are both at the northeast corner of their intersections.

  Proof: Of the two parallel lines, imagine that the bottom one moves toward the top one, while keeping the two lines parallel. This pushes angle D upward, but does not change it. We keep moving the bottom line upward until it coincides with the top line. At that moment, angle D coincides with angle A, so we can see that angles D and A are congruent.

- *Alternate interior angles are congruent.*
  - B and D are alternate interior angles in the above drawing.

  Proof: (This proof should only be given orally to the students.) We know that angles A and D are congruent because they are corresponding angles, and we know that angles A and B are congruent because they are vertical angles. And because angles B and D are both congruent to angle A, they must be congruent to each other.

- *Same-side interior angles add to 180°.*
  - C and D are same-side interior angles in the above drawing.

  Proof: (This proof should only be given orally to the students.) We know that angles A and C are supplementary, because they form a straight line. Angles A and D are corresponding angles and therefore congruent. So instead of saying that A and C are supplementary, we can replace "A" with "D" and therefore say that D and C are supplementary.

The Angles in a Triangle add to180°

Two visual proofs:
- *Cutting Out Angles.* Construct any random triangle, and then use a colored pencil to shade-in inside the vertex of each angle. Cut out the three angles with scissors. Place the shaded-in angles point to point in order to see that they form a straight line (180°). While this is not a "mathematically exact" proof, it is a wonderful way to give the children a sense of truth about the fact that the angles in a triangle add to 180°.

- *The Half-wheel Theorem.* Imagine that the base of the triangle moves upward. As it moves upward, the two base angles are pushed upward, but remain unchanged in size (degree measure). At the moment that the triangle has become infinitely small, we can see that the three angles of the triangles form a straight line (180°). This sequence can be made clearer by coloring in the angles rather than labeling them as A, B, C. In the above drawing, all the angles labeled A could be green, the B angles could be red, and the C angles could be blue.

The Angles in Polygons other than Triangles (optional)

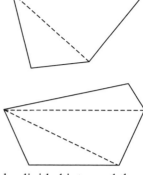

- *The angles in any quadrilateral add to 360°.*
  - To prove this, simply demonstrate that any quadrilateral can be divided into 2 triangles. Since the number of degrees in one triangle is 180°, then a quadrilateral must have 2·180°, which is 360°.
- *The angles in any pentagon add to 540°.*
  - To prove this, simply demonstrate that any pentagon can be divided into 3 triangles. Since the number of degrees in one triangle is 180°, then a pentagon must have 3·180°, which is 540°.
- *For any polygon* we simply need to figure out how many triangles (N) it can be divided into, and then multiply that number (N) times 180°.
  Example: Any octagon can be divided into 6 triangles, so the number of degrees in any octagon is:
  6·180° = 1080°.

Angle Puzzles (optional)

- There are limitless possibilities for making puzzles with angles.
- Build up to problems like this (see drawing at the right):
  Example: Fill in all the missing angles, given that the top and bottom lines are parallel, and X = 60° and Y = 110°.
  Solution: We use all that we know about two parallel lines and a transversal, supplementary angles, and the fact that the angles in a triangle add to 180°. A key realization is that Q and X are corresponding angles (and therefore equal), and so are angles Y and F.
  A = B = R = T = 120°; C = Q = S = 60; L = F = D = 110°;
  E = G = M = P = 70°; J = H = 50°; K = I = 130°

Theorem of Thales
- The theorem states:
  Any triangle (or angle) inscribed in a semi-circle is a right triangle (or right angle).

Theorem of Morley (optional) (**See Appendix A** for drawing.)
- The theorem states:
  The six angle trisectors of any triangle meet to form an equilateral triangle.
- Since there is no general method for trisecting an angle, the students will need to use a protractor in order to do this construction.
- This drawing is a wonderful example of how order can emerge from chaos.

Pythagorean Theorem

With any right triangle, the area of the square of the hypotenuse is equal to the sum of the areas of the squares of the other two sides.

- *Important!* The emphasis in seventh grade is on the general concept of the theorem − the relationship between the areas of the squares − rather than using the theorem to find the length of a missing side.

Visual proofs

- *A cutout puzzle.*
  With any non-isosceles right triangle (perhaps students work in groups, and each group draws a slightly different right triangle), draw a square coming off each of the three sides. Extend two lines from the sides of the largest square so that they cut through the other two squares, in each case dividing the squares into a triangle and a trapezoid. Draw a line perpendicular to the line that divided the second largest square, by starting at the intersection point on the edge of that square. The second largest square has now been cut into three pieces: two triangles and a quadrilateral having two right angles. Cut the 5 pieces (see drawing on the right) out of the two smaller squares. Place these 5 pieces on top of the large square so that they fit perfectly. This is a great geometric puzzle! Have the class do this <u>before</u> saying anything about the theorem, and then ask them what the drawing shows. It shows that the sum of the areas of the two smaller squares equals the area of the largest square.

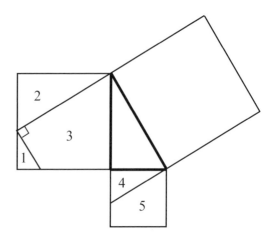

- *The case of the isosceles right triangle.*
  With an isosceles right triangle, draw squares off each of the triangles. Draw two diagonals across the large square, and one diagonal across each of the smaller squares. We now see that there are nine equal-sized triangles in the drawing, and that the largest square therefore is composed of the same number of triangles (four) as the sum of the number of triangles found in the two smaller squares.

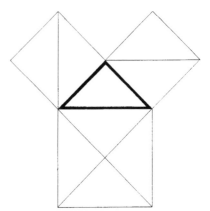

The Isosceles Right Triangle

- *The case of the 3-4-5 triangle.*
  - Draw a 3" by 4" by 5" right triangle with squares off each of the three sides of the triangle. Divide each square into a grid of one-inch squares. The students can now easily count the number of square inches found inside each square, and therefore see for themselves that the area of the two smaller squares (9 and 16 square inches) adds up to the area of the largest square (25 square inches).
  - This construction can be done for any right triangle where the three sides work out to be a Pythagorean triple. (e.g., 5-12-13; See *Pythagorean triples*, below.)

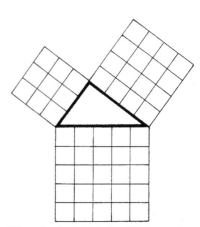

The 3-4-5 Right Triangle

Pythagorean Triples (optional – can instead be covered in eighth grade)

- Pythagorean triples are the three sides of a right triangle, where all three sides work out as whole numbers.

    Example: If the two legs are 28 and 96, then we calculate the areas of the squares of these two sides to be 28^2 and 96^2, which is 784 and 9216. According to the Pythagorean Theorem, the area of the third square (off the side of the hypotenuse), must be the sum of these two squares, 784 + 9216, which is 10,000. The length the hypotenuse is therefore equal to $\sqrt{10000}$, which is 100 (a whole number). Therefore, all three sides are whole numbers, and 28, 96, and 100 make a Pythagorean triple. This triple can be reduced (by dividing all three sides by 4) to the *primitive* triple 7, 24, 25.

    Example: If the two legs of a right triangle are 2 and 3, then by using the Pythagorean theorem, we see that the area of the square attached to the hypotenuse must be $2^2 + 3^2 = 13$. The length of the hypotenuse must therefore be $\sqrt{13}$, which is not a whole number. Therefore the three sides of this right triangle ($2, 3, \sqrt{13}$) do *not* constitute a Pythagorean triple.

- *Pythagoras's formula* for creating Pythagorean triples.
    $$X = 2n + 1 ; \qquad Y = 2n^2 + 2n ; \qquad Z = 2n^2 + 2n + 1$$
    - Choose any positive whole number value for n, put it into the above formulas, and X, Y, and Z will be a Pythagorean triple.
    - This formula only produces the triples that have two sides that are one apart (e.g., 5, 12, 13).

    Example: Choosing n = 5 we get X = 2·5+1 = <u>11</u>; Y = 2·5^2 + 2·5 = <u>60</u>; and Z = 2·5^2 + 2·5 + 1 = <u>61</u>.

- *Plato's formula* for creating Pythagorean triples.
    $$X = 2n ; \qquad Y = n^2 - 1; \qquad Z = n^2 + 1 \qquad \text{(beginning with n = 2)}$$
    - This formula only produces the triples that have two sides that are two apart (e.g., 8, 15, 17), and some of them are not reduced triples (e.g., 6, 8, 10).

    Example: Choosing n = 5 we get X = 2·5 = <u>10</u>; Y = 5^2 − 1 = <u>24</u>; and Z = 5^2 + 1 = <u>26</u>.

- *The Arabian formula* for creating Pythagorean triples.
    $$X = u^2 - v^2 ; \qquad Y = 2uv ; \qquad Z = u^2 + v^2$$
    - This is similar to what Euclid did.
    - This is a more sophisticated formula that produces all the Pythagorean triples. By choosing any positive whole numbers for u and v, where u is greater than v, the above formulas will generate a Pythagorean triple. As opposed to the Pythagorean formula and Plato's formula, it generates all the Pythagorean triples.
    - In order to produce a reduced Pythagorean triple, you must choose u and v so that one is odd and one is even, and so that they are relatively prime (i.e., so that they don't have any common factor).

    Example: Choosing u = 7, and v = 4, we get X = 7^2 − 4^2 = <u>33</u>; Y = 2·7·4 = <u>56</u>; and Z = 7^2 + 4^2 = <u>65</u>.

- If a Pythagorean triple cannot be reduced (e.g., 6,8,10 reduces to 3,4,5) then we refer to it as *primitive*. The following is a list of the *primitive Pythagorean triples* that have all three numbers less than 100:

3,4,5	20,21,29	11,60,61	13,84,85
5,12,13	12,35,37	16,63,65	36,77,85
8,15,17	9,40,41	33,56,65	39,80,89
7,24,25	28,45,53	48,55,73	65,72,97

Calculating Missing Sides of Triangles

- Given the lengths of two sides of a right triangle, find the length of the missing side.
- Don't introduce the formula $c^2 = a^2 + b^2$ until eighth grade.
- Give only a few simple examples. Much practice using the Pythagorean Theorem is done in eighth grade.

    Example: Find the length of the hypotenuse of a triangle that has legs of length 10 and 24 feet.

    Solution: Using the Pythagorean Theorem, we can say that the areas of the squares off the two given sides are 100 (which is 10^2) square feet and 576 (which is 24^2) square feet. The Pythagorean Theorem says that the area off the hypotenuse must have an area equal to 100 + 576 = 676 square feet. It follows that the length of the square is $\sqrt{676}$, which we determine either by using the square root algorithm, or a bit of trial and error, giving us an answer of <u>26 feet</u>.

Other Topics

- *Perspective Drawing.*
  - See Baravalle's book: *Perspective Drawing.*
  - Often done in the track classes, or as the "artistic element" of another main lesson.
- (optional) Islamic Art, which often deals with geometric designs and symmetry.
- (optional) Drawings showing *reflection*. (**See Appendix A,** *Reflection of a Figure,* for drawing.)
- (optional) Drawings showing *reducing/enlarging*. (**See Appendix A,** *Perspective Reduction,* for drawing.)
- (optional) Drawings with shadows (e.g., a circle often has an elliptical shadow). (See Stockmeyer p63.)
- (optional) Curves arising out of a network of lines (e.g., string boards). (See Sheen's book p47-51.)
- (optional) Wilderness navigating and orienteering (done on a camping/nature trip) put geometry into practice.

Eighth Grade

The year before high school

What is covered in the eighth grade year may vary somewhat depending on whether the students will be attending a Waldorf high school, or going elsewhere. At my school, we have a high school and, for the most part, I go on the assumption that the eighth graders will be continuing on into our high school. Most of our students who leave our school after eighth grade and go to a public high school, end up doing fine in math, even though they have had a different middle school math curriculum. What about the topics covered in public school (e.g., probability) that we haven't covered yet? It is my experience that solid basic math skills, a healthy imagination, and enthusiasm for learning, more than compensate for this. It is best to avoid the temptation to sacrifice the real goals of a math program in order to "prepare" our students for what we think they must have before high school. Also, avoid the temptation to fall back on what is familiar (e.g., lots of algebra), because it's easier to teach. They will get the algebra they need at whatever high school they attend.

The order of topics

The order of the units in my workbook is as follows:

- Number Bases
- Pythagorean Theorem
- Mensuration
- Percents & Growth
- Dimensional Analysis and Proportions
- Algebra
- Yearend Review

Main Lessons and Priorities

I recommend that two math main lessons be taught (each one with two independent topics):

- Number Bases & Loci
- Mensuration & Stereometry

If there is only room in the main lesson schedule for one math main lesson during the year, then number bases and mensuration are topics that could instead be done during the track class, which leaves one math main lesson consisting of stereometry and loci. This, of course, may result in some topic(s) needing to be left out of eighth grade altogether. If time is running short in the eighth grade year, and you must decide what to leave out, then it is recommended that it be number bases and/or loci (even though they are two of my most favorite topics). The rest of the units (Pythagorean theorem, mensuration, percents & growth, dimensional analysis and proportions) are topics that students ought to have some exposure to before entering high school.

Arithmetic

Number Bases

- This unit gives students insights into our base-ten system while learning other "counting" systems. The students journey back, in a manner of speaking, to their earlier years of school, and relearn how to count and do basic arithmetic, but in other bases. The real purpose of this unit is to stretch the students' thinking. In the end, they also get a general idea of how a computer stores information in its memory (see **8th grade Computers**, below).
- This unit works well as half a main lesson block, at the beginning of the year, perhaps with the topic *loci* (**see 8th Grade Geometry**, *Loci*) as the other half.
- It is best to cover this unit at the beginning of the year, so that it comes before the computer unit and before the unit on the Pythagorean Theorem, which requires the use of the square root algorithm (which is part of the computer unit).
- See Ulin's *Finding the Path* and Baravalle's *The Waldorf Approach to Arithmetic* for a detailed account of Number Bases.

Ancient Number Systems
- Briefly cover the Babylonian, Egyptian, and Roman number systems thereby giving a picture of the history of numbers. (See Ulin's book for details.)

Expanded Notation
- Only spend a brief amount of time on this.
  Example: $6472 \rightarrow 6 \cdot 10^3 + 4 \cdot 10^2 + 7 \cdot 10^1 + 2 \cdot 10^0$ (where 10^0 is equal to 1)[1].

Scientific Notation
- Only spend a brief amount of time on this.
  Example: $2{,}384{,}000{,}000$ in scientific notation is $2.384 \cdot 10^9$
  Example: 0.0000451 in scientific notation is $4.51 \cdot 10^{-5}$
  Note: A full treatment of negative exponents should be handled in ninth grade. Here, we only say that a negative exponent makes the decimal point move to the left, thereby making the number smaller.

Base-Eight, Octal
- A good question to start with is: How would our number system be different if we only had 8 fingers?
- *What are the digits?* A key realization for the students to come to is that the octal system uses only the digits 0 through 7. The digits 8 and 9 would be completely unrecognizable by anyone familiar with only the octal system. (This is assuming that all the digits used in the octal system (0, 1, 2, 3, 4, 5, 6, 7) are digits used in our base-ten number system.)
- *Counting.*
  - Have the students count in octal. It is best if they come to the realization on their own that they shouldn't use the digits 8 or 9.
- *A Key Example.* (It will probably take the class a while to really get this.)
  Bob (who uses base-ten) and Fred (who uses octal) are looking at a field of sheep. Draw dots on the board to represent the sheep. Then show how Bob counts by grouping in 10's, 100's, and 1000's, etc., and Fred counts by grouping in 8's, 64's, and 512's, etc. Why 64? Because 64 is eight 8's, just like our 100 place is ten 10's. Similarly, Fred uses 512 because it is eight 64's, just like our 1000 is ten 100's. A slightly different perspective is that 512 is 8^3, just like our 1000 is 10^3.

  Example: If Bob writes down 35 as the number of sheep, how would Fred write it?
  Solution: Fred sees 4 groups of eight, and then there are 3 left over. The answer is then: <u>43</u>.

  Example: If Bob writes down 153 as the number of sheep, how would Fred write it?
  Solution: Fred first sees 2 groups of 64. That leaves 25 sheep ($153 - 2 \cdot 64$) that are uncounted. From these 25 sheep, Fred sees 3 groups of eight with one left over. So Fred writes it as <u>231</u>.

- *Notation.* The number base of a given number is indicated with a subscript at the end of the number.
  bin = base-two (binary)
  oct = base-eight (octal)
  five = base-five
  dec = base-ten (decimal)
  hex = base-sixteen (hexadecimal)

  Example: Using the problem given above we can say that $35_{dec} = 43_{oct}$ and $153_{dec} = 231_{oct}$. The first one should be read as, "Three-five decimal is equal to four-three octal".

- *The place values* with the Octal system. (See, also, **Appendix C**, *Place Value Table.*)
  - The right-most place is the 1s' place.
  - The second place (from the right) is the 8s' place.
  - The third place (from the right) is the 64s' place. (because $8^2 = 64$).
  - The fourth place (from the right) is the 512s' place. (because $8^3 = 512$).
  - The fifth place (from the right) is the 4096s' place. (because $8^4 = 4096$).
  - The six place (from the right) is the 32768s' place. (because $8^5 = 32768$).

---

[1] This odd fact (that $10^0 = 1$) isn't really explained fully until 9th grade. But in eighth grade, we could say the following: just as there is an invisible 1 in front of the x^2 in the expression $6 + x^2$, there is also an invisible 1 in front of 10^0. Now, the exponent always tells us how many of something we have. For example, 7^3 tells us that there are three 7's being multiplied by one another. Therefore 10^0 really means $1 \cdot 10^0$, and since the exponent says that we have zero 10's, we are left with just the (invisible) 1 in front. This is why 10^0 is 1. Similarly, it follows that anything to the zero is 1 (e.g., $13^0 = 1$).

- *In summary*, the place values (from right to left) are: 1, 8, 64, 512, 4096, 32768, etc.
- *Conversion problems with Octal.* Build up to problems like these:

Example: What is 26573_{oct} in base-ten?

Solution: Be careful that the students don't just memorize some procedure. Before writing anything down for this problem, they should say to themselves, "This number is three 1's, seven 8's, five 64's, six 512's, and two 4096's." Only after they say this to themselves should they write this as:
$$2\cdot4096 + 6\cdot512 + 5\cdot64 + 7\cdot8 + 3\cdot1 = \underline{11643}_{dec}$$

Example: What is 1383_{dec} in octal?

Solution: Going from base-ten is more difficult. The question that we must ask ourselves is: "How many of each octal place value can we take out of the given base-ten number (1383)?" Of course, we are limited to a single digit of each place value. Another way of looking at it is to think that each octal place value is an empty box, and we need to fill in all the boxes with a single octal digit so that all these digits together form an octal number that is equal to the given base-ten number. Here are the empty boxes:

4096s' place	512s' place	64s' place	8s' place	1s' place

We first look to see what the largest octal place value is that goes into 1383_{dec}. 4096 is too big, so it will be left empty. Therefore the 512's place is the biggest that will fit into 1383. It goes in **2** times. We therefore put a 2 in the 512's place, and we get this:

4096s' place	512s' place	64s' place	8s' place	1s' place
	2			

We now have accounted for $2\cdot512 = 1024$ out of the original number (1383_{dec}). Subtracting this 1024 from 1383 gives us 359 that is still unaccounted for. So we ask: "How many 64's can we get out of 359?" 64 goes into 359 **5** times. So we put a 5 in the 64s' place, giving us, for the moment:

4096s' place	512s' place	64s' place	8s' place	1s' place
	2	5		

These five 64's account for another 320 out of the 359 that was remaining. Subtracting 320 from 359, tells us that we still have 39 that is unaccounted for. We then ask: "How many 8's can we get out 39?" 8 goes into 39 **4** times. So we write 4 into the 8s' place, giving us:

4096s' place	512s' place	64s' place	8s' place	1s' place
	2	5	4	

These four 8's account for another 32 out of the 39 that was left. Subtracting 32 from 39 tells us that we have **7** 1's left over. So we write 7 into the 1s' place, and get:

4096s' place	512s' place	64s' place	8s' place	1s' place
	2	5	4	7

Our final answer is, therefore, $\underline{2547}_{oct}$, which is indeed equal to 1383_{dec}.

Base-Five

- Done in a similar fashion to the octal system, but covered more quickly.
- *What are the digits?* The five digits in a base-five system are 0, 1, 2, 3, 4.
- *Counting.* Have the students count in base-five.
- *The place values* (from right to left) are $5^0, 5^1, 5^2, 5^3, 5^4, 5^5$ etc., which is: 1, 5, 25, 125, 625, 3125 etc. (See, also, **Appendix C**, *Place Value Table.*)

- *Conversion problems.* Do a few conversion problems with base-five, such as:

Example: What is 2243_{five} in base-ten?

Solution: Again, the students first need to say to themselves, "This number is three 1's, four 5's, two 25's, and two 125's". Then they simply do the calculation: $2 \cdot 125 + 2 \cdot 25 + 4 \cdot 5 + 3 \cdot 1 = \underline{323}_{dec}$.

Example: What is 967_{dec} in base-five?

Solution: Again, going from base-ten is more difficult. Carefully look over the above conversion problem that converted 1383_{dec} to octal. The question with this new problem that we must ask ourselves is: "How many of each base-five place value can we take out of the given base-ten number (967)?" Of course, we are limited to a single digit of each place value. Another way of looking at it is to think that each base-five place value is an empty box, and we need to fill in all the boxes with a single base-five digit so that all these digits together form a base-five number that is equal to the given base-ten number (967). Here are the empty boxes:

3125s'	625s'	125s'	25s'	5s'	1s'
place	place	place	place	place	place

We first look to see what the largest base-five place value is that goes into 967. It is the 625s' place (since 3125 is too big, its box shall be left empty). It goes in **1** time, so we put a 1 into the 625s' place (box), and then subtract that from 967, resulting in a remainder of 342. 125 goes into 342 **2** times, so we put a 2 into the 125s' place, and subtract to get a remainder of 92. 25 goes into 92 **3** times (so we put a 3 in the 25s' place) with a remainder of 17. 5 goes into 17 **3** times, so a 3 goes into the 5s' place, which leaves us with a remainder of **2** to be put into the 1s' place. In the end we get this:

	1	2	3	3	2
3125s'	625s'	125s'	25s'	5s'	1s'
place	place	place	place	place	place

so our answer is $\underline{12332}_{five}$, which equals 967_{dec}.

Base-Sixteen, Hexadecimal

- The hexadecimal number system is used frequently in computers as a shorthand way to represent a binary number (**see** *binary numbers,* below).

- *What are the digits?* Here we need a total of 16 digits, so we must add digits to our standard 10 digits. The hexadecimal digits that we will use are 0, 1, 2, 3, 4, 5, 6, 7, 8, 9, A, B, C, D, E, F. These new single digits represent the base-ten equivalents of 10, 11, 12, 13, 14, 15.

- *The place values* (from right to left) for hexadecimal are 16^0, 16^1, 16^2, 16^3, 16^4 etc., which is: 1, 16, 256, 4096, 65536, etc. (See, also, **Appendix C**, *Place Value Table*.)

- *Counting.* Have the students count in hexadecimal.

Example: What is the hexadecimal number that follows each of these:
  - 9? (answer: A)
  - F? (answer: 10)
  - 3B49? (answer: 3B4A)
  - D374F? (answer: D3750)
  - 69FF? (answer: 6A00)

- *Conversion problems.* Do many conversion problems with hexadecimal. Build up to problems like these:

Example: What is $3C4D_{hex}$ in base-ten?

Solution: Again, the students first need to say to themselves, "This number is D (thirteen) 1's, four 16's, C (twelve) 256's, and three 4096's. Therefore, we get $3 \cdot 4096 + 12 \cdot 256 + 4 \cdot 16 + 13 \cdot 1 = \underline{15437}_{dec}$

Example: What is 15076_dec in hexadecimal (hexadecimal)?

Solution: Again, going from base-ten is more difficult. Carefully look over the above conversion problem that converts 1383_dec to octal. The question with this new problem that we must ask ourselves is: "How many of each hexadecimal place value can we take out of the given base-ten number (15076)?" Of course, we are limited to a single digit (0,1,2,3..up to F) of each place value. Another way of looking at it is to think that each hexadecimal place value is an empty box, and we need to fill in all the boxes with a single hexadecimal digit so that all these digits together form a hexadecimal number that is equal to the given base-ten number. Here are the empty boxes:

65536s' place	4096s' place	256s' place	16s' place	1s' place

We first look to see what the largest hexadecimal place value is that goes into 15076. It is the 4096s' place. It goes in **3** times, so we put a 3 into the 4096s' place. This accounts for 3·4096, which, when subtracted from 15076, results in a remainder of 2788. 256 goes into 2788 ten times (which in hexadecimal is the single digit **A**). So we put "A" into the 256s' place. When we subtract these ten 256's from what was the remainder (2788), we get a new remainder of 228. 16 goes into 228 fourteen times (which is **E** in hexadecimal). So we put "E" into the 16s' place. Then we subtract these fourteen 16's from the remainder 228, and get a new remainder of **4**, which we put into the 1s' place. In the end our boxes look like this:

	3	A	E	4
65536s' place	4096s' place	256s' place	16s' place	1s' place

so our answer is 3AE4_hex, which equals 15076_dec.

Base-Two, Binary

- *What are the digits?* Here we have only two digits: 0 and 1.
- *The place values* (from right to left) for binary are $2^0, 2^1, 2^2, 2^3, 2^4$ etc., which is: 1, 2, 4, 8, 16, etc. (See, also, **Appendix C**, *Place Value Table.*)
- *The connection with computers.* Here, with the binary number base, we see some real practical application of number bases – specifically with computers (see **8th grade Computers**, below).
- *Counting in binary.*
  Example: What is the binary number that comes after:
      (a) 1101?   (answer: 1110)
      (b) 101011? (answer: 101100)
      (c) 111?   (answer: 1000)
- *Counting Race.* Be sure to do a row of 5 students counting in binary by raising and lowering their hands. A hand up represents "1" and a hand down is "0". They then count from zero (all hands down) to 31 (all hands up). See if the students can state a rule about under what conditions someone must raise their arm. The rule is this: the person in the 1s' place simply moves his hand up and down, while all the other people only change their position following the moment that all those before them have their hands up. For an added challenge, you can have three people using both of their hands (6 digits therefore) and counting from 0 to 63 as fast as possible.

- *Conversions problems.* Do many conversion problems with binary, such as:

  Example: What is 10011_{bin} in base-ten?

  Solution: Converting from binary is much easier than converting from other bases, because there is no need to multiply. It's never a question of how many of a certain place value you have − it's either there (a "1") or it's not there (a "0"). Therefore, in the case of 10011_{bin}, we can say "This number has a 1, a 2, and a 16", because those are the places that have a "1" in them. (The two zeroes in 10011 signify that there is no 4 and no 8.) Therefore our answer is: $1+2+16 = \underline{19_{dec}}$.

  Example: What is 38_{dec} in Binary (base-two)?

  Solution: Again, going from base-ten is more difficult. Carefully look over the above conversion problem that converted 1383_{dec} to octal. The question with this new problem that we must ask ourselves is: "What is the largest binary place value that can go into the given base-ten number (38)?" Another way of looking at it is to think that each binary place value is an empty box, and we need to fill in all the boxes with a single binary digit (0 or 1) so that all these digits together form a binary number that is equal to the given base-ten number. Here are the empty boxes:

  128s' place, 64s' place, 32s' place, 16s' place, 8s' place, 4s' place, 2s' place, 1s' place

  We first look to see what the largest binary place value is that goes into 38_{dec}. The 64s' place and the 128s' place are both too big, so we'll leave them empty. The first place we can use is the 32s' place. Recall, that we don't have to ask "how many times does 32 go into 38?", because it can't be more than 1. It either goes in once or not at all (recall that "2" is not a legal digit in binary). So we put a **1** in the 32s' place, and then subtract 32 from 38 to get a remainder of 6. We can't get a 16 or an 8 out of this remainder, so we put a **0** in the 16s' place and a **0** in the 8s' place. But we can get a 4 out of our remainder of 6, so we put a **1** in the 4s' place, and, after we subtract this 4 from the 6, we are left with a new remainder of 2. Now, we put a **1** in the 2s' place, and since there's no remainder left, we finish by putting a **0** in the 1s' place. In the end, our boxes look like this:

		1	0	0	1	1	0

  128s' place, 64s' place, 32s' place, 16s' place, 8s' place, 4s' place, 2s' place, 1s' place

  so our answer is $\underline{100110_{bin}}$, which equals 38_{dec}.

Arithmetic in Various Bases

- When doing an arithmetic problem in a certain base, be sure to do all work in that base. You shouldn't convert into base-ten in order to do the calculation, and then convert back − that would take too long, and it misses the point.

  Example: $6_{eight} + 5_{eight}$ should not be thought of as: "6 plus 5 is normally 11, and that is 13_{eight}"; but rather: "if we take 2 from the 5, then it can be combined with the 6 to make one 8 with a 3 left over, giving us a base eight answer of 13_{eight}."

  Example: With $34_{five} + 23_{five}$ we add the 4 and 3 in the right column and think that it is two beyond 5, so 4+3 is 12. We write down the 2 and carry the 1. Now with the left column, 3+2 is just 5, plus the 1 that we carried gives us 11, so we write that down, which gives us a final answer of 112_{five}.

- *Multiplication tables.* Students should make the multiplication tables for the various bases. They should look for patterns. Perhaps the hexadecimal multiplication table should be a challenge problem. They can then use these multiplication tables in order to do multiplication and division problems in different bases. The students become appreciative of the fact that people don't have 16 fingers − the hexadecimal table would have been very difficult to memorize! They may well wish that we had always operated with the binary (base-two) system − its table would have been a piece of cake!

- *The climax of the unit.*
  - See **Appendix C**, *Multiplication Tables for Number Bases*, for the Octal, Base-five, Binary, and Hexadecimal multiplication tables. These tables will be needed for multiplication and division problems. Do many arithmetic problems, such as:

Example: $110_{bin} + 11_{bin} + 101_{bin}$
Solution: Starting with the right-most column, 0+1+1 is 10, so we write down 0 and carry the 1. With the next column, we have 1 (the carry) +1+1+0, which is 11, so we write down 1 and carry 1. The last column is the 1 (the carry) +1+1, which is 11. So our answer is $\underline{1110}_{bin}$.

Example: $132_{five} - 34_{five}$
Solution: Borrowing from the 3 in the middle column gives us 12-4 in the right-most column, which is 3 (12 is 3 numbers up from 4). We write down the 3 and then do the next column 12-3, which is 4. Our answer is $\underline{43}_{five}$.

Example: $64_{oct} \cdot 26_{oct}$
Solution: Using the Octal Times Table, we first do 6·4 = 30, so we write down the 0 and carry the 3. Then, 6·6 = 44, plus the 3 that was carried is 47. The rest of the problem is shown at the right. The answer is $\underline{2170}_{oct}$.

Example: $BC8_{hex} + 9A5_{hex}$
Solution: The solution is $\underline{156D}_{hex}$, and is shown at the right.

Example: $9C_{hex} \cdot B5_{hex}$
Solution: The Hexadecimal Times Table is needed. The solution is $\underline{6E4C}_{hex}$, and is shown at the right.

Example: $2AF8_{hex} \div C8_{hex}$
Solution: The Hexadecimal Times Table is needed. The solution is $\underline{37}_{hex}$, and is shown at the right.

- *Multiplication with zeroes.* We know that in base-ten we can multiply 3496·100 and quickly get 349600. We can do the same in other bases.
  Example: In binary   11011·100 = 1101100. (This is 27·4 = 108 in base-ten.)
  Example: In hexadecimal   E8F·1000 = E8F000. (This is 3727·4096 = 15265792 in base-ten.)

(optional) Converting between Binary and Hexadecimal

Decimal	Binary	Hexadecimal		Decimal	Binary	Hexadecimal
0	0000	0		8	1000	8
1	0001	1		9	1001	9
2	0010	2		10	1010	A
3	0011	3		11	1011	B
4	0100	4		12	1100	C
5	0101	5		13	1101	D
6	0110	6		14	1110	E
7	0111	7		15	1111	F

- Notice that the "Decimal" column in the above table is only for reference, and is not actually used when doing a conversion straight from hexadecimal to binary, or back.

- It is much easier to convert straight from binary to hexadecimal (or straight from hexadecimal to binary) rather than to convert first into decimal and then from decimal into the desired base.
  Example: What is $3A8_{hex}$ in binary?
  Solution: We simply look up each hexadecimal digit on the table to see what its equivalent four digits are in binary. We see that 3 is 0011, A is 1010, and 8 is 1000. This gives us $(00)\underline{11\ 1010\ 1000}_{bin}$.

  Example: What is 1001111110_{bin} in hexadecimal?
  Solution: Starting from the right, we separate the digits into groups of four. The right-most group is 1110, which we look up on the table and get "E" in hexadecimal. The next group, 0111 in binary, is 7 in hexadecimal. The last group is 10, so we add two zeroes on the front, and look up 0010 on the table resulting in a 2 in hexadecimal. Putting these hexadecimal digits together we get $27E_{hex}$.

The World of Numbers

The Square Root Algorithm (without zeroes)

- The *Square Root Algorithm – without zeroes* (**see Appendix C**) should be taught in eighth grade even if it wasn't taught in seventh grade.
- The square root algorithm, if done in seventh grade as outlined in Appendix C, is very challenging, because it focuses on getting the students to understand *why* it works. In eighth grade, the task is much easier – the students simply memorize a step-by-step procedure (called an *algorithm*), which allows them to calculate square roots by hand.
- *The Square Root Algorithm – without Zeroes* (as taught here in eighth grade) is a slight variation of *The Square Root Algorithm – with Zeroes* (as taught in seventh grade). Specifically, in the eighth grade version:
  - Extra zeroes are not written down.
  - We bring down only two digits at a time, similar to what happens in long division.
  - We can more easily calculate decimal approximations for uneven square roots (e.g., $\sqrt{30}$).
- The unit on computers (**see** *Computers*, below) should be done just before this unit on the square root algorithm since it culminates nicely with the square root algorithm.
- Have students calculate the square roots of 2 through 10 to three decimal places by using *the Square Root Algorithm* (**see 8th Grade,** *Computers*) and then memorize these approximations as shown below.

$$\sqrt{2} \approx 1.414 \quad \sqrt{3} \approx 1.73 \quad \sqrt{4} = 2 \quad \sqrt{5} \approx 2.24$$
$$\sqrt{6} \approx 2.45 \quad \sqrt{7} \approx 2.65 \quad \sqrt{8} \approx 2.83 \quad \sqrt{9} = 3 \quad \sqrt{10} \approx 3.16$$

- *Simplifying Square Roots* is saved for ninth grade. (e.g., $\sqrt{75}$ simplifies to $5\sqrt{3}$)

The Pythagorean Theorem
With any right triangle, (the area of) the square of the hypotenuse is equal to the sum (of the areas) of the squares of the other two sides.

- In seventh grade, the Pythagorean Theorem talked only about *the area of the squares*. Now, in eighth grade, we will use the Pythagorean Theorem as a tool for finding the length of the missing side of right triangles. We therefore don't need to visualize the squares each time, but can do things more mechanically. To make this transition, we can take the above statement and, surprisingly, drop the words in the parentheses, and then it becomes clear that the word "square" has two meanings - a geometrical figure, and an exponent of two. Through this, we introduce these two formulas (in each case a and b are the lengths of the two legs and c is the length of the hypotenuse):

The Hypotenuse Formula: $c^2 = a^2 + b^2$ which is used to find the length of the hypotenuse.

The Leg Formula: $a^2 = c^2 - b^2$ which is used to find the length of one of the legs.

- **See eighth grade Geometry,** *Mensuration,* for Baravalle's proof of the Pythagorean Theorem, which should be done during the mensuration unit.
- *Do many problems* that find the missing sides of right triangles including answers that are *not* whole numbers. This is a good opportunity to practice *the Square Root Algorithm*.

Example (using ratios): What is the length of the hypotenuse of a right triangle if the two legs are 36cm and 105cm long?

Solution: With this problem we can work out the answer by simply using ratios, without using a formula. The ratio 36:105 reduces (÷3) to 12:35. The primitive Pythagorean triple (**see 7th Grade Geometry,** *Pythagorean Theorem*) is 12,35,**37**. Therefore the answer is: 37x3 = <u>111</u>.

Example (using algebra and the square root algorithm): If the length of the hypotenuse of a right triangle is 9 inches and one leg is 5 inches long, then what is the length of the other leg?

Solution #1: Using the *Hypotenuse Formula*, we first need to know that "C" is always the hypotenuse ("9" in this case). The "5" can be either "a" or "b". Using this formula and solving, we get:

$$c^2 = a^2 + b^2 \qquad a^2 = 56$$
$$9^2 = a^2 + 5^2 \qquad a = \sqrt{56}$$
$$81 = a^2 + 25$$
$$81 - 25 = a^2 \qquad \text{Using the } \textit{square root algorithm}\text{, we get } \underline{a \approx 7.48}.$$

Solution #2: Most students usually prefer to use the *Leg Formula*, $a^2 = c^2 - b^2$, for this type of problem where we need to find a leg. We simply do:

$$a^2 = 9^2 - 5^2 \rightarrow a^2 = 81 - 25 \rightarrow a^2 = 56 \rightarrow a = \sqrt{56} \rightarrow \underline{a \approx 7.48}.$$

Percents and Growth

Review percents from sixth and seventh grade very thoroughly.

Calculators. The teacher needs to decide whether or not it is appropriate for the students to use calculators for this unit.

Four Ways to Find the Base

- Review 7th grade, *Finding the Base* (**see 7th Grade Percents**).

- *An Easy Problem*: Joe has 20% as much money as Kate. How much does Kate have if Joe has $12?

   The Even Multiple Method: (This method is only possible for "easy" problems where the given percentage translates quickly to a fraction with a "1" in the numerator, such as 10%, 20%, 25%, etc.) With the above problem, 20% translates into $^1/_5$ as a fraction. Therefore, since Joe has $^1/_5$ as much as Kate, we can say that Kate has 5 times as much as Joe. Our answer is that Kate has 5·12 = $60.

- *A Harder Problem*: Joe has 37.5% as much money as Kate. How much does Kate have if Joe has $12?

   The Decimal Method: Thinking of 37.5% as a decimal, we can say that Joe has 0.375 times as much as Kate. We can then see that the opposite is also true: Kate has Joe's amount divided by 0.375. So our answer is 12÷0.375 = $32.

   The Fraction Method: Thinking of 37.5% as a fraction, we can say that Joe has $^3/_8$ as much as Kate. So we know that the opposite is also true: Kate has $^8/_3$ as much as Joe. So our answer is: 12·$^8/_3$ = $32.

   The Algebra Method: (Use this method only in eighth grade, and only if you're really stuck.) We use the formula $N = P·B$, which says that a *number* (N) is a certain *percentage* (P) of a *base* (B). For this problem, N is 12, and P is $^{37.5}/_{100}$, which is more easily expressed as $^3/_8$ or as 0.375. This gives the equation: 12 = $^3/_8$ · B   or   12 = 0.375·B   Solving either equation gives us B = $32.

   Example: Jill is 86% as tall as Fred. If Fred is 1.72m tall, then how tall is *Jill* (to the nearest cm)?
   Solution: This is a "normal" percent problem; we are finding the smaller number. The easiest way is to multiply 1.72 times 0.86, which is 1.4792. Our rounded answer is 1.48m.

   Example: Jill is 86% as tall as Fred. If Jill is 1.62m tall, then how tall is *Fred* (to the nearest cm)?
   Solution: Here we are finding the larger number. We can use the *decimal method* (1.62÷0.86), the *fraction method* (1.62·$\frac{100}{86}$), or the *algebra method* (1.62=0.86·B). The answer (rounded) is 1.88m.

Increase/Decrease Problems

- *Rewording a percent increase problem.*

   Example: "My rent has increased by 50%", is the same as saying, "My rent is 150% of what it was".

   Example: "My rent has increased by 150%", is the same as saying, "My rent is 250% of what it was".

   Example: Increasing a number by 100% is the same as taking 200% of that number, or multiplying by two.

   Example: Increasing a number by 20% is the same as taking 120% of that number, or multiplying by 1.2.

   Example: What is 48 increased by 7%?
   Solution: We simply change the wording to: "What is 107% of 48?", which gives us 1.07·48 → 51.36.

- *Rewording a percent decrease problem.*
   Example: Decreasing a number by 20% is the same as 80% (which is 100%−20%) of that number, or multiplying that number by 0.8.

   Example: What is 32 decreased by 20%?
   Solution: We change the wording to: "What is 80% of 32?", which gives us 0.8·32 → 25.6.

   Example: What is 510 decreased by 15%?
   Solution: The wording is changed to: "What is 85% of 510?", which gives us 0.85·510 → 433.5

- *Calculating the Percentage of Increase or Decrease.*
   - Review seventh grade, *Calculating the Percentage of Increase or Decrease,* especially the formulas:

$$\% \text{ increase} = \frac{\text{amount of increase}}{\text{starting point}} \qquad \% \text{ decrease} = \frac{\text{amount of decrease}}{\text{starting point}}$$

- In eighth grade, we can do the calculation more directly, by dividing the *ending point* by the *starting point*. How far this answer is from 100% tells us the percentage of increase or decrease.

Example: Going from 120 to 162 is what percent increase?

Solution: We simply divide 162 by 120 (the starting point), which gives us 1.35. This tells us that 162 is 135% of 120, and therefore we can say that it is a <u>35% increase</u>.

Example: Going from 75 to 63 is what percent decrease?

Solution: We divide 63 by 75 (the starting point), which gives us 0.84. This tells us that 63 is 84% of 75, and therefore we can say that it is a <u>16% decrease</u>. (100% − 84% = 16%)

Example: If Jill is 1.81m tall and Fred is 1.45m tall, then
- (A) Jill is what percent of Fred's height?
- (B) Jill is what percent taller than Fred?

Solutions: (A) We do $1.81 \div 1.45 \rightarrow P \approx 1.248 \rightarrow$ Jill is <u>124.8%</u> of Fred's height.

(B) Looking at the solution from part A, we can see that Jill is <u>24.8%</u> taller. Alternatively, we can use the method introduced in seventh grade: We determine the amount of increase and then divide by the starting point. So we do $0.36 \div 1.45$, which is 0.248, or <u>24.8%</u>.

- *Calculating the Starting Point.*
  - These are the trickiest problems. They can be done using algebra, but I would recommend the following: First, *reword* (see above) the problem, and then solve it using one of the methods described above in *Four Ways to Find the Base*. The following examples should help clarify things:

Example: In a basketball game, the Frogs scored 12.5% more than the Pigs. If the Frogs scored 99 points, how many points did the Pigs score?

Solution: The problem is first *reworded* as: *The Frogs' score (99) is 112.5% of the Pigs' score.* This can then be further simplified to: *99 is 112.5% of what number?* Now, we can use any of the last three methods described under *Four Ways to Find the Base*:

    The decimal method: 112.5% is written as 1.125, and then we do $99 \div 1.125$
    The fraction method: 112.5% is written as $^9/_8$, and then we do $99 \cdot {^8/_9}$
    The algebra method: we solve the equation $99 = 1.125 \cdot B$ or $99 = {^9/_8} \cdot B$
Using any of these methods, we get $B = \underline{88}$.

Example: Larry sold a car for $22,400. If this is a 36% loss from the price that he originally paid, then what was that original price?

Solution: Knowing that 36% less than 100% is 64%, we reword the problem as: *Larry sold the car ($22,400) for 64% of what he paid.* This can then become further simplified to: *$22,400 is 64% of what number?* Here, we can use the *decimal method*, and do $22,400 \div 0.64$ to get an answer of <u>$35,000</u>.

Exponential Growth

- *Review seventh grade Doubling.*
- The difference between linear growth and exponential growth (constant percentage growth) can be nicely shown by using the example of a town that starts with a population of 5000:
  - **Linear growth** is when the population *increases by the same amount* every year. If the town grows by 550 people per year, then it goes from 5000 to 5550 to 6100 to 6650 to 7200, etc.
  - **Exponential growth** is when the population *increases by the same percentage* every year. For 10% annual growth, the population goes from 5000 to 5500 to 6050 to 6655 to 7320.5, etc.
- Exponential growth is exemplified by population growth, bank accounts (compound interest), inflation, and with many things in nature. Linear growth is exemplified by rates (e.g., rate of speed, rate of pay).
- In the long run, exponential growth *always* outstrips linear growth - it's just a matter of time before it catches up.

The Exponential Growth Formula $P = P_0(1 + r)^t$, where P_0 ("P sub zero") is the initial amount,

r is the percentage growth rate as a decimal, t is the time (i.e., number of years), P is the end amount after t years.

- This formula is used for compound interest or population growth. "P" can stand for principle or population.

- Review seventh grade compound interest.

- *Understanding why the formula works is important.* For example, 5% interest compounded annually means that we calculate a particular year's balance by taking 105% (which means multiplying by 1.05) of the previous year's balance. If the account starts at $2000, then the balance at the end of the first year is 105% of 2000, which is $1.05 \cdot 2000$, or $2100. To get the next year, we multiply by 1.05 again. And to get the balance after the third year, we multiply once again by 1.05.

  So, if the question is to find the balance after three years at 5% interest of an account that starts at $2000, then what we must do is multiply $2000 by 1.05, and that result by 1.05, and then that result again by 1.05. This can be written as $2000 \cdot 1.05 \cdot 1.05 \cdot 1.05$, or more succinctly as $2000 \cdot 1.05^3$, which is exactly what the formula $P = P_0(1 + r)^t$ says that you must do, using $P_0 = 2000$, $r = 0.05$, $t = 3$. (Recall that you must cube 1.05 before multiplying by 2000.) The final answer is: $2000 \cdot 1.05^3 \rightarrow 2000 \cdot 1.157625$, which is <u>$2315.25</u>.

- *The Growth Rate Table.* (**See Appendix C.**) This table compares different growth rates over a 200-year period.

  - The table gives values for $(1+r)^t$ given various values of t and r.
  - Each column uses a different rate (1+r). Each row shows a different period of time (t). The calculated value of $(1+r)^t$ appears in the box.
  - *This table can be used in various ways.* For one, we can determine how much percent increase we get with given values for r and t. For example, with 5% annual growth over a 20-year period, the table shows 2.6533, which tells us that the initial value is now about 265% as much as when it started. This is about a 165% increase.

    Also, we can solve specific problems, like:

    Example: What is the balance in a savings account after 20 years at 5% interest if the initial deposit was $300?

    Solution: Here, we use the formula $P = P_0(1+r)^t$. Now, using 20 for the value t, and 1.05 for the value for (1+r), and see that the table tells us that $(1+r)^t$ is 2.6533. Then we get the final balance by multiplying that number by the value of P_0, which is 300. This gives us an answer of <u>$795.99</u>.

  - *Doubling times.* The table shows that at 10% it takes a little more than 7 years for the initial investment to double.

- *Dramatic results.* Have the students do many calculations that use the formula $P = P_0(1 + r)^t$. Do some dramatic examples, such as:

  Example: If $50 is invested and earns a return of 15% annually, how much money will be in the account after (a) 3 years (b) 20 years (c) 100 years

  Solutions: (a) $76.04   (b) $818.33   (c) $58,715,650 using table, or $58,715,672.53 using calculator.

  Example: If a town starts with a population of 700 residents and then grows at an annual rate of 8% annually, what will its population be (to the nearest whole person) after
  (a) 10 years (b) 50 years (c) 200 years

  Solutions: (a) 1511   (b) 32,831   (c) 3,387,265,000 (from table), or 3,387,264,709 (calculator)
  This is about half the current population of the planet!

(optional) Depreciation

- Depreciation is when the value of something drops, usually at a fairly steady annual percentage rate. For example, the depreciation of a car is typically 30% in the first year.

- The formula for depreciation is a slight variation of the *Exponential Growth Formula*; we simply change the plus to a minus to get: $P = P_0(1 - r)^t$.

  Example: If Betty buys a used car for $14,000 and it depreciates at a rate of 12% annually, then how much will it be worth after eight years?

  Solution: The depreciation formula gives us: $P = 14000(0.88)^8$, which, after plugging into a calculator, gives us an answer of <u>$5034.88</u>.

The Rule of 72

- This is a trick that allows us to quickly estimate the number of years required for an amount to double given an annual growth rate, or to estimate the growth rate given the number of years for the amount to double. The rule is:

$$R \cdot T \approx 72$$

Where R is the annual growth rate (in percentage points), and T is the number years it takes to double. In some cases, we choose 70 instead of 72, depending on which one makes the division problem easier.

Example: How long does it take a city's population to double if its current annual growth rate is 6%?
Solution: We simply divide 6 into 72 for a result of 12. We can therefore conclude that the population is doubling about every <u>12 years</u>. (The exact answer is 11.90 years.)

Example: If somebody's investment is doubling every 5 years, then what approximately is the annual rate of return?
Solution: Here we choose 70 instead of 72, because it is easier. We simply divide 5 into 70 for a result of 14. We can therefore estimate that the annual rate of return (annual profit) is about <u>14%</u>. (The exact answer is 14.87%.)

Dimensional Analysis[1]

<u>Review</u> seventh grade metric system.

A Few Thoughts on this Unit

- This unit is important in order for the students to be adequately prepared for high school science.
- This unit should be done after *mensuration*, and after the physics main lesson block. I usually do it towards the end of the year.
- *Calculators.* For this whole unit, it is best to allow the students to use a calculator, so they don't get bogged down in tedious calculations.
- *Conversion table.* **See Appendix C** *Conversion Table* for a table listing useful conversion factors. Keep in mind that most of these are approximations. The students should memorize the ones indicated.
- *Accuracy.* Since the conversion factors are approximations, it is likely that students will get answers that are slightly different, especially if they do the problems differently. I generally tell them to go to *three significant digits* (see **6th grade**, *Statistics*). The third digit may be slightly off.
- *Showing work.* The students need to be sure that they show their work, and write down the numbers that they put into the calculator, so they can find any mistakes that they make.

Two Methods for doing Unit Conversion Problems

Example: How many cups are in 5.2 liters?

Solution using The Intuitive Approach:
Since there is nothing on the *Conversion Table* that tells us how to go directly from liters to cups, we must do the problem in two steps. One possibility is to first convert from liters to fluid ounces, and then from fluid ounces to cups. In converting from liters to fluid ounces, we know that one liter is about 33.8 fluid ounces. We then ask ourselves whether we should multiply 5.2 by 33.8, or divide 5.2 by 33.8. Only multiplying gives a reasonable answer. Therefore: 5.2·33.8 = 175.76 fluid ounces.
Now, in converting to cups, we know that one cup is 8 fluid ounces. We ask ourselves whether to multiply 175.76 by 8 or divide 175.76 by 8. Only dividing gives a reasonable answer. Therefore, our final answer is: 175.76÷8 = <u>21.97 cups</u>.

Solution using The Chain Method:
The *Chain Method* focuses on the idea of getting units to cancel until only the desired unit is left. Mathematically speaking, we are multiplying our original amount by fractions that are equal to one – in

---

[1] *Dimensional analysis* is the study of units of measurement. Often, it focuses on changing a quantity from one unit base to another. (e.g., From *miles per hour* to *meters per second*.)

other words, where their numerators and denominators are equal. The work looks like this:

$$\frac{5.2\,\ell}{1} \cdot \frac{33.8\text{ fl oz}}{1\,\ell} \cdot \frac{1\text{ cup}}{8\text{ fl oz}}$$

Notice that all the units cross cancel, except for "cup", and the arithmetic amounts to $5.2 \cdot 33.8 \div 8$, which gives our answer of <u>21.97 cups</u>. Also notice that the second two fractions have a value equal to one, because the denominators are equal to the numerators.

Converting between the U.S. and Metric System Here are some examples:

Example: 350 yards is how many meters?

Solution Using the Intuitive Approach: $350\text{yd} \cdot 3 \rightarrow 1050\text{ft}$ $1050\text{ft} \div 3.28 \rightarrow \underline{320.12\text{m}}$

Solution Using the Chain Method: $\frac{350\text{yd}}{1} \cdot \frac{3\text{ft}}{1\text{yd}} \cdot \frac{1\text{m}}{3.28\text{ft}} \rightarrow \underline{320.12\text{m}}$

Example: Mount Everest has a height of 8850m. How many miles is this?

Solution Using the Intuitive Approach: $8850\text{m} \cdot 3.28 \rightarrow 29028\text{ft}.$ $29028\text{ft} \div 5280 \rightarrow \underline{5.50\text{mi}}$

Solution Using the Chain Method: $\frac{8850\text{m}}{1} \cdot \frac{3.28\text{ft}}{1\text{m}} \cdot \frac{1\text{mi}}{5280\text{ft}} \rightarrow \underline{5.50\text{mi}}$

Converting Units for Rates

- *Review* seventh grade *average rate of speed.*
- *Converting units of speed.*

   Example: If a train is traveling 38 m/s (meters per second), how fast is this in mph (mi/hr)?

   Solution Using the Intuitive Approach (<u>Note</u>: "m" means meters, and "mi" means miles.):

   $38\frac{\text{m}}{\text{s}} \cdot 3600 \rightarrow 136800\frac{\text{m}}{\text{hr}}$ (because 1 hr = 3600 sec)

   $136800\frac{\text{m}}{\text{hr}} \div 1000 \rightarrow 136.8\frac{\text{km}}{\text{hr}}$ (because 1 km = 1000 m)

   $136.8\frac{\text{km}}{\text{hr}} \div 1.61 \rightarrow \underline{84.97\frac{\text{mi}}{\text{hr}}}$ (because 1 mi ≈ 1.61 km)

   Solution Using the Chain Method:

   $\frac{38\text{m}}{\text{s}} \cdot \frac{3600\text{sec}}{\text{hr}} \cdot \frac{1\text{km}}{1000\text{m}} \cdot \frac{1\text{mi}}{1.61\text{km}} \rightarrow \underline{84.97\text{ mph}}$

- The students should be able to picture the train traveling 84.97 miles every hour, and imagine that this is the equivalent of traveling 38 meters every second.

- *Unit cost.*

   Example: On April 21, 2002 the cost of gasoline at a station in the U.S. was $1.59 per gallon, and at a station in Holland it was 1.21 euros per liter. If the exchange rate for buying euros is 85¢ per euro, then how much more expensive (as a percentage) is gasoline in Holland than in the U.S.?

   Solution Using the Intuitive Approach: Given 1 gallon ≈ 3.785 liters, we convert the price at the station in Holland into dollars per gallon:

   $$1.21\,\frac{\text{euros}}{\text{liter}} \cdot 3.785 \rightarrow 4.580\,\frac{\text{euros}}{\text{gal}}$$

   $$4.580\,\frac{\text{euros}}{\text{gal}} \cdot 0.85 \rightarrow \$3.89/\text{gal.}$$

   To find out how much more expensive, as a percentage, $3.89 is than $1.59, we divide 1.59 into 3.89 which is 2.45, which means that $3.89 is 245% of $1.59. Therefore, we can say that gasoline is <u>145% more</u> expensive in Holland than in the U.S.

   Solution Using the Chain Method: $\frac{1.21\text{ euros}}{\text{liter}} \cdot \frac{3.785\text{ liters}}{\text{gal}} \cdot \frac{\$0.85}{\text{euro}} \rightarrow \$3.89/\text{gal},$

   which is 145% more expensive than $1.59. (See solution #1, above.)

- *Inverse ratios and reciprocals.*
  Example: Given that 1 meter is about 3.28 feet, how many meters is 1 foot?
  Solution: We want to know how many *meters per feet* ($^m/_{ft}$) there are, and we are given 3.28 *feet per meter* ($^{ft}/_m$). Since $^m/_{ft}$ and $^{ft}/_m$ and are reciprocals of each other, it seems reasonable that we simply need to take the reciprocal of 3.28, which is $\frac{1}{3.28}$. Dividing 3.28 into 1 gives us: $1ft \approx 0.305m$. The important thing to realize is that we got our answer by taking the *reciprocal* of 3.28.
  Example: Given that 1 mile is about 1.61 kilometers, how many miles is 1 kilometer?
  Solution: We simply take the reciprocal (see above solution) of 1.61. So we divide 1.61 into 1 to get $1km \approx 0.621mi$.

Converting Areas and Volumes

- Try to have the students derive the following relationships, and give them problems that practice them:

  $1\text{ ft}^2 = 144\text{ in}^2$ (which is 12in·12in) $1\text{ ft}^3 = 1728\text{ in}^3$ (which is 12in·12in·12in)
  $1\text{ yd}^2 = 9\text{ ft}^2$ $1\text{ yd}^3 = 27\text{ ft}^3$
  $1\text{ m}^2 = 10,000\text{ cm}^2$ $1\text{ m}^3 = 1,000,000\text{ cm}^3$
  $1\text{ km}^2 = 1,000,000\text{ m}^2$ $1\text{ km}^3 = 1,000,000,000\text{ m}^3$
  $1\text{ in}^2 \approx 6.45\text{ cm}^2$ (which is 2.54^2) $1\text{ in}^3 \approx 16.39\text{ cm}^3$ (which is 2.54^3)
  $1\text{ m}^2 \approx 10.76\text{ ft}^2$ $1\text{ m}^3 \approx 35.31\text{ ft}^3$

  Example: 4 cubic yards is equal to how many cubic meters?
  Solution (using the Intuitive Approach): $4yd^3 \cdot 27 \rightarrow 108ft^3$ $108ft^3 \div 35.31 \rightarrow 3.06m^3$
  Solution (using the Chain Method): $\frac{4yd^3}{1} \cdot \frac{27ft^3}{1\ yd^3} \cdot \frac{1m^3}{35.31ft^3}$ The answer is $\underline{3.06m^3}$.

- *Grains of rice problem.* (**See Appendix C,** *The Grains of Rice Problem.*)
  - This is a great problem to do in order to review *Doubling* from seventh grade, and at the same time to practice *Volumes* and *Dimensional Analysis*.
  Question: A wise man is granted a request. He requests that a single grain of rice be placed on the first square of a chess board, 2 grains on the second square, 4 grains on the third, 8 grains on the fourth, and so on, doubling with every square up until the last square - the 64th square. How many grains of rice is that, and what is the total volume of that much rice?
  Solution: The answer is $\underline{163.9\text{ mi}^3}$ (Yes, cubic *miles*!). For the detailed story and solution, **See Appendix C,** *The Grains of Rice Problem.*

Density

- *The key idea* is that density is *weight per volume*. For example, the density of gold is 1205 lb/ft³, which tells us that a cubic foot of gold weighs 1205 pounds. The density of gold can also be given as 19.3 g/cm³, which says that a cubic centimeter weighs 19.3 grams.
- Density can be expressed in many different ways, such as grams per cubic centimeter (g/cm³), pounds per cubic foot (lb/ft³), or ounces per cubic inch (oz/in³). We can go between these different units of density by using these conversion facts:

$$1\tfrac{g}{cm^3} \approx 62.43\tfrac{lb}{ft^3} \approx 0.578\tfrac{oz}{in^3} \qquad 1\tfrac{oz}{in^3} \approx 1.73\tfrac{g}{cm^3}$$

- Notice that water is used as a standard − it has a density of 1 in both the metric and the U.S. systems.
  - 1 mℓ (i.e. 1 cm³) of water (at 4°C) weighs exactly 1 gram[A].
  - 1 liter of water (at 4°C) weighs exactly 1 kilogram.
  - 1 cubic meter of water (at 4°C) weighs exactly 1 metric ton (1000 kg).
  - 1 fl.oz. of water (at 100°C) weighs exactly 1 ounce[B]. (1 fl.oz. of water at 4°C weighs 1.043 ounces[C].)

[A] This is the temperature where water has maximum density.
[B] This is the boiling point of water, where water has its least density.
[C] The fact that water has different densities (and therefore weights) at different temperatures is usually handled during the *Heat* unit of the seventh grade physics main lesson block.

Eighth Grade

- When a density is given in terms of g/cm³ we can easily compare it to water, which has a density (at 4°C) of exactly 1 g/cm³ (1 cm³ of water weighs 1 gram). For example, with gold's density of 19.3 g/cm³, we can say that gold is 19.3 times heavier than water.
- For densities of various materials **see Appendix C** *Conversion Table*.
- In order to calculate density, we divide weight by volume.
Example: What is the density (in g/cm³) of a rock that has a weight of 2.41kg and a volume of 502cm³?
Solution: 2.41kg is 2410g. So we divide 2410g by 502cm³ to get an answer of <u>4.80 g/cm³</u>.

- Do several density word problems building up to ones like these:
Example: How much does a block of gold weigh that is 10cm x 12cm x 24cm (the size of a tissue box)?
Solution: We calculate the volume as 10cm·12cm·24cm, which is 2880cm³. Looking on the *Conversion Table*, we see that the density of gold is 19.3g/cm³, we then calculate:

$$\frac{2880cm^3}{1}\cdot\frac{19.3g}{cm^3}\cdot\frac{1kg}{1000g}\approx \underline{55.58kg}\text{ (or about 123 lb.)}$$

Example: How much does a cube of iron weigh that measures 8 inches on a side?
Solution: Given that the density of iron is 443 lb per ft³, we can do the problem in two possible ways:
The intuitive approach: 8 inches is ⅔ of a foot, thereby giving the cube a volume of (⅔)³ or ⁸⁄₂₇ of a cubic foot. Our answer is thus: ⁸⁄₂₇ · 443, which is about <u>131.3 lb</u>.

The Chain Method: The volume is 8³ or 512 in³. We do $\frac{512\,in^3}{1}\cdot\frac{1\,ft^3}{1728in^3}\cdot\frac{443lb}{1\,ft^3}$ which is <u>131.3 lb</u>.

Example: A small stone pyramid weighs 5.52 kg, has a square base with a length 20 cm, and is 12 cm high.
(a) What is its density?
(b) What is its weight in water?
Solution: (a) In order to calculate the density in terms of grams per cubic centimeter, we first convert the weight to 5520 grams. Next, to find the volume of the pyramid, we use the formula
V = ⅓ A_base · H (**see 8th Grade**, *Mensuration*), which results in ⅓(20)²·12, which is 1600cm³. We get the density by dividing 5520 by 1600, which results in <u>3.45g/cm³</u>.
(b) To find its weight in water, the class must be familiar with Archimedes' Principle from the eighth grade Physics (*hydraulics*) main lesson block. Archimedes said that an object that sinks becomes lighter by the weight of the water that it displaces. Since it displaces 1600cm³ of water, and that amount of water weighs 1600 grams (assuming water temperature of 4°C), then we can say that, once the pyramid is submerged in water, it weighs 5520 − 1600 = 3920 grams, or <u>3.92 kg</u>.

Example: Does a plastic ball float, given that it weighs exactly 9 pounds and is 8 inches in diameter?
Solution: We need to calculate its density. First, we find the volume by using the formula V = ⁴⁄₃ π r³ (**See 8th Grade**, *Mensuration*), and since the radius of the ball is 4, we get:
V = ⁴⁄₃ π 4³ → V = ⁴⁄₃ · (3.14) ·64 (because 4³ is 64), which works out to 267.9 in³.
In order to get ounces per cubic inch, we convert the 9 pounds to 144 ounces. Then, to get the density, we divide its weight (144) by its volume (267.9), for a result of 0.537 oz/cm³. Since this density is less than that of water, which has a density of 0.578 oz/cm³ (**see Appendix C,** *Conversion Table*), we can say that <u>it floats</u>.

Example: A cylindrical bucket is 10 inches in both diameter and height.
(a) What is the volume of the bucket, both in cubic inches and in gallons?
(b) How much do the contents of the bucket weigh if it is filled with water?
(c) How much do the contents of the bucket weigh if it is filled with mercury?
Solution: (a) We get the area of the base by using the formula for the area of a circle, A = π·r², which gives us an area of π·5² = 25π. The volume equals the area of the base times the height, giving us 250π or <u>785in³</u>. Given that there are 231 in³ in a gallon (**see Appendix C,** *Conversion Table*) we divide 785 by 231 to get an answer of approximately <u>3.40 gallons</u>.
(b) Given that a gallon of water weighs 8.345 pounds, we do 8.345·3.40, which is <u>28.4 lb</u>.
(c) *The Chain Method*: Given: 1 ft³ mercury weighs 843 lb, and 1 ft³ ≈ 7.481 gallons:
$$\frac{3.40gal}{1}\cdot\frac{1\,ft^3}{7.481gal}\cdot\frac{843\,lb}{1\,ft^3}=\underline{383.1\,lb}.$$
The Intuitive Method: Given that mercury is 13.5 times denser than water, we simply multiply the weight of the bucket filled with water (28.4) by 13.5 to get <u>383.4 lb</u>.

Proportions

- Review seventh grade ratios.
- When two ratios are equal to each other, we can use an equation to set the two ratios (as fractions) equal. This kind of equation is called a *proportion*. (e.g., $\frac{3}{4} = \frac{X}{8}$). A proportion is an equation with a ratio or fraction on each side, such as: $6:x = 4:7$, which is the same as $\frac{6}{X} = \frac{4}{7}$ (See example below for solution.)

<u>Shortcuts</u> for solving proportions.

- *Moving along diagonals.*

   Explanation: Starting with $\frac{3}{4} = \frac{6}{8}$ we notice that any of the four terms can be moved diagonally across the equal sign to produce a number of variations (each one still being a true statement), such as:

   $$\frac{3 \cdot 8}{4} = \frac{6}{1} \quad \text{or} \quad \frac{3}{1} = \frac{4 \cdot 6}{8} \quad \text{or} \quad \frac{3}{6} = \frac{4}{8} \quad \text{or} \quad \frac{3}{4 \cdot 6} = \frac{1}{8} \quad \text{or} \quad 3 \cdot 8 = 4 \cdot 6 \quad \text{(There are more possibilities.)}$$

   The idea, is that as long as we start with a proportion (equation) that is in balance (equal), then we can move any of the four terms along a diagonal, and the equation will still be valid.

   Example: Solve: $\frac{6}{X} = \frac{4}{7}$

   Solution: Our objective is to get X on the top of a fraction, and then to get it alone on one side of the equation, with all the constants on the other side. We do this by taking the original equation and first moving the X up to the right, giving us for the moment:

   $$\frac{6}{1} = \frac{4X}{7}.$$

   We can now move the 4 and 7 along diagonals to the other side, allowing us to finally reach our goal, where X is alone on one side: $\frac{6 \cdot 7}{4} = X$, which becomes X = <u>10½</u>. With practice, this can be done very quickly.

- *Cross multiplying*

   - Cross multiplying is a variation of the theme *Moving Along Diagonals*, but a popular way of eliminating fractions. The idea is simply to move both of the denominators up along diagonals to the other side of the equation.

   Example: Using the same example as above: $\frac{6}{X} = \frac{4}{7}$

   Solution: Cross multiplying means to move both denominators up along the diagonals to get: $6 \cdot 7 = 4 \cdot X$. Dividing both sides by 4 then gives an answer of   <u>X = 10½</u>.

   - See *cross multiplying* in the eighth grade *algebra unit* for a more complicated example.

- *Caution!* Both *moving along diagonals* and *cross multiplication* can only be used for "true" proportions, namely *only if the equation is such that one fraction is equal to one fraction*. It cannot be immediately used for equations such as: $3 + \frac{2}{X} = \frac{5}{7}$. (the left side is not a single fraction.) This is solved in high school.

<u>Word Problems</u> that use proportions.

- This unit can be done simultaneously with *dimensional analysis* (See **8th Grade Arithmetic**, *Dimensional Analysis*).
- Review seventh grade *similar triangles*.
- *Recipe problems*

   Example: If a recipe calls for 6 cups of flour and 4 cups of water, then how much water is needed if the recipe is expanded and 10 cups of flour are used?

   Solution: We set up a proportion in terms of flour:water = flour:water

   $$6:4 = 10:x \quad \rightarrow \quad \frac{6}{4} = \frac{10}{X}$$

   By *moving along diagonals* we get: $X = \frac{10 \cdot 4}{6}$

   which results in an answer of $\frac{20}{3}$ or <u>6⅔</u> cups of water.

- *Gas mileage problems.*
  Example: If a car goes 220 miles on 15 gallons of gas, how far can it go on 9 gallons of gasoline?

  Solution: We set up a proportion in terms of mi:gal = mi:gal → 220:15 = X:9 → $\frac{220}{15} = \frac{X}{9}$

  Using the *moving along diagonals*, we get $X = \frac{220 \cdot 9}{15}$ resulting in an answer of <u>132</u> miles.

- *Map scale problems.* Maps can have two possible types of scales:
  - <u>Fractional scale.</u> This is given usually as a ratio. For example, a scale of 1:24,000 means that real distances are 24,000 times greater than the distances between points on the map. This kind of scale is common outside the U.S.
  - <u>Verbal scale.</u> This kind of scale, which is common in the U.S., states how many miles in the real world are represented by one inch on the map. For example, a scale of 1 inch = 60 miles means that every inch on the map represents 60 miles in reality.

  Example: A verbal scale of 1 inch = 50 miles, is the equivalent of what fractional scale?
  Solution: Multiplying 50 by 5280 and 12, we see that 50 miles is equal to 3,168,000 inches. We can then say that 1 inch on the map represents 3,168,000 inches in the real world, and therefore the fractional scale is <u>1:3,168,000.</u>

  Example: If Greenville and Browntown are 3¾ inches apart on a map, and the scale is 1 inch = 40 miles, then how far apart are they in reality?
  Solution: We set up a proportion in terms of inches:miles = inches:miles, which gives us: 1:40 = 3.75:X. This leads to X = 40·3¾, which gives an answer of <u>150 miles.</u>

  Example: A map of China has a scale of 1:6,000,000. If Wuhan and Shanghai are 11.4 cm apart on the map, then how far apart (in kilometers) are they in reality?
  Solution: We can set up a proportion in terms of centimeters:kilometers = centimeters:kilometers, or we can simply realize that the distance in reality is 6 million times further than the distance on the map, so we multiply 11.4 times 6 million, which gives the result that the two cities are 68,400,000 cm apart. Since there are 100,000cm in a kilometer, we move the decimal point 5 places to get <u>684 km.</u>

- *Rate problems.*
  - Review seventh Grade rate problems. Also include rate problems from *Dimensional Analysis*, above.
  - Do new rate problems, such as the following:

  Example: Which of the following is a better buy: A 12-ounce block of cheese for $3.32, or a kilogram of cheese for $10.12?
  Solution: One way to solve this problem is to convert both prices to dollars per pound. The 12-ounce block costs 3.32÷12 = 0.27\overline{6}$/oz. We multiply this by 16 to get $4.43/lb. The kilo block of cheese costs 10.12÷2.2 = $4.60/lb. Therefore, the 12-ounce block is a better buy.

  Example: At Bill's Bikes, Tina can assemble 4 bikes in 7 hours.
  (A) How many bikes can she assemble in 20 hours?
  (B) How long does it take her to assemble 13 bikes?

  Solution: (A) Since she can assemble 4 bikes in 7 hours, she can do $^1/_7$ as much in one hour, which is $^4/_7$ of a bike. In other words, her rate of work is $^4/_7$ of a bike per hour. Therefore, in 20 hours she can assemble 20·$^4/_7$, which is $^{80}/_7$ or <u>11$^3/_7$ bikes.</u> Alternatively, we can do the problem by setting up a proportion of bikes:hours = bikes:hours, which gives us the equation 4:7 = X:20. This becomes $^4/_7 = {}^X/_{20}$, and *moving along diagonals* (see above) gives us X = $^{80}/_7$, which gives us an answer of <u>11$^3/_7$ bikes.</u>

  (B) Since she does 4 bikes in 7 hours, it takes ¼ as long to do one bike, which is $^7/_4$, or 1¾ of an hour. 13 bikes then take 13·$^7/_4$ or <u>22¾ hours.</u> Alternatively, we can do the problem by setting up a proportion of bikes:hours = bikes:hours, which gives us the equation 4:7 = 13:X. This becomes $^4/_7 = {}^{13}/_X$, and *moving along diagonals* (see above) gives us X = $^{91}/_4$, which gives us an answer of <u>22¾ hours.</u>

Eighth Grade Algebra

- For some general thoughts on teaching algebra, see the introduction, *Algebra*.
- A reminder: don't do too much algebra for the sake of (perhaps unconsciously) showing people that the class is advanced in mathematics, or because it is what you are most familiar with. The only algebra topics that are absolutely necessary in eighth grade are a review of the seventh grade main lesson block, and *proportions*.

   Any high school algebra course begins with a review of the basic algebra concepts we cover in our seventh grade *algebra* main lesson. If you don't get to a topic that is listed here under eighth grade algebra, then you can be assured that the students will have it in high school. On the other hand, many of the non-algebra eighth grade math topics listed here (e.g., number bases, Platonic solids, loci, etc.) are not covered in high school.

<u>Review</u> seventh grade algebra *very* thoroughly.   Very important!

Expressions

Order of Operations

- The *order* is: (<u>P</u>lease <u>E</u>xcuse <u>M</u>y <u>D</u>ear <u>A</u>unt <u>S</u>ally).
   1. Simplify Inside <u>P</u>arentheses
   2. <u>E</u>xponents
   3. <u>M</u>ultiplication or <u>D</u>ivision (left to right)
   4. <u>A</u>ddition or <u>S</u>ubtraction (left to right)

- Give several problems so that the students can practice the *order of operations*, such as:

   Example: Simplify $25 - 5 \cdot 3$

   Solution: Before we do the subtraction, we must first multiply 5 times 3. We take that result (15), and subtract it from 25 to get a final answer of <u>10</u>.

   Example: Simplify $16 - 5 \cdot 3^2 - 20 + 5 - (10-8)^3$

   Solution: First, we do inside the parentheses, which is 2, and then becomes 8 when cubed. Next, we simplify the $5 \cdot 3^2$ by first squaring the 3 to get 9, and then we multiply that by 5, which gives us 45. At this point, the original problem has become $16 - 45 - 20 + 5 - 8$, which can be rearranged to $16+5-45-20-8$, which leads to our final answer of -52. The work should be written down somewhat like this:

   $$16 - 5 \cdot 3^2 - 20 + 5 - (10-8)^3$$
   $$16 - 5 \cdot 9 - 20 + 5 - (2)^3$$
   $$16 - 45 - 20 + 5 - 8$$
   $$16 + 5 - 45 - 20 - 8$$
   $$21 - 73$$
   $$\boxed{-52}$$

Evaluating Expressions

- Evaluate expressions by plugging in values

   Example: Evaluate $x^2 + 4y - xy$ given $x = -3$; $y = -2$

   Solution: Everywhere we see an X, we put in -3, and for each Y we put in -2. The problem now becomes $(-3)^2 + 4(-2) - (-3)(-2)$. Order of operations says we must first do $(-3)^2$, which is 9. Then we do each of the multiplications where $4(-2)$ is -8, and $(-3)(-2)$ is $+6$. At this point we have $9 + (-8) - (+6)$, which is just $9 - 8 - 6$. Here we can combine the -8 and -6 to get -14. The final answer is $9 - 14$, which is -5. The work should be written down somewhat like this:

   $$x^2 + 4y - xy \qquad \text{(given } x = -3; y = -2\text{)}$$
   $$(-3)^2 + 4(-2) - (-3)(-2)$$
   $$9 + -8 - +6$$
   $$9 - 8 - 6$$
   $$9 - 14$$
   $$\boxed{-5}$$

The Laws of Exponents

- These rules should be covered fairly briefly. They receive much attention in ninth grade.
- Don't give the general formulas (e.g., $x^n \cdot x^m = x^{(n+m)}$). This is too abstract for eighth grade.
  - *Add exponents* when multiplying terms with the same base.
    Example: $2^5 \cdot 2^3 \rightarrow 2^8$
    Example: $x^4 \cdot x^3 \rightarrow x^7$
  - *Multiply exponents* if one exponent is raised to another.
    Example: $(3^4)^2 \rightarrow 3^8$
    Example: $(x^4)^3 \rightarrow x^{12}$
    Example: $(3y^2)^3 \rightarrow 27y^6$
  - *When adding like terms* with exponents, the exponents don't change.
    Example: $3x^5 + 4x^5 \rightarrow 7x^5$
    Example: $3x^2 + 4x^3$ can't be simplified.
  - (optional) *Square rooting* a term with an exponent.
    Example: $\sqrt{5^6} \rightarrow 5^3$
    Example: $\sqrt{x^{16}} \rightarrow x^8$

Fractions and Negatives

- It doesn't matter where the negative sign goes in a fraction.
  Example: $\frac{3}{-4}$ is the same as $\frac{-3}{4}$ and the same as $-\frac{3}{4}$

Equations

Use of Equal Sign (for the teacher only)

- There are three different ways to show work when simplifying or evaluating expressions:
  1. Use an *arrow* ($\rightarrow$) to show going from one step to the next.
  2. Use an *equivalence sign* ($\equiv$) to show going from one step to the next.
  3. Show the steps under one another.

- Use equal signs ($=$) only for equations, otherwise some students will incorrectly think that they have an equation that needs to be solved.
  Example: Simplify $6x - 5 + 4x + 11$
  Solution: There are three possibilities to show the work:
  1. $6x - 5 + 4x + 11 \rightarrow \boxed{10x + 6}$
  2. $6x - 5 + 4x + 11 \equiv \boxed{10x + 6}$
  3. $6x - 5 + 4x + 11$
     $\boxed{10x + 6}$

Incorrect: The work shouldn't be shown like this: $6x - 5 + 4x + 11 = 10x + 6$ because now it looks like an equation and some students will try to "solve" it.

Distributive Property

- Do lots of practice, especially when the distributive property is used in equations, such as:
  Example: Solve: $5 - 3(2x-3) - x = 7x - 2 + 4(x+3)$
  Solution: Start by simplifying both sides.

$$5 - 3(2x-3) - x = 7x - 2 + 4(x+3)$$
$$5 - 6x + 9 - x = 7x - 2 + 4x + 12$$
$$-7x + 14 = 11x + 10$$
$$\underline{+7x - 10 \quad +7x - 10}$$
$$4 = 18x$$
$$\div 18 \quad \div 18$$
$$\frac{4}{18} = x \rightarrow \text{Answer is } x = \frac{2}{9}$$

Equations with Fractions

- This is a great way to integrate fraction review.
- Show that fractional answers can be plugged in and will work.
  Example: The answer for the previous problem was $^2/_9$. Check to see that it is correct.
  Solution: We simply put $^2/_9$ in the original equation to see if it really balances.

$$5 - 3(2x{-}3) - x = 7x - 2 + 4(x{+}3)$$
$$5 - 3(2{\cdot}\tfrac{2}{9}{-}3) - \tfrac{2}{9} = 7{\cdot}\tfrac{2}{9} - 2 + 4(\tfrac{2}{9}{+}3)$$
$$5 - 3(\tfrac{4}{9}{-}3) - \tfrac{2}{9} = \tfrac{14}{9} - 2 + 4(3\tfrac{2}{9})$$
$$5 - 3(\tfrac{4}{9}{-}\tfrac{27}{9}) - \tfrac{2}{9} = \tfrac{14}{9} - 2 + 4(\tfrac{29}{9})$$
$$5 - 3(-\tfrac{23}{9}) - \tfrac{2}{9} = \tfrac{14}{9} - 2 + \tfrac{116}{9}$$
$$\tfrac{45}{9} + \tfrac{69}{9} - \tfrac{2}{9} = \tfrac{14}{9} - \tfrac{18}{9} + \tfrac{116}{9}$$
$$\tfrac{112}{9} = \tfrac{112}{9} \quad \text{Both sides are equal, so x} = \tfrac{2}{9} \text{ works!}$$

- *Equations with Fractional Constants and Coefficients.* Do many of these, such as:
  Example: $\tfrac{2}{3}X - \tfrac{3}{4} = \tfrac{1}{5}X + \tfrac{2}{5}$

  Solution: $\tfrac{2}{3}X - \tfrac{3}{4} = \tfrac{1}{5}X + \tfrac{2}{5}$

  $\underline{-\tfrac{1}{5}X + \tfrac{3}{4} \quad -\tfrac{1}{5}X + \tfrac{3}{4}} \qquad (\tfrac{2}{3} - \tfrac{1}{5} \to \tfrac{7}{15} \text{ and } \tfrac{2}{5} + \tfrac{3}{4} \to \tfrac{23}{20})$

  $\tfrac{7}{15}X = \tfrac{23}{20}$

  $\div\tfrac{7}{15} \qquad \div\tfrac{7}{15}$

  $X = \tfrac{23}{20} \cdot \tfrac{15}{7} \text{ cross canceling} \to X = \tfrac{23}{4} \cdot \tfrac{3}{7} \to X = \tfrac{69}{28} \text{ or } 2\tfrac{13}{28}$

- *Cross Multiplying.*
  - See *Moving along Diagonals* and *Cross Multiplying* in the eighth grade *Proportions* unit, above.
  - In the algebra unit, cross multiplying is taken a step further to include problems where the X appears on both sides of the equation.

  Example: $\tfrac{X+3}{2} = \tfrac{2X-4}{3}$
  Solution: We simply cross multiply to get: $3(X{+}3) = 2(2X{-}4)$. Solving gives an answer of X = $\underline{17}$.

(Optional) Strange Solutions

- These are best introduced once the class is fairly confident with solving basic equations.
- There are three types of situations to discuss here:
  - *Equations with a solution of X = 0.* (There is one solution.)
    Example: $8x + 5 = 3x + 5$
    - There is only one solution, and that solution happens to be X = 0.
  - *Equations where any value for X will work.* (There are infinitely many solutions.)
    Example: $8x + 7 = 4 + 8x + 3$
    - When we start to solve this, we get $8x + 7 = 8x + 7$, and notice that both sides of the equation are identical. If we continued solving this equation (which would be unnecessary), then X would disappear and we would end up with just $0 = 0$, *which is always true.*
    - No matter what we put in for X in the original equation, the equation will balance. Try it!
  - *Equations with no solution.*
    Example: $8x + 3 = 8x - 7$
    - This occurs when we notice that the X's disappear, leaving us with zero on one side of the equation, and some constant on the other side. In the above example, we end up with $0 = -10$, *which is never true.* No matter what we put into X, the equation cannot balance.

(Optional) <u>Converting Repeating Decimals into Fractions</u>

- Review the sixth grade method for converting repeating decimals into fractions. (**See 6th Grade,** *Converting Repeating Decimals to Fractions.*)
- Introduce the following new method that uses algebra.

Example: What is $0.3\overline{42}$ as a fraction?

Solution: Let $x = 0.3\overline{42}$. Therefore $100x = 34.2\overline{42}$. We chose 100 because there are two digits under the repeat bar. Subtracting the former equation from the latter, we get:

$$100x = 34.2\overline{42}.$$
$$-\ (1x) = -(0.3\overline{42}) \quad \text{(Notice how the repeating parts line up and cancel!)}$$
$$99x = 33.9,$$

which leads to $x = \frac{33.9}{99}$ which is $\frac{339}{990}$ and this reduces to a final answer of $\frac{113}{330}$.

Example: What is $0.12\overline{037}$ as a fraction?

Solution: Let $x = 0.12\overline{037}$. Therefore $1000x = 120.37\overline{037}$. We chose 1000 because there are three digits under the repeat bar. Subtracting the former equation from the latter, we get:

$$1000x = 120.37\overline{037}$$
$$-\ (1x) = -(0.12\overline{037})$$
$$999x = 120.25$$

which leads to $x = \frac{120.25}{999}$ which is $\frac{12025}{99900}$ reducing to a final answer of $\frac{13}{108}$.

Eighth Grade Computers

(See the section on *Computers* in the Introduction.)

Computer memory and ASCII code

- This should be done after the unit on number bases. (**See 8th Grade Arithmetic,** *Number Bases.*)
- ASCII stands for <u>A</u>merican <u>S</u>tandard <u>C</u>ode for <u>I</u>nformation <u>I</u>nterchange.
- *Binary Codes using Flags.* Try introducing this by imagining that you are sending codes from one tower to another with a line of flags, where each flag can be one of two possible colors. How many codes are possible with a row of 4 flags? (answer: $2^4 = 16$) How many codes are possible with 8 flags? (answer: $2^8 = 256$) Computers do basically the same thing, but use bits instead of flags.
- *A Computer Bit as a Switch.* Computers use the ASCII coding system, which is based on binary digits. A *bit* is a very small circuit in the computer that can be thought of as a switch; it is either "on" or "off". At any given moment, an electrical current is either passing through it, or not. We represent these two possibilities in binary either as "1" (for "on") or "0" (for "off"). This is why people say that the memory of a computer is just a bunch of zeroes and ones – it really means that it's a bunch of switches, with each one either "on" or "off". The students need to understand that when any key on the computer keyboard is hit, that its ASCII code is "written" into the computer memory as a string of binary digits – switches that are either on or off.
- *One Byte of Memory.* One byte consists (usually) of 8 bits. A single keyboard character has a binary code that is one byte (8 bits) long. One 8-bit byte has 256 possible codes, just like our 8 flags on the tower had 256 possible codes.

  Example: How is the character "L" represented in the computer's memory?

  Solution: In the ASCII code table (**see Appendix C**), we see that the hex code for "L" is 4C. Since 4 in hexadecimal is equal to 0100 in binary, and C in hexadecimal is equal to 1100 in binary, we can say that "L" is represented in binary ASCII code as 01001100.

- *Decoding Strings of Binary Code.*
  - **See Appendix C** for the *ASCII Code Table.*
  - Have the students decode one byte at a time from binary to hexadecimal, then look up the code in the *ASCII Code Table.*

  Example: Decode this string: 01101000, 01101111, 01110010, 01110011, 01100101

  Solution: These five bytes are written as 68,6F,72,73,65 in hexadecimal, which is then converted (by looking on the *ASCII code table*) into the five characters, "horse".

  Example: The following string of binary code is actually a riddle. Decode it and answer the riddle.
  01010111, 01101000, 01100001, 01110100, 00100000, 01100010, 01100001, 01110011, 01100101, 00100000, 01101001, 01110011, 00100000, 01110100, 01101000, 01101001, 01110011, 00111010, 00100000, 00110011, 00110100, 00101011, 00110100, 00110100, 00111101, 00110001, 00110000, 00110000, 00111111

  Solution: The binary bytes are first converted into the following in hexadecimal (in the same order):

57	68	61	74	20	62	61	73
65	20	69	73	20	74	68	69
73	3A	20	33	34	2B	34	34
3D	31	30	30	3F			

  Using the ASCII code table in Appendix C, we decode these bytes to (in the same order):

W	h	a	t	space	b	a	s
e	space	i	s	space	t	h	i
s	:	space	3	4	+	4	4
=	1	0	0	?			

  which is the string: "What base is this: 34+44=100?". The answer to this riddle is that it is <u>octal</u>, since 34+44 is equal to 100 in octal (**see 8th Grade Arithmetic,** *Number Bases*).

Computer Algorithms (Computer programming)

- This unit deals with how computers manipulate information through computer programming.
- Only spend a couple of days on this unit. Even a brief amount of time gives the students a glimpse into the basic idea of a computer program.
- The term *Algorithm* (coming from al-Khwarizmi's name) existed in mathematics long before computers, and has become popularized with their development. *An algorithm is a procedure that is described in a detailed, step-by-step manner.*
- *Computers don't think.* The computer programmer does the thinking. *The computer simply follows the step-by-step instructions as given in the computer program.*
- *Some key words* that an algorithm (or program) may use are: **If..then..else, Until, Goto, Input, Print.**
- Students should not be expected to write algorithms on their own. For the most part, that kind of thinking is for tenth and eleventh grade. The idea here is simply to give them an idea of how computers work, and to be able to follow the steps of these algorithms thereby gaining a basic understanding of what a computer does when a program is being executed.

Writing Familiar Algorithms

Take a familiar procedure (e.g., addition, long division) and describe it thoroughly in words. Then write it down as an algorithm. The language is English, but careful thought must be given when choosing the wording.

- *An algorithm for addition.*
  - **See Appendix C** for the *Addition Algorithm* written out in the style of a computer program, but in English.
  - The class should try to create it together on the board, so that everyone sees it evolve.
- (Optional) *An algorithm for long division.*
  - **See Appendix C** for the *Algorithm for Long Division* written out in the style of a computer program, but in English.
  - Students wanting an extra challenge may attempt to write this on their own. They should imagine that they have a friend who knows how to add, subtract, and multiply, but does not know how to do long division. They have to write a letter to this friend and explain how to do long division, step-by-step, and without referring to a specific example.
  - Emphasize to the students that there are many possible answers for writing down this algorithm.

Examples of New Algorithms

Below are a couple of new algorithms for the students to try to follow. The students should simply follow the step-by-step instructions stated in the program, thereby imitating what a computer does when it executes a program.

- *The prime number algorithm* (similar to the Sieve of Eratosthenes).
  - **See Appendix C** for the *Prime Number Algorithm* written out in the style of a computer program, but in English.
  - Don't explain any of the steps to the students. The main purpose is for the students to experience how a computer operates – it simply follows instructions. They should do the same!
- *The square root algorithm – without zeroes.*
  - **See Appendix C** for the *Square Root Algorithm – without zeroes* written out in the style of a computer program, but in English.
  - Read my notes given in eighth grade Arithmetic for the importance of teaching the square root algorithm so that students can calculate square roots by hand.

Eighth Grade Geometry

Mensuration (Areas and Volumes)

Beware of Formulas!

- A common approach to teaching *areas* and *volumes* is to have the students use, and therefore memorize, a lot of formulas. This approach reduces math to blindly sticking numbers into formulas, often without the students having a clue about what they are really doing. I do the opposite − I try to use as few formulas as possible. Almost always, I show the students where a formula comes from, and most of my formulas are quite general (e.g., One of my formulas can be used for either a cone or a pyramid). I encourage the students to think their way through every problem.

Area

Review

- Review seventh grade *area*.
- Review one, two, three dimensions from sixth grade.
- *Emphasize* that length is measured using lines (e.g., meter, foot, etc.); area is measured using squares (e.g., m^2, ft^2, in^2, etc.); and volume is measured using cubes (e.g., m^3, ft^3, in^3, etc.).

The Pythagorean Theorem

- *Review shear and stretch* from seventh grade.
- *Give Baravalle's[1] proof* using the sheer and stretch, as shown below.

Hermann von Baravalle's
Proof of the
Pythagorean Theorem

---

[1] Hermann von Baravalle was a math teacher at the first Waldorf school.

Area of a Trapezoid

- The formula for calculating the area of a trapezoid $A = \frac{1}{2}H(B_1 + B_2)$ is given in math textbooks, but I don't give it to the students. As a challenge problem, I often ask a student to come up with the formula.
- Have the students find the area of any trapezoid by dividing it into a triangle and a parallelogram (or a rectangle), or into two triangles.

    Example: Find the area of the trapezoid shown on the right. Assume all measurements are given in meters.

    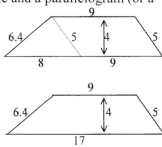

    Solution: We first divide the trapezoid by drawing a line parallel to one side from one of the obtuse angles, as shown in the drawing at the right. We then calculate the area of the parallelogram as its base (9) times its height, which is 4 (not 5!), resulting in an area of 36m². The triangle also has a height of 4, and its base is 8, so its area is ½(8)(4), which is 16m². The whole trapezoid, therefore, has an area of 36+16 = <u>52m²</u>.

Heron's Formula for the Area of a Triangle

Area $\triangle ABC$ $= \sqrt{s \cdot (s-a) \cdot (s-b) \cdot (s-c)}$, where $s = \frac{1}{2}(a + b + c)$ is the semi-perimeter.

- This formula is attributed to the Greek, Heron (fl.≈75A.D.), but it may have been Archimedes that came up with it first.
- Heron's amazing proof of this formula is, for me, the climax of the tenth grade year of studying geometry.
- Before seeing this formula, the students should first be able to calculate the areas of non-right triangles where the base and height are given. (**See 7th grade Geometry,** *Area.*)
- The beauty of this little-known formula is that you don't need to know the height of the triangle. Without this formula, you would have to use trigonometry (studied in high school) to calculate the height, and it would be more complicated.

    Example: Find the area of the triangle that has sides of length 5m, 6m, and 7m.

    Solution: The perimeter is 18m, so the semi-perimeter is 9m. Putting all the numbers into the formula, we get: Area $= \sqrt{9(9-5)(9-6)(9-7)}$, which is $\sqrt{9 \cdot 4 \cdot 3 \cdot 2}$, and becomes $\sqrt{216}$. Using the square root algorithm, we get an area of <u>14.70m²</u> (rounded).

Calculating the Area of Four Types of Triangles

- *A right triangle.* We are given the base and the height, so finding the area is easy.

    Example: With the triangle here, the area is: $A = \frac{1}{2} \cdot B \cdot H \rightarrow A = \frac{1}{2} \cdot 20 \cdot 21 \rightarrow A = \underline{210 \text{ ft}^2}$

- *An isosceles triangle.* Here, we can use the Pythagorean Theorem in order to calculate the height. We then use this height in order to calculate the area.

    Example: We start with a triangle with one side 20' long and two sides 26' long. To find the height, we cut the triangle in half, which makes a right triangle with sides 26', 10', and H, which is the height of the original triangle. Using the *leg formula* we get:

    $H^2 = 26^2 - 10^2 \quad \rightarrow \quad H^2 = 676 - 100 \quad \rightarrow \quad H^2 = 576 \quad \rightarrow \quad H = 24$

    (We also could have determined H more quickly by using Pythagorean triples.)
    Now we know that the height of the original triangle is 24. So the area is:
    $A = \frac{1}{2} \cdot B \cdot H \quad \rightarrow \quad A = \frac{1}{2} \cdot 20 \cdot 24 \quad \rightarrow \quad A = \underline{240 \text{ ft}^2}$

- *An equilateral triangle.* In this case, we could use the same method as described above for the isosceles triangle, but Heron's formula is generally easier.

    Example: With an equilateral triangle that has all sides equal to 10cm, the perimeter is 30cm, so the semi-perimeter (S) is 15. The area of the triangle is then:

    Area $= \sqrt{15 \cdot (15-10) \cdot (15-10) \cdot (15-10)} \rightarrow \sqrt{15 \cdot 5 \cdot 5 \cdot 5} \rightarrow \sqrt{3 \cdot 5^2 \cdot 5^2} \rightarrow 5 \cdot 5 \cdot \sqrt{3} \rightarrow 25 \cdot (1.73) \approx \underline{43.25 \text{ ft}^2}$

- *A scalene triangle* (each side is different). In this case, we must use Heron's formula.

    Example: Using Heron's formula with the triangle here, the perimeter is 72', so the semi-perimeter (S) is half of 72, which is 36. The area of the triangle is then:

    Area $= \sqrt{36 \cdot (36-28) \cdot (36-24) \cdot (36-20)} \rightarrow \sqrt{36 \cdot 8 \cdot 12 \cdot 16} \rightarrow \sqrt{55296} \approx \underline{235.1 \text{ ft}^2}$

Area of a Circle $A = \pi \cdot r^2$

Proof: Have students (perhaps in groups) derive the formula by
following this procedure:

1. Cut three congruent circles, each with a radius of 2 inches, into 4,
   8, and 16 pie pieces.
2. From each circle, take the pie pieces and put them side-by-side,
   alternating top up and top down, so that a kind of parallelogram is
   formed that has a wavy top and bottom. (Only the case of 16
   pieces is shown at the right.)

16 pie pieces

3. Compare the three cases. Ask the class the following questions:
   Question: What happens as the circle is cut into more and more
      pie pieces?
   Answer: The pie pieces become thinner and thinner, and the
      wavy parallelogram gets closer and closer to becoming a
      rectangle. *It becomes a rectangle once the circle is cut into
      infinitely many pieces.*

Infinitely many pieces

Question: What is the area of this rectangle, and of the circle?
Answer: The area of the rectangle is the same as the area of the circle, because the rectangle was
   made from the pieces of the circle. The height of the rectangle is 2 inches (the radius of the
   circle). The base of the rectangle is half the circle's circumference (which is 2π), since half the
   circumference is on the top of the rectangle and half is on the bottom. Therefore, the area of the
   rectangle, and also the area of the circle, is $2(2\pi) = 4\pi \approx \underline{12.56 \text{ in}^2}$.

Question: What is the formula for the area of a circle?
Answer: To determine the formula, we do the same process as just done above, except we use r
   for the radius instead of 2 inches. The height of the rectangle is r, and the base is r·π. So the
   area of the rectangle, and also the area of the circle, is (π·r)·r, or $\underline{\text{Area} = \pi \cdot r^2}$.

- *Archimedes' version of the area of a circle.*
  - Archimedes saw the area of a circle as being
    equal to the area of the right triangle that has a
    base equal to the circumference of the circle,
    and a height equal to the circle's radius. This
    triangle is twice as long as the above rectangle.
    And since the triangle's area is ½·base·height,
    we calculate the area of this triangle, and also the circle, to be: $\frac{1}{2} \cdot 2\pi r \cdot r = \pi \cdot r^2$

Portions of Circles

- *Finding the length of an arc (an arc is part of the circumference of a circle).*
  Example: What is the length of an 80° arc of a circle that has a diameter of 20m?
  Solution: The circumference of the whole circle (using C=π·D) is 20π. Since the whole circle consists
     of 360°, the arc is $\frac{2}{9}$ (reducing $\frac{80}{360}$) as long as the circumference of the whole circle. So the

     length of the arc is: $\frac{2}{9} \cdot 20\pi$ → $\frac{40\pi}{9}$ → $\frac{40 \cdot 3.14}{9} \approx \underline{13.96m}$.

- *Finding the area of a segment of a circle.*
  Example: Find the area of a circle with a radius of 5 inches that has a 60° segment (pie piece) missing.
  Solution: The circle is 300° out of 360°, or $\frac{5}{6}$ complete. The area of the segment is therefore $\frac{5}{6}$ of the

     area of the whole circle (A=π·r^2). The segment's area is then: $\frac{5}{6} \cdot \pi (5)^2 \rightarrow \frac{125\pi}{6} \approx \underline{65.42 \text{in}^2}$.

Volumes of Solids

The Basics

- *Cubic Measurement.*
    - Introduce the concept of volume with models of various cubes (cubic inch, cubic foot, cubic cm, etc.), and talk about how each one of these cubes can be used to measure volume.
- *Notation.*
    - Be sure when using the abbreviated form that you are careful to say "cubic inches" and not "inches cubed".
    - Be aware that some students may look at 8 in^3 and think that we should calculate 8^3.
- *Don't give many formulas.*
    - Don't give the students separate formulas for each specific solid (e.g., cylinder, pyramid, cone, prism, etc.). (**See above**, *Beware of Formulas*, for more details.) Instead, I mostly use two general formulas, both of which the students (ideally) derive for themselves.

Volumes of Prisms and Cylinders

- *The transition from area to volume.*
    - Imagine a rectangular room, 20ft by 12ft, which is filling with water. We should lead the students through the following sequence of questions:

        Question: How much water is there in the room when the water is 1 foot deep?

        Answer: Here we should be able to picture *one* layer of boxes placed next to one another on the floor, where each box is one cubic foot and filled with water. The total number of cubic feet (boxes) is then 20·12 = 240 cubic feet.

        Question: How much water is there if the water is 2 feet deep?

        Answer: The picture is basically the same, except now there are two layers, each layer having 240 cubic feet. Therefore, our answer is 2·240 = 480 cubic feet.

        Question: How much water is there if the water reaches the ceiling (8 feet tall)?

        Answer: Now there are 8 layers of boxes, where each layer has 240 boxes. Our answer is: 8·240 = 1920 ft^3.

        Conclusion: The students should now be able to derive the general formula for this situation, which is our first volume formula:

$$V = A_{Base} \cdot H$$

Where A_{Base} is the area of the base, and H is the height. This formula is used for solids where the top and bottom are flat and identical (e.g., prisms, cylinders, etc.).

- *3-D shear and stretch* for finding volumes.
    - *Use a deck of cards* (or a stack of books). The volume of a deck of cards is the same whether the deck is straight up, or knocked over slightly and rising up at a angle.
    - *Imagination exercise.* In the corner of the room there is a prism (box), such that the base of the prism, placed on the floor, is a square, two feet on each side, and the top of the prism (square of the same size) is positioned directly above the base and sits on the ceiling. The four sides of the prism are rectangles and are made of a thin stretchable substance. If the height of the prism is 8 feet, then the volume is 2x2x8, or 32 cubic feet.

        Now, imagine that the top of the prism is allowed to slide anywhere along the ceiling of the room while the bottom remains fixed in the corner of the room. The four sides of the prism then become stretched out to form parallelograms. As the top moves further away from the bottom, the prism becomes longer and thinner. We can imagine this to be the same scenario as the deck of cards; the prism is just a stack of squares, no matter where the top of the prism is on the ceiling, and therefore we can see that the volume of the prism always remains at 32 cubic feet.

    Conclusion: The volume of a prism, whether "tilted" or perfectly vertical, depends only on the area of its base and on its height above the ground, and thus the formula given above (V = $A_{Base} \cdot$ H) is valid for this case as well.

- *A surprising variation.*

  If we take any 4 points in space (not all points on the same plane), then we have a tetrahedron (probably irregular). The volume of the tetrahedron will remain the same if we slide two of the points anywhere along the line that they lie on. This can be explained by thinking of the tetrahedron as lying on a table. The volume of this tetrahedron is ⅓ the area of the base times the tetrahedron's height (see volume formulas, below). If we slide two of the three points of the triangular base along the line that they share, then the area of this triangular base does not change (**see 7th Grade Geometry,** *The Shear and Stretch*); nor is the height of the whole tetrahedron altered. Since area of the base and the height are unchanged, then we can say that the volume is also unchanged.

Volumes of Pyramids and Cones

- *Three pyramids in a cube.*

  Demonstration (Must do!): We start with a normal, Egyptian-style, pyramid, but it is made so that the height is equal to the length of its square base. This allows the pyramid to fit perfectly into a cube (with an open top) that has the same size square base as the pyramid. Both the cube and the pyramid also have the same height. We now construct three "tilting pyramids". Each one is identical, with the same square base and the same height as the original pyramid. However, with each tilting pyramid, *its apex is located directly above one of the corners of the square base.*

  Now we have a puzzle. The objective is to fit the three tilting pyramids perfectly together inside the cube. (It really works!) This shows that the volume of one tilting pyramid is ⅓ the volume of the cube. And since the shear and stretch principle says that the original pyramid has the same volume as one of the tilting pyramids, we can say that the original pyramid has a volume equal to ⅓ of the volume of the cube. The net below (try enlarging it in a photocopier) folds up into a tilting pyramid.

  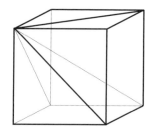

A Net for Constructing a Tilting Pyramid   A Tilting Pyramid   3 Tilting Pyramids in a Cube

Conclusion (drawn from the above demonstration): The students should now be able to derive the formula for a pyramid, which is:

$$V = \frac{1}{3} A_{Base} \cdot H$$

Where A_{Base} is the area of the base, and H is the height. This formula can be used when the bottom of a solid is flat and the top is a point (e.g., pyramid, cone). It was discovered by Democritus, ca. 430B.C.

Archimedes' Ratio

- Imagine that a sphere fits perfectly into a cylinder such that the diameter of the sphere is equal to both the height and the base diameter of the cylinder. Imagine a cone, which also fits perfectly into the cylinder, since its height and base diameter are the same as the cylinder's.
- Archimedes discovered that the ratio of the volume of the Cone to the Sphere to the Cylinder is:

Cone : Sphere : Cylinder = 1 : 2 : 3

- This means that the Cone's volume is ⅓ of the volume of the cylinder (which the formula $V = ⅓ A_{Base} \cdot H$ tells us), and that the sphere's volume is twice the volume of the cone, and ⅔ the volume of the cylinder.

- We can also say that the volume of the cylinder is equal to the sum of the volumes of the cone and the sphere. The following demonstration can be done if you have a cone, ball, and cylinder (with an open top) all with the same height, or alternatively, you can lead the students through it imaginatively:

  Demonstration: Fill the cone completely with water and pour the water into the cylinder. The cylinder is now ⅓ full with water. Slowly push the ball (sphere) into the cylinder. The water should rise exactly to the top of the cylinder, without spilling, thereby showing that the volume of the cylinder is equal to the sum of the volumes of the cone and the sphere.

- The proof of Archimedes' Ratio is done in tenth grade.

The Formula for the Volume of a Sphere

$$V = \tfrac{4}{3}\pi r^3$$ where r is the radius of the sphere.

Derivation of this formula (given Archimedes' ratio):
A cylinder with a height equal to its base diameter has a volume equal to the area of its base times its height, which is $\pi r^2 \cdot 2r$, or $2\pi r^3$. Archimedes' ratio says that the volume of the sphere is ⅔ the volume of this cylinder. Therefore: $V = \tfrac{2}{3}(2\pi r^3) = \tfrac{4}{3}\pi r^3$

Surface Area

- Surface area can be covered fairly briefly.

  Example: What is the surface area of a cube that has an edge of length 10cm?
  Solution: We add up six squares, each with an area of 100cm^2, and get <u>600cm^2</u>.

  Example: What is the surface area of a box that is 2ft by 3ft by 4ft?
  Solution: We have two rectangles that are 2 by 3, two that are 3 by 4, and two that are 2 by 4. The total surface area is therefore: $2(2 \cdot 3) + 2(3 \cdot 4) + 2(2 \cdot 4) \rightarrow$ <u>52 ft^2</u>

  Example: What is the surface area of a cylinder that is 3 ft tall and has a base diameter of 10 ft?
  Solution: We can see that the cylinder has three parts. First, we imagine removing the top and bottom, and then cutting the side (tube) of the cylinder vertically, so that it rolls out flat into a rectangle. This rectangle has a height of 3 ft and a length equal to the cylinder's circumference (10π ft), which results in the rectangle's area being $3 \cdot 10\pi = 30\pi \text{ ft}^2$. The top and bottom of the cylinder each have an area of $\pi(5)^2$, which is $25\pi \text{ ft}^2$. The total surface area is the sum of these three parts: $30\pi + 25\pi + 25\pi$, which is <u>80π</u> or <u>$\approx 251.2 \text{ ft}^2$</u>.

  Example: What is the surface area of an icosahedron that has edges 10cm long?
  Solution: Each of the twenty triangular faces has a height of $\sqrt{75}$ cm and an area of 43.3 cm^2. (This was calculated in *Volume Practice Problems: A triangular prism*, above.) Since there are 20 triangles on an icosahedron, the total area is: $20 \cdot 43.3 \rightarrow$ <u>$\approx 866\text{cm}^2$</u>.

Surface Area of a Sphere $S = 4\pi r^2$

- This formula tells us that the area of the hemisphere (half the sphere) is twice the area of the circle on which it sits, or that the whole sphere's surface area is 4 times the area of the greatest circle inside it.
  Example: What is the surface area of a sphere that has a radius of 5 cm?
  Solution: The answer is $4\pi(5)^2$, which is $100\pi \text{ cm}^2 \approx$ <u>314cm^2</u>.

(optional) Surface Area of a Cone $S = \pi k r$

- r is the radius of the base of the cone, and k is the distance along the edge of the cone.
- This formula does not include the area of the circular base.
  Example: What is the surface area of a cone (without its base), with a 10cm diameter and a 12cm height?
  Solution: We must find the length of the cone's edge. Here we need to imagine the right triangle that goes from the vertex of the cone, straight down along the central axis of the cone to the center of the circular base, then out to the edge of the base, and finally, from there, up along the edge of the cone, returning to the vertex. The two legs of this triangle have been given as 5cm and 12cm, and by using the *Hypotenuse Formula* we find the length of the hypotenuse of the triangle (which is the same as the edge of the cone) to be 13cm. Putting k = 13 and r = 5 into our formula, we find that the surface area of the cone is $\pi \cdot 13 \cdot 5$, which is 65π, or $\approx$ <u>204.1cm^2</u>.

Proof of the formula $S = \pi k r$

    We can cut any cone (with edge length k and base radius r) straight down the edge, and then press it flat onto a table. We now have a *segment* of a circle ("a portion of a pie"), which has a radius equal to k. We can imagine that if the cone is tall and narrow, that it will produce a circle segment that is only a small portion of the pie. Likewise, if the cone is short and wide, then it will produce a circle segment that, when flattened out, is nearly a whole pie (only a narrow sliver is missing).

    With a given cone, how can we know exactly what portion of the pie we have? The answer is that the cone, once it is flattened, is $r/_k$ of the pie. This means that if k is 6 and r is 3, then the circle segment that results from flattening the cone is $^3/_6$ or ½ of the pie (a semi-circle). If k is 8 and r is 6, then the cone, which is fairly short and wide, will be flattened into a circle segment that is $^6/_8$, or ¾ of the whole pie[1]. Now we can say that the area of the circle segment (which is equal to the cone's surface area) is

$r/_k$ of the area of the whole pie (πk^2).   Therefore: $S = (r/_k) \cdot \pi k^2 = \pi k r$

Mensuration Practice Problems

Example: What is the volume of a cylindrical can with a height of 8 inches and a base diameter of 6 inches?

Solution: The radius of the base is 3, so the area of the base is $\pi \cdot 3^2$, which is 9π. The volume is simply equal to the area of the base times the height (8), which gives an answer of:
$8 \cdot 9\pi \rightarrow 72\pi \text{ in}^3 \approx \underline{226.08 \text{ in}^3}$.

Example: What is the volume of a box that is 18 inches by 3 feet by 4 feet?

Solution: We can say that the base is 3 by 4, which has an area of 12 ft². Multiplying this area by 1½ (the height) gives a volume of $\underline{18 \text{ ft}^3}$.

Example: What is the volume of a sphere that has a radius of 5 inches?

Solution: Using the formula $V = {}^4/_3 \pi r^3$, we simply put 5 into r, which gives $V = {}^4/_3 \pi 5^3$. Remembering to first cube the 5 (which is 125), we get:
$V = {}^4/_3 \pi 5^3 \rightarrow \frac{4 \cdot 125}{3} \cdot \pi \rightarrow \frac{500}{3} \cdot \pi \rightarrow \frac{500 \cdot 3.14}{3} \approx \underline{523 \text{in}^3}$.

Example: What is the volume of the cone shown on the right?

Solution: We first need to calculate the height of the cone. So we draw a right triangle inside the cone that goes from the top of the cone down to the middle of the base (this is the height, H), then out to the edge of the base (a distance of 39 feet, which is the radius of the circular base), and then up along the outside of the cone back to the top (a distance of 89 feet). We use the leg formula to find H: $H^2 = 89^2 - 39^2 \rightarrow H^2 = 7921 - 1521 \rightarrow H^2 = 6400 \rightarrow H = 80$.

    Now that we have determined the height, we can easily find the volume:
$V = {}^1/_3 A_{Base} \cdot H \rightarrow V = {}^1/_3 (\pi \cdot 39^2) \cdot 80$, which gives an answer of $\approx \underline{127358.4 \text{ft}^3}$

Example: *A triangular prism.* What is the volume of a triangular prism where the edges of the triangles are all 10cm, and the length of the rectangular sides is 15cm?

Solution: It is easiest if we view the prism as standing on one of its triangular ends, so that the rectangular sides are standing vertically. The volume can then be seen to be equal to the area of the triangular base times the height (which is the length of any of the rectangles). We can find the area of the triangular base either by splitting the triangle in half (as shown on the right) and using the leg formula to find the height: $H^2 = 10^2 - 5^2$, leading to $H = \sqrt{75} \approx 8.66$, and then the area of the triangular base is: $A_{Base} \approx ½ \cdot 10 \cdot \sqrt{75} \rightarrow 5\sqrt{75} \rightarrow 43.3 \text{cm}^2$. Alternatively, we could have more easily used Heron's formula, as was done above for the same triangle (see, above, *Calculating the Area of Four Types of Triangles*). Either way, once we have the area of the triangular base, we can then calculate the volume of the whole prism: $V = A_{Base} \cdot H \rightarrow 43.3 \cdot 15 \rightarrow \underline{649.5 \text{cm}^3}$.

---

[1] The reason for this ratio ($r/_k$) is that the circumference of the whole pie is $2\pi k$, and the distance along the pie's circumference of just the circle segment is equal to the circumference of the base of the cone, which is $2\pi r$. The ratio of these two circumferences is $2\pi r : 2\pi k$, which is $r:k$. This ratio (r:k) is therefore also the ratio of the area of the cone to the area of the "full" circle (which has a radius of k).

Example: Given the pyramid shown on the right...
    (a) Calculate the volume.
    (b) Calculate the surface area.

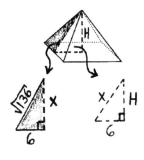

Solution for (a): This is one of the most difficult problems in this unit, because we are not given the height of the pyramid, and calculating this height is fairly difficult. The height (shown as "H" in the drawing on the right) can be imagined as the distance that a ball would fall if it were dropped from the top of the pyramid onto the middle of the floor, which is a square. We can then draw a triangle that has H as one of its sides. (It stands inside the pyramid, and is shown on the right with dotted lines.) We could find H fairly quickly if we knew the other two sides of this dotted triangle, but unfortunately, we only know the length of one of the sides. So we draw a second triangle, which is half of one of the sides of the pyramid (it is shaded in the drawing). The advantage of the shaded triangle is that we know two of its sides and it shares a side with the dotted triangle. Using the *leg formula* (**see 8th grade, The World of Numbers,** *Pythagorean Theorem*) with the shaded triangle, we get: $x^2 = (\sqrt{136})^2 - 6^2 \rightarrow x^2 = 136 - 36 \rightarrow x^2 = 100 \rightarrow x = 10$. Finding x is a major step, because now we have the length for a second side of the dotted triangle. Now, using the *leg formula* with the dotted triangle, we get:
$$H^2 = x^2 - 6^2 \rightarrow H^2 = 10^2 - 6^2 \rightarrow H^2 = 100 - 36 \rightarrow H^2 = 64 \rightarrow H = 8$$
Now that we have found the height of the entire pyramid (H), finding the volume is easy:
$$V = \tfrac{1}{3}(A_{base}) \cdot H \rightarrow V = \tfrac{1}{3}(144) \cdot 8 \rightarrow \underline{\mathbf{V = 384ft^3}}$$

Solution for (b): To find the surface area, we simply add up the area of the five faces of the pyramid (four equal triangles and a square). Each triangle has a base of 12 feet, and a height of 10 feet. (Notice that this height is given as x, and was calculated in the solution for part a. Also, note that x is the height of a triangle, and H is the height of the whole pyramid.) Each triangle, therefore, has an area of $A = \tfrac{1}{2}(12)(10) \rightarrow 60 \text{ ft}^2$. The whole pyramid then has a surface area equal to the area of the four triangles plus the area of the square, which is
$$4 \cdot 60 + 144 \rightarrow \underline{\mathbf{S = 384ft^2}}.$$
    (It is coincidental that 384 also appeared in the answer for the volume. It is, of course, not correct to say that the volume is equal to the surface area, since ft^2 and ft^3 are completely different units. If we had instead measured in inches, or in meters, then the volume and surface area would have produced completely different numbers.)

Example: A conical drinking glass is 12cm deep and 10cm across at the top.
    (a) What is its volume in cm^3 ?
    (b) What is its volume in fluid ounces (Hint: $1cm^3 = 1m\ell$ and $1fl.oz. \approx 29.58m\ell$)?
    (c) If it is filled halfway to the top with water, then how much water is that (in fluid ounces)?

Solution: (a) Using the formula $V = \tfrac{1}{3} \cdot A_{Base} \cdot H$, we get $\tfrac{1}{3} \cdot (\pi \cdot 5^2) \cdot (12) \approx \underline{314cm^3}$

    (b) Since $1cm^3$ equals one milliliter, the volume of the glass is $314m\ell$. And since 1 fluid ounce is approximately $29.58m\ell$ (**see Appendix C,** *Conversion Table*), we divide 314 by 29.58 to get about <u>10.6 fluid ounces</u>.

    (c) This is deceptive! Filling it halfway up means that *both* the diameter and the height are cut in half. Using then a depth of 6 cm, and a diameter of 5 cm, we get:
$V = \tfrac{1}{3} \cdot A_{Base} \cdot H \rightarrow V = \tfrac{1}{3} \cdot (\pi \cdot 2.5^2) \cdot 6 \approx 39.25cm^3$. Now, dividing 39.25 (the volume of the glass filled halfway to the top) by 314 (the volume of the glass filled), we get 0.125, which is equal to $\tfrac{1}{8}$. Surprisingly, the glass has only been filled to $\tfrac{1}{8}$ of its full volume!

The Volume of an Octahedron and Tetrahedron   (**See Appendix C for details.**)

• These are great problems for those students needing an extra challenge.

"Tricks" with Dimensions

- A volume of a given shape can be "made" into a one-dimensional straight line.

    Example: There is a room that has a floor measuring 30 feet by 22 feet and is 8 feet high. The volume of the room is therefore 30x22x8 = 5280 cubic feet. We can picture that 5280 boxes, each one exactly one cubic foot in size, could be neatly stacked into this room.

    Alternatively, we can imagine taking all the boxes out of the room, and putting them side by side into a straight line. Surprisingly, this line of boxes would be one mile (5280 feet) long!

    More dramatically, we can imagine filling the same room with very small boxes that are only one cubic inch in size. Since there are 12x12x12 = 1728 cubic inches in a cubic foot, we can say that the room has a volume of 5280x1728 = 9,123,840 cubic inches. If these boxes were put into a straight line, then the line would be 9,123,840 inches or 144 miles long. Note that the room and both of the above mentioned lines of boxes all have the same volume.

- Often, people try to make sense of large numbers by translating them into something visual. The results are often intentionally distorted.

    Question: *Are there too many people on the earth?* (Assume 7 billion people.)

    Answer #1 (One-dimensional): Yes, far too many people! If all the people in the world were to join hands, the line would be about 26 times longer than the distance to the moon, or about 253 times around the equator. (This assumes that an average person's arm span is 4'9".)

    Answer #2 (Three-dimensional): No, there are not so many people at all! We could take all the people in the world, put each one in a box that has a floor area of 2000 square feet with eight-foot high ceilings, and adding all these boxes together gives a total volume of about 761 cubic miles, which is considerably less than the volume of the Grand Canyon, which is estimated to be very close to 1000 cubic miles.

    Answer #3 (Two-dimensional): There is enough room, for now! If we spread everyone out evenly around the world, there would be one person per 5.3 acres. (This is based on a total land area on the earth of 57,500,000 mi^2, and that there are 640 acres in a square mile.) If we use the fact that an estimated 32% of the earth's land is "wasteland" (i.e., too rocky, dry, cold, or barren to grow anything), then that would amount to 14.3 acres of "fertile land" (i.e., farmland, pasture, forest) per household, given that everyone is in a 4-person household.

    Note that this is the most relevant of the three solutions because it is dealing with the real issue: the amount of land per person.

Stereometry (The study of 3-D forms including the Platonic and Archimedean solids)

Highly recommended reading! I highly encourage anyone planning to teach Platonic and/or Archimedean solids to read Daud Sutton's book, titled *Platonic & Archimedean Solids*.

Vocabulary

The following definitions are intended for the teacher only. The students should come to a familiarity with each of these terms, through talking about them and experiencing them, not through definitions.

- *Polyhedron*: a 3-D solid with flat polygons for faces.
- *Edge*: a line along which two faces of a polyhedron meet. (A cube has 12 edges.)
- *Vertex*: a corner, or point, of a polyhedron. (A cube has eight *vertices*.)
- *Dihedral angle*: the angle at which two planes meet along an edge. Specifically, it is measured as the angle formed by two lines (one lying on each plane) drawn perpendicularly from a point on that edge. More simply, we can think of the dihedral angle by placing the polyhedron on a table, and measuring the angle at which a face meets the table. Looking in this way, we can understand better that the dihedral angle of a cube is 90°; the dihedral angle of a tetrahedron is approximately 70½° –

Dihedral Angles of a Cube, Tetrahedron, and Octahedron

it's less than vertical; and the dihedral angle of an octahedron is approximately 109½° – it's more than vertical. Furthermore, a dodecahedron has a dihedral angle equal to approximately 116½°, and an icosahedron has a dihedral angle of about 138°. (Again, this explanation is for the teacher. Try not to show the tetrahedron, octahedron, dodecahedron, or icosahedron yet. Let the students discover these for themselves, as described below in *Transformations of the Cube*.)

Types of Polyhedra

| **Hexagonal Prism** | **Hexagonal Bipyramid** | **Pentagonal Anti-prism** | **Pentagonal Trapezohedron** |

- *The following definitions are intended for the teacher only*. The students need to become familiar with these terms, but they shouldn't be given these definitions. Instead, the students should learn about these forms through experience and observation.
- A *Platonic solid* is a regular polyhedron. (**See** *Platonic Solids* below for details.)
- An *Archimedean solid* or an *Archimedean dual* is a semi-regular polyhedra. (**See** *Archimedean Solids*.)
- A *pyramid* has a polygon as a base, a point as a top, and triangular faces for its sides. The pyramids of Egypt are called square pyramids because they have a square base. A tetrahedron is a pyramid with a triangular base. A pyramid can be created with any polygon as its base.
- A *prism* is a polyhedron that has its top and bottom faces both congruent and parallel, and the faces on its sides are all parallelograms. A right prism has rectangles for side faces. A cube is a right square prism.
- A *bipyramid* consists of two congruent (or mirror-reflected) pyramids that are combined to form one solid by joining their bases together. An octahedron (**See** *Platonic Solids*, below) is a special case of a bipyramid; it is a square bipyramid with congruent faces.
- An *anti-prism* has its top and bottom faces both congruent and parallel, but in a different orientation. It has triangular side faces. An octahedron (surprisingly) is a special case of an anti-prism, and can be seen as such when sitting on a flat surface; it has a triangular top and bottom (in different orientations), and it has six triangular side faces.
- A *trapezohedron* looks like a "twisted" bipyramid. It has a zigzag ring of edges going around its mid-section and its faces are all kites. Surprisingly, a cube is a special case of a trapezohedron, where the kites have all become squares. If we balance a cube on its point, and then we can see a zigzag ring consisting of six edges.

The Platonic Solids

Tetrahedron   **_Octahedron_**   **_Cube_**   **_Dodecahedron_**   **_Icosahedron_**

- *The four properties.*

    A Platonic solid is a perfectly symmetrical polyhedron having four properties. Try to get the students to arrive at these properties by observing the Platonic solids, rather than listing the properties immediately on the board. They will likely come up with other additional properties on their own. The four properties[1] are:
    - Every face is regular (i.e., an equilateral triangle, square, regular pentagon, etc.).
    - Every vertex is identical (i.e., every point is surrounded by the same kind of faces).
    - Every face is identical.
    - Every dihedral angle is identical.

- *There exist only five Platonic solids.* They are:
    - *The Tetrahedron,* which has four triangular faces.
    - *The Cube (Hexahedron),* which has six square faces.
    - *The Octahedron,* which has eight triangular faces.
    - *The Dodecahedron,* which has twelve pentagonal faces.
    - *The Icosahedron,* which has twenty triangular faces.

- *Give the proof* that there exist only five Platonic solids. (**See Appendix C.**)

- *Plato's Academy.*

    Plato's study of mathematics included four subjects: Arithmetic, Geometry, Astronomy, and Stereometry. Stereometry means "the putting together of the cosmic figures." The Greeks considered the Platonic solids to be the most perfect forms (along with the sphere). Plato did not discover these solids, but he studied them in depth, and about them wrote in his book *Timaeus.* Above the door of the Academy was written "*Let no one unversed in geometry enter here*".

    Plato said that when God created the universe, he first created the element of *fire*, for which he used the tetrahedron. Then he created the element *air*, for which he used the octahedron. He then created *water* using the icosahedron, and then used the hexahedron (cube) to create the *earth* element. Lastly, he used the dodecahedron to create the *life* element, or *quintessence*.

- *Kepler's universe.*

    During Johannes Kepler's quest to discover how it was that the planets revolve around the sun, he was, for a while, convinced that the five Platonic solids were the key. In 1596 he published the book, *Mysterium Cosmographicum* in which he stated his hypothesis on the movement of the planets. It was based on careful astronomical observations, and central to his theory was a way that the Platonic solids could be nested inside one another. Starting with Mercury moving along the surface of a sphere (with the sun at the center), an octahedron was then circumscribed about that sphere.[2] Venus was then said to travel along the surface of a second (and larger) sphere that was circumscribed about the octahedron. (The octahedron now sits in the space between the two spheres.)

    This pattern of alternating Platonic solids and spheres, each nested inside the other, continued all the way up to Saturn. In short, the order was: sphere (Mercury), octahedron, sphere (Venus), icosahedron, sphere (Earth), dodecahedron, sphere (Mars), tetrahedron, sphere (Jupiter), cube, sphere (Saturn). The astonishing thing is that the spacing created by such an arrangement of the Platonic solids is very close to the actual spacing between the orbits of the planets.

    Shortly after the publication of this book, Kepler received more accurate astronomical data, which indicated that his hypothesis was wrong. In 1609, Kepler published his remarkable (and correct) laws of planetary motion, which included the fact that the planets travel along elliptical paths around the sun. Yet, it remained a mystery to Kepler what kept the planets in orbit; unto his death, he believed the planets were pushed along their orbits by angels!

---

[1] It is taken for granted that the solid is required to be *convex*, meaning that it cannot be "indented" anywhere. This eliminates the stellated solids (see Sutton's book: pages 26-31) as possible Platonic solids.

[2] *Circumscribed* means "encircling" or "wrapped around". Since the octahedron is circumscribed about the sphere, we can say that the sphere sits inside the octahedron, and the sphere barely touches the center of each face of the octahedron.

The Transformation of Solids Do each transformation mentally first, and then in clay.

- *The transformation of solids in the mind.*

    The process of transformation is first attempted mentally as a quiet, meditative exercise with the class as a whole. The students concentrate on picturing the specific solid in their mind as the teacher guides the children slowly through, describing in as much detail as possible how the form is changing from one step to the next. If successful, the children can experience each transformation clearly in their mind. It is a powerful experience for them to "see" a new shape for the very first time by picturing it exactly in their mind. This mental process is then replicated with clay (usually the next day).

- *The transformation of solids using clay.*

    As the students are working on a transformation with clay, they can recall how far they were able to go in their mind the previous day. When working with the clay, the students should be careful that even if they can quickly see the whole transformation process happening, they should not rush the process - they should slowly live into it. Also, the students should be careful not to make one portion of the clay too perfect before moving on to another portion of the solid. Ideally, the whole piece of clay is transformed at the same time (e.g., each face changes at the same time). Practically speaking, this is impossible. So we strive toward this ideal by working on a small area of clay, making a slight improvement, and then quickly, and randomly, rotating it in order to work on another section. Also, when doing a transformation in clay, make sure the edges and points are not too sharply defined, otherwise the transformation becomes too difficult.

- *The evolution of solids.*

    The sphere is the perfect solid. In the end, the students should come to realize that any solid could evolve from the transformation of the sphere. However, I find it to be a better imaginative exercise to first arrive at a new solid through the transformation of another familiar solid (e.g., the cube). For example, we can arrive at a dodecahedron in two ways: (1) the transformation of the sphere by starting with 12 equally-spaced points on a sphere and then pushing in on these points until the twelve pentagons emerge; or (2) the transformation of the cube by growing roofs off a cube (see detailed description, below). With any new solid, it is good to first arrive at it by transforming the cube, and then, perhaps later, to try to arrive at it through the transformation of the sphere.

- *Transforming a cube into an octahedron*
    - This is, I feel, the most basic and important of the transformations. It needs to be done thoroughly (perhaps repeated in some way three days in a row) so that all the students really "get it."
    - The procedure starts with the cube, and then we (slowly!) push in all the points, thereby creating eight small triangles. These triangles slowly grow until the moment comes that they are touching one another point-to-point. The most difficult part comes now as these triangles continue to grow. Their points push against each other causing new edges to arise, thereby transforming the triangles into hexagons. Next, these hexagons continue to grow and they get transformed into large triangles that take over the whole solid. This final form is the octahedron, which consists of eight triangles.

Cube	**Truncated Cube**	**Cuboctahedron**	**Truncated Octahedron**	**Octahedron**
6 squares, 8 pts	6 octagons, 8 Δs	6 squares, 8 Δs	6 squares, 8 hexagons	6 points, 8 Δs

Returning back to the start with the cube, we shall now turn our attention to the faces of the cube. We picture that while the eight points of the cube become the eight triangles of the octahedron, the six faces of the cube transform themselves, shrink down, and eventually become the six points of the octahedron.

The challenge with doing this transformation in the mind, is to picture the whole solid fluidly transforming itself - points into faces, and faces into points - all simultaneously.

When working "meditatively" with the students to get them to visualize this process, it is best to have them visualize colors, for example a cube with yellow faces and red points. We then visualize the red points turning into red triangles, and then the red areas get larger and larger, while at the same time, the yellow areas get smaller and smaller, until, in the end, the result is an octahedron with red faces and yellow points.

- *Transforming a cube into a tetrahedron.*
  - One way is to push in on four oppositely oriented points of the cube (see drawing at right). These four points become four triangles which grow bigger and bigger until they all come together to become a tetrahedron.
  - Alternatively, we can use a knife and deeply cut off the four corners of the cube in order to expose the tetrahedron hiding inside the cube.

- *Transforming a cube into a dodecahedron.*
  - This is an interesting, and surprising, way of creating a dodecahedron.
  - This process grows roofs off each of the faces of the cube. Each roof is designed like the drawing on the left, but any two neighboring roofs have to be oppositely oriented (i.e., the top lines of neighboring roofs are perpendicular to one another). After the roofs grow higher off the faces of the cube, sections of neighboring roofs merge together to form pentagons. In the drawing on the right, the cube is shown with dotted lines, and the top lines of the roofs are shown with heavy lines. When working with clay, it makes it considerably easier to start with a small cube and *add* small bits of clay, thereby slowly building roofs off each face of the cube.
  - After doing this process, we can ask: "How is it that a cube can sit inside a dodecahedron?" We can then have the students take a dodecahedron, and make six cuts with a knife thereby cutting off six roofs of the dodecahedron in order to expose the cube hiding inside the dodecahedron.

- *Transforming a cube into a rhombic dodecahedron.*
  - Similar to transforming a cube into a dodecahedron, here we grow pyramids off each of the faces of a cube. Once again, it is easiest to do this in clay by starting with a small cube, and then adding clay, bit-by-bit, onto each face of the cube, thereby allowing the pyramids to grow taller and taller until triangles from the pyramids merge together in pairs to form rhombuses (diamonds). The end result is a solid with 12 rhombic faces, called the rhombic dodecahedron. **Rhombic Dodeca.**

  Demonstration: Construct a rhombic dodecahedron from paper. All four sides of the rhombus are congruent, and the angles in the rhombus are 109½° and 70½°. (The exact shape of this rhombus is found in **Appendix A**, *Patterns for the Archimedean solids and their duals.*) Then draw red lines along the long diagonals of all the rhombuses, and green lines along all the short diagonals. Surprisingly, the red lines form an octahedron, and the green lines form a cube!
  - The ratio of the lengths of the two diagonals of the rhombic face is $\sqrt{2}:1$, which is also the ratio of a square's diagonal to its side.
  - The volume of the rhombic dodecahedron is exactly twice the volume of the cube (formed by the green lines) that sits inside the rhombic dodecahedron. This is due to the fact that the rhombic dodecahedron can be generated by growing pyramids onto the faces of a cube. If you imagine that a second equal-sized set of pyramids grew from the cube's faces inward toward the cube's center, then these six pyramids have their apexes meet at the center. Therefore, the volume of the cube (or the six inner pyramids) equals the volume of the outer pyramids, and the volume of the rhombic dodecahedron is twice that of the cube.

- *Transforming a dodecahedron into an icosahedron.*
  - This is basically the same transformation that led us from the cube to the octahedron (see above). We push in on the points, and continue until the points become faces, and the faces become points.
  - This is very difficult in clay! For most students, it is much easier to get an icosahedron by first clearly marking 12 equally-spaced points on the surface of a sphere, and then pushing in on the space in-between the points, thereby producing the icosahedron's 20 triangles.

Dodecahedron	**Truncated dodeca.**	**Icosidodecahedron**	**Truncated icosa.**	**Icosahedron**
12 pentagons, 20 pts	12 decagons, 20 Δs	12 pentagons, 20 Δs	12 pent., 20 hexagons	12 points, 20 Δs

- *Pushing in the points of a tetrahedron.*
  - The biggest surprise here is that we don't end up with a new solid. The end result is another tetrahedron, where the first and last stages are "turned inside-out" from one another.
  - When doing the meditative imagination of this, it is again best to imagine it in color. For example, the original tetrahedron has four red faces and four green points, then the next stage has four red hexagons and four green triangles, and the octahedron has four red triangles and four green triangles, then four red triangles and four green hexagons, and finally four red points and four green points.

Tetrahedron	**Truncated Tetra.**	**Octahedron**	**Truncated Tetra.**	**Tetrahedron**
4 Δs, 4 points	4 hexagons, 4 Δs	8 Δs	4 Δs, 4 hexagons	4 points, 4 Δs

Orthogonal Views

- An orthogonal view (or projection) of a solid is the outline that is seen when looking at the solid in a certain orientation. Essentially, it is a 2-D drawing of a 3-D object. Often "special" orientations are chosen in order to clearly see the symmetry of the solid.
- It is interesting to see the similarity of the orthogonal views of the tetrahedron, cube, octahedron, and rhombic dodecahedron. Here are two orthogonal views for each of these four solids:

             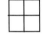

Tetrahedron	**Octahedron**	**Cube**	**Rhombic dodecahedron**

- Because the rhombic dodecahedron and the cube have one orthogonal view that is identical (a hexagon), it is actually possible to show someone a rhombic dodecahedron (in that perspective, and at a fair distance) and they will be tricked into seeing a cube!

Duality

- In *transforming a cube into an octahedron* (see above), we saw a step-by-step description of how to make the dual form of a polyhedron. The dual of a cube is an octahedron, and the dual of an octahedron is a cube. In making the dual in this way, we see that *the points become faces, and the faces become points*.

- *Another way to envision the dual* of a solid is to imagine that the dual sits inside the solid. For example, we can picture that the octahedron sits inside the cube such that its six vertices lie on the six center points of the faces of the cube, and that each of the eight faces of the octahedron lie directly under each of the eight vertices of the cube. In the same way, we can picture that inside the octahedron sits its dual - another cube.

- Notice that if a *face* of a solid is a square (i.e., it is bounded by four edges), then the *vertex* of the dual under that square face will have four edges coming to it. Using another example, since a dodecahedron has pentagonal *faces* (faces that are bounded by five edges around them), its dual (an icosahedron) has five edges coming together at each of its *vertices*.

- *Examples of dual solids*:
  - The cube and the octahedron are duals of one another.
  - The dodecahedron and icosahedron are duals of one another.
  - The tetrahedron is self-dual. (In other words, the dual of a tetrahedron is another tetrahedron.)
  - The dual of a rhombic dodecahedron is a cuboctahedron, which is halfway between a cube and an octahedron. (See *Transforming a Cube into an Octahedron*, above.)
  - The dual of a hexagonal prism is a hexagonal bipyramid. (See *Types of Polyhedron*, above, for the drawing.)
  - The dual of a pentagonal anti-prism is a pentagonal trapezohedron. (See *Types of Polyhedron*, above, for the drawing.)

The Archimedean Solids (**See Appendix A**, *The Archimedean Solids and their Duals,* for drawings.)

- There are 13 Archimedean solids.
- These solids all satisfy the first two of the *four properties* of the Platonic solids (see above). Namely, Archimedean solids have (1) identical vertices, and (2) regular, non-identical faces.[1]
- Seven out of the 13 Archimedean solids have already been mentioned as intermediate stages that are reached when transforming a Platonic solid into its dual (see above). These seven are:

Truncated tetrahedron	4 triangles & 4 hexagons
Truncated cube	6 octagons & 8 triangles
Cuboctahedron	6 squares & 8 triangles
Truncated octahedron	6 squares & 8 hexagons
Truncated dodecahedron	12 decagons & 20 triangles
Icosidodecahedron	12 pentagons & 20 triangles
Truncated icosahedron (soccer ball)	12 pentagons & 20 hexagons

- The other six Archimedean solids result from "stretching" solids in the ways shown below.

The Stretching Process (**See Appendix A**, *The Archimedean Solids and their Duals,* for drawings.)

- These are great imaginative exercises for the students to try to visualize in their head. It is probably necessary for most students to actually look at a model of the form that they are attempting to "stretch". However, some students may be able to do the whole process in their head, with their eyes closed.
- The small rhombicuboctahedron. To create this, we start with a cube and imagine that it is bright yellow and is wrapped loosely in a translucent, stretchable covering. We then picture all the faces of the cube becoming disconnected and all moving slowly, and perpendicularly, away from the center of the cube. Imagine that a red light streams out from the center of the figure so that the spaces between the six square faces of the original cube are all glowing in red. At first, we see 12 red rectangles appear where each edge of the cube once was, and eight small red triangles appear at the vertices of the cube. The faces of the cube continue to move further apart, until, at a given moment, the 12 rectangles have become red squares, equal in size to the original six faces of the cube. This form is our new Archimedean solid. It has 18 squares (6 of which are from the original cube) and eight triangles for faces.
- The small rhombicosidodecahedron. We reach this form by doing the same "stretching" process, as described above, but we start with the dodecahedron. The resulting solid has 12 pentagons, 30 squares, and 20 triangles.
- The great rhombicuboctahedron. We reach this by starting with a truncated cube and imagining that the triangular faces are "holes" defined by the translucent covering that goes over them. The six octagonal faces move away from the center resulting in squares appearing at the edges between the octagons, and the triangles becoming transformed into hexagons. The end result is a solid with six octagons, 12 squares, and eight hexagons.
- The great rhombicosidodecahedron. We reach this by starting with a truncated dodecahedron and imagining that the triangular faces are "holes" defined by the translucent covering that goes over them. The 12 decagonal (10-sided) faces move away from the center resulting in squares appearing at the edges between the decagons, and the triangles becoming transformed into hexagons. The end result is a solid with 12 decagons, 30 squares, and 20 hexagons.
- The snub cube. Here we do the same transformation that led us to the small rhombicuboctahedron, but we take the process one step further. From the small rhombicuboctahedron, we take the original six yellow squares and rotate each one of them a bit clockwise (22.5°). This transforms each of the 12 squares defined by the translucent covering into two triangles.[2] The result is a form with six squares and 32 triangles. This form is unique in that its mirror image is not identical to itself. It has a "left-hand" and "right-hand" version, depending on whether the yellow square faces were rotated clockwise or counter-clockwise.
- The snub dodecahedron. Here, we do the same as we did to get the snub cube, but we start with a dodecahedron, transform it into a small rhombicosidodecahedron, and then we rotate the 12 pentagons slightly clockwise (or counter-clockwise). The result is 12 pentagons and 80 triangles.

---

[1] Prisms and anti-prisms also have these two properties, but, as opposed to the Archimedean solids, they don't have genuine three-dimensional symmetry – i.e., they have two faces that can be said to be a top and a bottom.

[2] It is not the intention that the squares being transformed have their edges locked into place as the transformation occurs. If this was taken literally, then each of these squares would become a "twisted" parallelogram with a curved surface. Instead, the translucent covering shifts slightly, thereby allowing the squares to become transformed into two triangles.

- *Stretching Other Solids.* Other solids can also be stretched in a similar manner, but the results, in each of the below cases, will be something that we have already seen, such as:
  - An octahedron becomes a small rhombicuboctahedron when stretched.
  - An icosahedron becomes a small rhombicosidodecahedron when stretched.
  - A truncated octahedron (with small square holes) becomes a great rhombicuboctahedron when stretched.
  - A truncated icosahedron (with small pentagonal holes) becomes a great rhombicosidodecahedron when stretched.
  - A cuboctahedron with holes at its triangular faces becomes a truncated octahedron when stretched.
  - A cuboctahedron with holes at its square faces becomes a truncated cube when stretched.
  - An icosidodecahedron with holes at its triangular faces becomes a truncated icosahedron when stretched.
  - An icosidodecahedron with holes at its pentagonal faces becomes a truncated dodecahedron when stretched.
  - A truncated tetrahedron (with small triangular holes) becomes a truncated octahedron when stretched.

The Archimedean Duals – Kepler's Solids. (**See Appendix A**, *The Archimedean Solids and their Duals*.)

- See *duality* (above) for an explanation of duality and its characteristics.
- We have seen that the dual of any Platonic solid is another Platonic solid. In contrast, the dual of an Archimedean solid is not an Archimedean solid. While Archimedean solids have the first two properties of the Platonic solids, all the Archimedean duals have the third and fourth properties of the Platonic solids - namely, all their faces are identical, and all their dihedral angles are identical.
- There are 13 Archimedean duals.
- *Faces and Points.*

  A solid and its dual have inverse numbers of faces and points. For example, a dodecahedron has 12 faces and 20 points, and its dual (an icosahedron) has 20 faces and 12 points. Furthermore, we can predict the kind of faces that a dual will have (**see** *Duality*, above). The cuboctahedron has 4 edges coming to each point, so its dual (the rhombic dodecahedron) has quadrilateral faces. Since the snub cube and the snub dodecahedron have 5 edges coming to each of their points, their duals have pentagonal faces. Seven of the Archimedean solids have 3 edges coming to each point, which corresponds to the fact that seven of the Archimedean duals have triangular faces. Likewise, the number of edges coming to a given point of an Archimedean dual, corresponds to the type of polygon that its dual (an Archimedean solid) sits under.

Constructing Paper Models

- After the students have become quite familiar with certain polyhedrons - through the mental imaginative exercises and through working with clay - they should construct some from paper. Over the course of the main lesson, I have them construct paper models of the five Platonic solids, and then they choose one of the Archimedean solids, or an Archimedean dual, as a final project.
- In order to construct a polyhedron, the students should try to figure out the *net* for themselves. (A *net* is the two-dimensional pattern that folds up into a three-dimensional shape.) Don't immediately give the students a photocopied net for them to cut out – this misses the pedagogical value of doing these constructions. (**See Appendix A,** *Nets of Selected Solids.*)
- *The number of possible nets.* Ask the students how many different nets there are for the tetrahedron, for the cube, and for the octahedron. The students enjoy writing all their nets on the board, and trying to see which ones are equivalent (e.g., through a rotation, or a reflection), and which are truly unique.
  - There are only two possible nets for the tetrahedron.
  - There are 11 possible nets for both the cube and the octahedron.

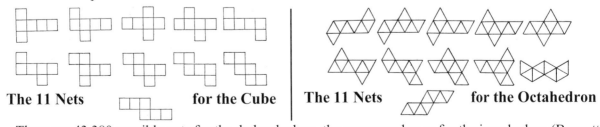

The 11 Nets for the Cube **The 11 Nets** for the Octahedron

- There are 43,380 possible nets for the dodecahedron, the same number as for the icosahedron (Bouzette and Vandamme, Hippenmeyer 1979, Buekenhout and Parker 1998).

- *Tips for constructing paper models.*
  - Constructing these models out of paper is a real exercise in accuracy and careful work. Careless work results in a form that can't come together properly.
  - It is important to use good paper. If the paper is too thin, then it won't hold its form; if it's too thick, then it won't fold nicely. The best paper that I have found is 80-pound cover (cardstock) paper at a cost of about 50¢ per sheet. Alternatively, I find that standard file folders work fairly well.
  - Use a very sharp pencil when drawing the net.
  - It is best for the students to do any art work on the paper after it has been cut out, and after the folds have been made, but before it has been glued together.

- *Drawing the net.*
  - Each polyhedron has faces with specific polygonal shapes. I give the students photocopies of the specific polygons that are needed to make the net of any solid. (**See Appendix A**, *Patterns for the Archimedean Solids and their Duals* for drawings of these polygons.) These pre-made polygons are especially necessary for the construction of an Archimedean dual, because for these solids, the faces (polygons) have to be made with specific angle measures in order for the form to come together properly.

    The students first need to make a nearly perfect *form* of their chosen polygon. This polygon form is then traced out carefully, and multiple times, in order to create a workable *net*. Since the polygon form on the photocopied paper is not stiff enough to use for tracing, they must make a duplicate of it on thick construction paper. To do this, put the photocopy of the desired polygon form on top of the sheet of construction paper. Then, using a pin, push through all the vertices of the photocopied polygon form thereby making tiny holes on the construction paper underneath. Put the photocopied piece of paper aside, and with a ruler carefully draw the polygon form on the construction paper by connecting the holes that were just made. Carefully cut out this polygon. In the case of making an Archimedean solid, more than one polygon form will need to be made.
  - Think carefully about how the net can be laid out so that it can be cut out and folded up into the desired polyhedron. For example, in order to make a cube, six square forms will have to be traced out in order to create the full net. As stated above, it is important that the students try to come up with the net on their own. (**See Appendix A**, *Nets of Selected Solids,* for the nets of some of the more difficult solids.)
  - Using the polygon form that has just been cut out, create the net by tracing adjacent polygons on the sheet of construction paper. For best results, leave a pencil's width (0.2mm) of space along the edge between adjacent polygons, in order to account for the fold that will occur along this edge.
  - Once the net has been made, placement of the tabs needs to be determined. A tab is a bit of extra paper (past the edge of a face) that is used to glue an edge together once the final polyhedron folds up into its proper shape. The tabs don't need to be drawn or cut out very neatly, since they won't be seen, but they need to run the length of the whole edge. It is important that no edges are left without a tab, and that no edge has two tabs joining it. Considering all this, draw all the tabs in the proper places. One possible net (with tabs) for constructing a cube is shown at the right. Can you see how this pattern will fold together, and how all the tabs will connect?

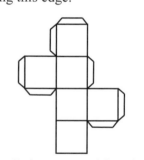

A Cube Net with tabs

- *Putting it together.*
  - After the net is cut out, folds need to be made along certain edges by placing a ruler along the edge, folding the paper up, and then going over the fold a couple of times with your finger nail.
  - The last part of the construction is gluing it together. This is a slow process, since after gluing a few tabs, it must be allowed to dry somewhat before gluing more tabs. It is best if the tabs were strategically placed in the net in such a way that the last face that gets glued has no tabs on it (this is the bottom square in the above drawing). This allows the last face to be gently pressed into place onto tabs (with glue on them) that are connected to other faces.

Close-Packing

- A polyhedron is said to *close-pack* when an indefinite amount of that exact same polyhedron can be packed together without there being any empty space between them. Spheres cannot be close-packed, because there is space between them.
- *What can be close-packed?* Any box (right-rectangular prism) obviously close-packs. Of all the Platonic solids, Archimedean solids and Archimedean duals (a total of 31 solids), there is only one solid from each group that close-packs. These special solids are the cube, the truncated octahedron, and the rhombic dodecahedron.

cubes   *truncated octahedra*   *rhombic dodecahedra*

Euler's Formula $edges = faces + points - 2$

- This formula relates the number of edges, faces, and points in any polyhedron.
- Descartes actually knew about this formula before Euler. The Greeks possibly knew about it as well.
- Allow the students to discover it. Perhaps it is best to make a table on the board where the columns are labeled: "solid", "number of faces", "number of points", and "number of edges". The solid can be any polyhedron – any of the Platonic or Archimedean solids, a triangular prism, a square pyramid, etc. The students carefully count the number of faces, points, and edges on each solid and enter the information in the table. Finally, they try to come up with Euler's Formula by asking: "How can we think of a formula that calculates the number of edges in any solid, based upon the number of faces and points?"

(Optional) Additional Imagination 3-D Transformation Exercises

- *The inner tube problem.*
  - This problem requires great concentration, but if done properly, the final result can be clearly "seen". Avoid the temptation to actually get a bicycle inner tube and do it. This is a great test of a person's power of "exact imagination".

    The Question: If you cut a hole (about the size of a quarter) out of a bicycle inner tube, reach through the hole with your fingers, and pull the entire inner tube through that hole, then what shape do you get? Picture this process exactly in your mind.

    Hint: It's not the same shape as the original inner tube. It is easily described, but probably not a shape that you've ever seen before. (I will not give the answer here!)

- *Reducing solids to tetrahedrons.*
  - Describe how it is possible to slice each one of the following solids into the least number of irregular tetrahedrons possible. It is best if the students first try to do it completely in their head, and then later try it with the aid of a paper model, or with clay.

    Question: How many tetrahedrons do you get by slicing a triangular prism?

    Answer: Start by placing the knife along an edge of one of the triangles, and then cut through the solid so that the cutting plane passes through the point that is opposite from the edge where you started to cut. This leaves us with two solids. One is an irregular tetrahedron (four triangular faces), and the other is a rectangular pyramid (a rectangle and four triangular faces). Cut the pyramid along the diagonal of the rectangle, toward and through the vertex where the four triangles meet. This divides the pyramid into two irregular tetrahedrons. Thus, the original triangular prism has been divided into <u>three tetrahedrons</u>.

    Question: How many tetrahedrons do you get by slicing a cube?

    Answer: Cut off four "opposite" corners, thereby exposing the tetrahedron that is enclosed in the cube. (**See above**, *Transforming a cube into a tetrahedron.*) This creates <u>five tetrahedrons</u>.

    Question: How many tetrahedrons do you get by slicing an octahedron?

    Answer: An octahedron can be sliced along any one of three planes in order to divide the octahedron into two square (Egyptian) pyramids. Simply cut along two of these planes in order to produce <u>four tetrahedrons</u>.

Loci

Key Ideas

- *What is Loci?* In essence, loci is the study of curves. *Loci* (pronounced like "low sigh") is the plural of *locus*. A *locus of points* is defined as *a collection of points, all of which satisfy some specific condition.* In every case that is considered in this unit, the condition has to do with distances to lines, points, or circles. The locus of points, which satisfies the given condition, forms a particular curve. We construct this curve by locating a few of the points that satisfy the condition, and then we connect the dots to draw the curve.

- *Why do we teach it?* The real purpose of teaching loci is that it works with the students' imagination through seeing curves in movement. Unfortunately, most students in mainstream education graduate from high school without studying any loci.

- *Loci as a main lesson.* Loci is best covered during a main lesson, but the amount of material is not enough to fill an entire three-week main lesson. I recommend that loci and number bases share a main lesson together; in some ways these two topics complement each other. Or, if there is only room for one math main lesson in the eighth grade, then loci can share a main lesson with stereometry.

- *Requirements?* The drawings done in this unit require great care and precision. High quality compasses (a few for drawing extra-large circles), and sharp pencils are essential. Shading-in should be simple.

- *The Treasure Hunt.* The language used for the subject of loci can seem awkward for the eighth grader. For this reason, it is good to use an analogy that demystifies the language. I use the idea of a treasure hunt. In this way we translate the standard mathematical loci definitions of curves into "treasure hunt" definitions.

- *The process is important.* Each definition given below is the *end result*. The students should be presented with each one as a puzzle that they need to figure out.

Curves Generated from Loci Problems

A Circle

- *As a treasure problem*: If a treasure is buried 100 feet from a tree in a field, then it could be found anywhere along the circle that has the tree at the center, and a radius equal to 100ft.
- *As a loci problem*: The locus of points that are a set distance from a given point (A) is a circle.

Construction: The students can do this drawing on their own.

**The Locus of Points
a Set Distance from a Point**

Two Parallel Lines

- *As a treasure problem*: If a treasure is buried 100 feet from a straight fence in a field, then it could be found anywhere along the two lines that are 100 feet from either side of the fence.
- *As a loci problem*: The locus of points that are a set distance from a given line (A) is two lines, one on each side of the given line.

Construction: The students can do this drawing on their own.

**The Locus of Points
a Set Distance from a Line**

Two Concentric Circles

- *As a treasure problem*: If a treasure is buried 100 feet from a circular fence (e.g., 500 feet in diameter), then it could be found anywhere along the two circles that are 100 feet from either side of that fence.
- *As a loci problem*: The locus of points that are a set distance from a given circle (A) is two circles, one on each side of the given circle.

Construction: The students can do this drawing on their own.

**The Locus of Points
a Set Distance from a Circle**

A Perpendicular Bisector

- *As a treasure problem*: If a treasure is buried such that it is an equal distance from two trees in a field, then it could be found anywhere along the line that cuts perpendicularly between the two trees.
- *As a loci problem*: The locus of points equidistant from two points (A and B) is the perpendicular bisector of the line segment that joins the two given points.

Construction: Review the sixth grade perpendicular bisector construction.

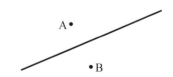

**The Locus of Points
Equidistant from Two Points**

Two Angle Bisectors

- *As a treasure problem*: If a treasure is buried such that it is an equal distance from two straight fences (lines A and B) that intersect (at a random angle) in a field, then it could be found anywhere along the two lines that are angle bisectors of the two fences.
- *As a loci problem*: The locus of points equidistant from two intersecting lines (A and B) is the two angle bisectors of the given lines.

The Locus of Points Equidistant from Two Intersecting Lines

Construction: Review the sixth grade angle bisector construction.

A Parabola (See **next page** for a drawing that has been slightly reduced in size.)

- *As a treasure problem*: If a treasure is buried an equal distance from a tree and a straight fence (where the tree is not on that fence), then it could be found anywhere along a curve known as a parabola.
- *As a loci problem*: The locus of points equidistant from a line and a point (not on that line) is a parabola.
- Note: The distance to a line is defined as the *shortest* distance, namely, approaching the line at 90°.
- The point is called the *focus,* and the line is called the *directrix*. The *vertex* of the parabola is the lowest point and is exactly halfway between the focus and the directrix.
- In nature, a parabola is the path followed by a rock thrown in the air, or the water shot from a fountain. The vertex is the highest point that it reaches.

Construction:
1. The paper should be set up with the long side running vertically. Space should be left at the top for a title. Draw a dark line (the directrix) 5 cm from the bottom of the page. Carefully, and lightly, draw lines parallel to this directrix at intervals of one centimeter all the way up and down the page.
2. A focal point (i.e., focus) is now to be chosen at a specific *set distance* away from the directrix line. This set distance should be 2cm, 4cm, 6cm, or 8cm. Have a quarter of the class do each distance, so that the results of varying this distance can be observed by the class. (Note: The drawing on the next page, which has been slightly reduced in size, used a set distance of 4cm.) Lightly draw circles, each one having the focus as its center, that have radii starting at 1cm and increasing by intervals of one centimeter. (These circles, with a common center, are called *concentric*.) Again, for clarity, see the drawing on the next page.
3. Now the students should try to answer the following question on their own: *Where are the points that are equidistant from the focus and the directrix?*
    The most obvious point that satisfies this condition is the *vertex*, which always turns out to be the point that is halfway between the directrix and the focus. Referring to the drawing on the next page, two more points that satisfy the condition can be found by considering the circle that is 3cm away from the focus, and the line that is 3cm away from the directrix. Every point on this circle is 3cm away from the focus, and every point on the line is 3cm away from the directrix. Therefore, we know that the two points of intersection of the circle and the line are *both* 3cm from the focus and 3cm from the directrix; so these two points also satisfy the condition. Now we have three points that satisfy the condition.
    The next two points that satisfy the condition are the two points of intersection between the next largest circle and the next furthest line – they are 4 centimeters away from both the focus and the directrix. Simply follow this pattern repeatedly, thereby finding points of intersection between larger circles and further-away lines until it runs off the page.
4. Draw the parabola by carefully connecting all the solution points with a colored pencil. All the points on this curve satisfy the condition of being equidistant from the focus and the directrix.

- *A parabola in movement.* How does the shape of the parabola vary as the focal point moves toward the directrix? The students answer this question by observing the differences in the parabolas that their classmates made (the distances from the focus to the directrix are varied from 2cm to 8cm). Then, without having a drawing to look at, the students should imagine the parabola changing shape (becoming narrower or wider) as the focus moves toward, or away from, the directrix.

The Parabola

The Locus of Points
Equidistant from a Point and a Line

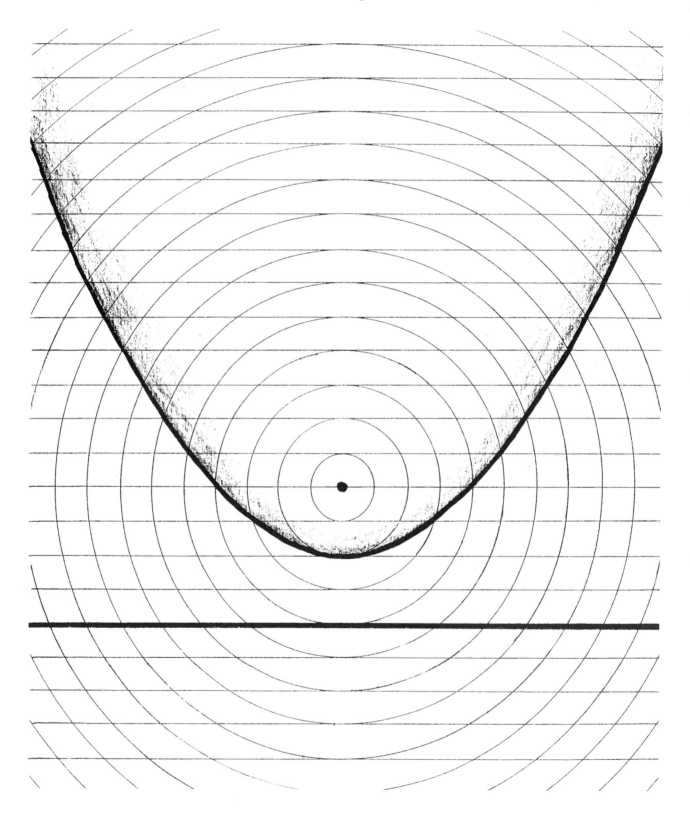

An Ellipse (**See below** for a drawing that has been reduced in size.)

- *As a treasure problem*: If a treasure is buried an equal distance from a circular fence and a tree *inside* that fence, then it could be found anywhere along a curve known as an ellipse.
- *As a loci problem*: The locus of points equidistant from a circle and a point *inside* that circle is an ellipse.
- Note: The distance from a point to a circle is defined as the *shortest* distance, namely, approaching the circle at 90°.
- The point is called the *focus* and the circle is called the *directrix*.

Construction:

1. Start by drawing a directrix circle that has a radius measuring an even number of centimeters, and is as large as possible. Lightly draw concentric circles from the directrix circle all the way in to the center having the radius get smaller by one centimeter with each circle.

2. A focus is now to be chosen. Pick the focus by selecting a point on one of the circles, which is an even number of circles in from the directrix. Mark this point clearly as the focus. Have students choose different locations for their focus so that the class can see how this affects the curve.

3. Using the focus as the center, draw concentric circles out from the focus, allowing the radii to grow by one centimeter with each circle.

4. Now the students should try to answer the following question on their own: *Where are the points that are equidistant from the focus and the directrix?*

   In order to find the points that are solutions to the above question, use a similar method to what was used with the parabola. The difference is that here we are finding points of intersection between two sets of circles, rather than the intersection of lines and circles, as was done in constructing the parabola. Now connect the solution points. The resulting curve is an ellipse, which falls within the directrix circle. Notice that the center of the directrix circle falls within the ellipse and is symmetrically opposite the focus.

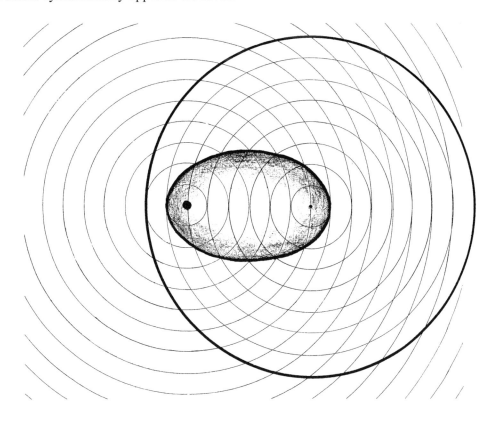

- *An ellipse in movement.* How does the shape of the ellipse change as the focus moves toward the center of the directrix circle? Have the students observe the differences in the ellipses their classmates made. Now, without having a drawing to look at, the students should imagine the ellipse changing shape as the focus moves from the directrix circle toward the center of the directrix, or back in the other direction.

A Hyperbola (**See below** for a drawing that has been reduced in size.)

- *As a treasure problem*: If a treasure is buried an equal distance from a circular fence and a tree *outside* that fence, then it could be found anywhere along a curve known as a hyperbola.
- *As a loci problem*: The locus of points equidistant from a circle and a point *outside* that circle is a hyperbola.
- Note: The distance from a point to a circle is defined as the *shortest* distance, namely, approaching the circle at 90°.
- Note: A compass that can draw large circles will be necessary for this construction.
- The point is called the *focus* and the circle is called the *directrix*.

Construction:
1. Start by drawing a directrix circle that has a diameter that is about one-third the length of the page, and position it to one side of the page. Lightly draw concentric circles from this directrix circle *outward* such that the radii get larger by one centimeter with each circle, until the page is filled.
2. A focus is now to be chosen. Pick the focus by selecting a point that is on one of circles and is centered on the opposite side of the page from the directrix circle. It is best if the circle chosen is an even number of centimeters beyond the directrix circle. Let students choose different foci so that their drawings can be compared later.
3. Using the focus as the center, draw concentric circles out from the focus, allowing the radii to grow by one centimeter with each circle.
4. Now the students should try to answer the following question on their own: *Where are the points that are equidistant from the focus and the directrix?*

    The solution is found in the same manner as with the ellipse.

    Connect the solution points, and the form of the hyperbola will emerge. It is similar to a parabola, but its sides tend to go outward as nearly straight lines as opposed to the parabola, which tends to have both of its sides get closer and closer to becoming parallel to each other.

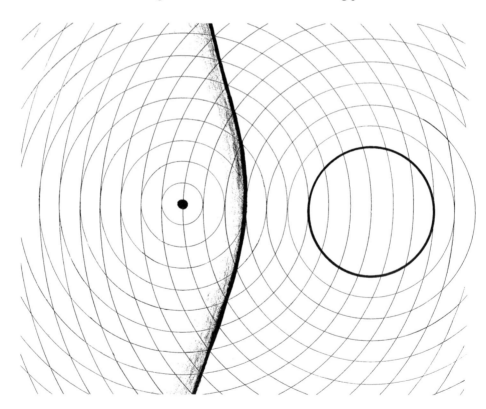

- *A hyperbola in movement.* How does the shape of the hyperbola change as the focus moves toward the directrix circle? Have the students observe the differences in the hyperbolas that their classmates made. Now, without having a drawing to look at, the students should imagine the hyperbola changing shape (becoming narrower or wider) as the focus moves toward, or away from, the directrix.

- *The two branches of a hyperbola.*
    It should be noted that a "real" hyperbola has two branches, which are mirror reflections of each other. Both branches get closer and closer to two intersecting lines, called *asymptotes*. Sometimes (e.g., with the loci drawing on the previous page) we only see one branch. We get the other branch when the positions of the focus and the center of the directrix circle are switched. Even though there are two branches to a hyperbola, it is considered to be one continuous curve. Explaining this strange notion is left until eleventh grade.

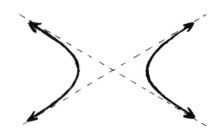

Alternative Definitions (optional)

- *The Ellipse.*
    - Above, the loci definition of an ellipse was given as "the locus of points equidistant from a directrix circle and a focus inside that circle". Alternatively, we can consider that the ellipse has *two* foci - the other one being the center of the directrix circle. The new definition is:

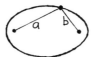

> An ellipse is the locus of points such that
> ## the sum of the distances
> *to the two focal points is constant.*

a <u>plus</u> b is always the same number.

- The truth of the above definition can be demonstrated by using two pushpins for the foci, and pushing them partway through a piece of cardboard. Next, a piece of string is tied end-to-end in order to form a loop and placed loosely around the two pushpins. A pencil is then placed inside the loop of string and pulled outward to make the string taut. The ellipse can now be drawn by moving the pencil around the pushpins while keeping the string taut.

- (optional) **Proof** that the two definitions of the ellipse are equivalent:

1. According to the loci definition of an ellipse, from any point, X, on the ellipse, the distance to the circle (AX) is equal to the distance to the focus (XF). As an equation, this is   XF = AX.

2. XC can be added to both sides of the above equation to get
    XF + XC = AX + XC.

3. The right side of the equation (AX+XC) is just equal to AC, which is the radius of the circle (r), giving us: XF + XC = r

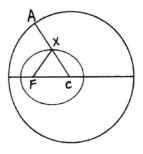

4. Imagine that point A is moving around the circle while point X is tracing the form of the ellipse. As this movement is happening, the lengths of AX, XF, and XC are continually changing, but what the above equation says is that *the sum of XF plus XC always remains constant* (equal to r).

- *The hyperbola.*
    - In light of the new definition of the ellipse, it may come as no surprise that the hyperbola can now be defined as:

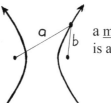

a <u>minus</u> b (or b minus a) is always the same number.

> *A hyperbola is the locus of points such that*
> ## the difference of the distances
> *to the two focal points is constant.*

- Here, as with the above ellipse, we have a second focal point rather than a directrix circle.
- This definition readily shows both branches of the hyperbola. One branch is closer to one focus and the other branch is closer to the other focus. From any point on the curve (with both branches) the difference of the distances to the two foci is always the same.

Conic Sections

- *What is a section?* A section of a three-dimensional solid is the two-dimensional "outline" that results from slicing straight through that solid.
  Examples:
  - What are the possible sections of a sphere? Answer: Only circles are possible.
  - What are the possible sections of a tetrahedron? Answer: Triangular sections are the most obvious, but a quadrilateral (or even a square) section is possible if the tetrahedron is sliced through all four faces.
  - What are the possible sections of a cube? Answer: By cutting parallel to the cube's face, we get a square section, and by cutting off a corner, we get a triangular section. But we can also get a hexagonal section if we balance the cube on a point, and then cut along a horizontal plane through the center of the cube. Pentagonal sections are also possible.
- *Conic sections in movement.*
  - A (double) cone is a single solid that resembles two "ice cream cones" joined at their points. It extends infinitely far in both directions.
  - *The sections of a cone.* Guide the students in seeing what curves arise from sectioning a cone. A (single) cone made of clay can be sectioned to show each possibility.

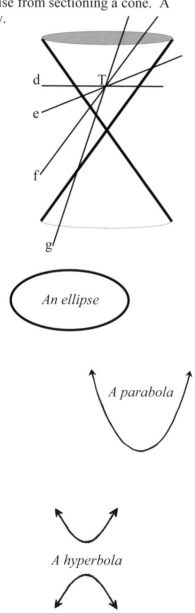

An ellipse

A parabola

A hyperbola

  - *The five conic sections in movement.* T is a point located inside the cone. Notice that what appear to be lines going through point T are really planes rising perpendicularly out of the page and slicing through the cone. We begin with plane d, which cuts horizontally through the upper half of the cone. We then allow the cutting plane to rotate about point T, from plane d to plane e, then to plane f, and finally to plane g, which cuts through both the top and the bottom half of the double cone. If we imagine this to be a continuous movement, then we can see that the drawing here shows just four snap-shots of this sequence.

    We can say the following regarding this sequence:
    - There is exactly one plane (d) that produces a <u>circle</u> as a section. This occurs only when the plane is perfectly horizontal. This circle is a special case of an ellipse.
    - There are infinitely many planes between plane d and plane f (plane e is only one of them). These planes cut through only the top half of the cone, and produce an <u>ellipse</u> as a section.
    - The section produced by plane f is the *critical instant* when the plane is parallel to the edge of the cone. An instant earlier, the section was an ellipse. But at this instant, the ellipse has been infinitely stretched out; its "end" is no longer connected together. If we advance an instant into the future from this stage, then we will have a hyperbola, which cuts through both halves of the cone. But at the present instant, the second branch of this soon-to-be hyperbola is hidden infinitely far away.
      The section produced at this critical instant (by plane f) is a <u>parabola</u>. *A parabola is the critical instant between an ellipse and a hyperbola.*
    - There are infinitely many planes that are rotated beyond plane f (plane g is only one of them). They each cut through both the top and bottom half of the cone, and produce a <u>hyperbola</u> as a section.

- *Conic sections from cones of light.*
  (It is best to make your own double cone of light, as described below, so that both branches of the hyperbola can be seen. A flashlight produces only one branch of the hyperbola.)
  Construction *of a double cone of light:*
  > Take a poster board and roll it into a cylinder by joining the two shorter sides. Cut a hole in the middle of the cylinder's side that is just big enough to insert the narrow end of a light bulb. The cylinder now acts as a lampshade that produces a double cone of light. (The light bulb is screwed in through the hole in the cylinder and sits inside the cylinder.) Make sure the students understand that although the lampshade is cylindrical, the light that comes out forms a double cone.

  Demonstration:
  - The chalkboard serves as the cutting plane for this double cone of light. After showing each stage separately, try several times to show the sequence in fluid movement.
    - A *circle* is seen when the light is directed straight at the board.
    - An *ellipse* is seen when the light is directed at the board at a slight angle.
    - A *parabola* is seen at the *critical instant* when the edge of the cone is parallel to the board.
    - A *hyperbola* is seen whenever the board cuts through both halves of the double cone of light. We can then see both branches of the hyperbola quite nicely.

Curves in Movement

A family of hyperbolas and ellipses. (See drawing, below.)

- Here the students can see both branches of the hyperbolas.
- This drawing nicely shows the movement of ellipses and hyperbolas due to the shrinking and expansion of the directrix circle.
- Make sure that it is clear to the students where the directrix circle and focus is for each hyperbola, and for each ellipse (there are two possibilities for each ellipse). They should be able to picture the directrix circle growing and shrinking and the movement of the resulting curves.

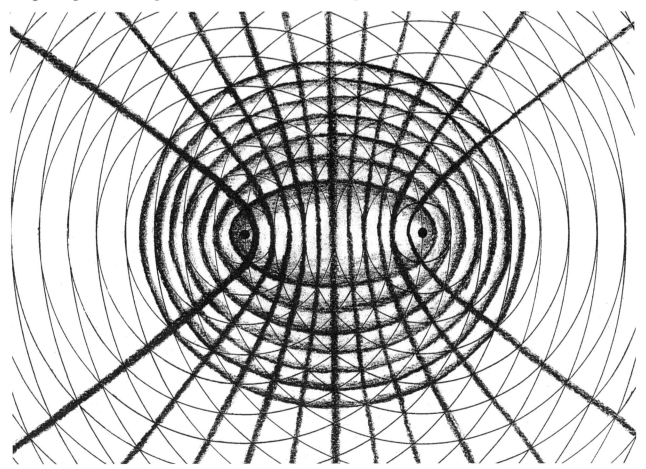

The movement of the focus to the outside of the directrix circle.

- This sequence doesn't include a parabola. Instead, the ellipse is transformed by flattening out into a ray, and then it emerges as one branch of a hyperbola. Remember that at any given moment the curve represents the locus of points equidistant from the directrix circle and the focus.

- The drawing on the right has been done as a sequence of five snapshots of the transformation of the curve as the focus moves from inside the directrix circle to outside the circle. The students should try to visualize the whole sequence in their heads as a continuous flowing movement. The five steps, as shown in the drawings from top to bottom, are as follows:

    1. The focus is well inside the circle, resulting in a fairly round ellipse.

    2. The focus has moved toward the edge of the directrix circle, resulting in a fairly thin ellipse.

    3. The focus is on the edge of the directrix circle resulting in a ray that starts from the center of the circle, and then passes through the focus, and then infinitely far beyond the circle. Notice that this ray is a combination of a flattened ellipse and a flattened hyperbola.

    4. The focus is now outside the directrix circle, but close to its edge, resulting in a fairly narrow hyperbola.

    5. The focus is well outside the directrix circle, resulting in a fairly wide hyperbola.

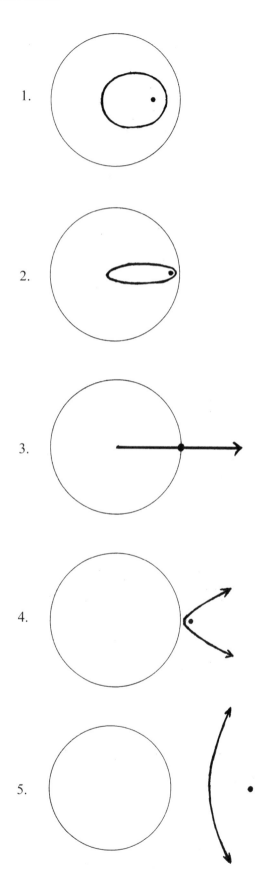

Turning the directrix circle inside-out

- This sequence nicely shows one branch of a hyperbola transforming into a parabola, and then into an ellipse. This happens by having the directrix circle growing and then shrinking while the focus remains fixed. The students should try to visualize the whole sequence in their heads as a continuous flowing movement. With the drawing below, notice that the focus is the same for each curve, and is the dot in the center of the drawing. The four steps are as follows:

1. The Hyperbola. The directrix circle is the circle furthest to the left. The resulting locus of points is the hyperbola (the shaded curve furthest to the left). We can imagine that this directrix circle is growing, and, *as it grows, its right-most point is fixed*, resulting in the directrix circle expanding to the left, while its center is moving to the left and off the page. As the directrix circle is growing, we visualize that the ends of the hyperbola are being pushed together. The bigger the directrix circle becomes, the more the hyperbola looks like a parabola.

2. The Parabola. The directrix circle is now infinitely large – so large that it appears as a vertical line in the drawing. This is the *critical instant* when the curve becomes a parabola – the instant between a hyperbola and an ellipse.

3. The Ellipse. The directrix circle (shown as a large, incomplete circle) has now turned inside out. Its center, which was initially to the left of the focus, is now to the right of the focus. In the process of encircling the focus, the directrix circle gathers in, and joins together what had been the ends of the hyperbola in order to form an ellipse. We can imagine that the directrix circle now begins to shrink, and, as it shrinks, the ellipse goes from becoming infinitely stretched out (a parabola), to becoming smaller and rounder. At this stage, the directrix circle and the ellipse are like a womb and its egg.

4. The Circle. The directrix circle (shown as a small, thin circle to the right of the vertical line) continues to shrink until the instant occurs that the center of the directrix circle coincides with the focus. At this point, the ellipse has become a perfect circle (shown as a small, shaded circle) that has a radius equal to half the radius of the directrix circle.

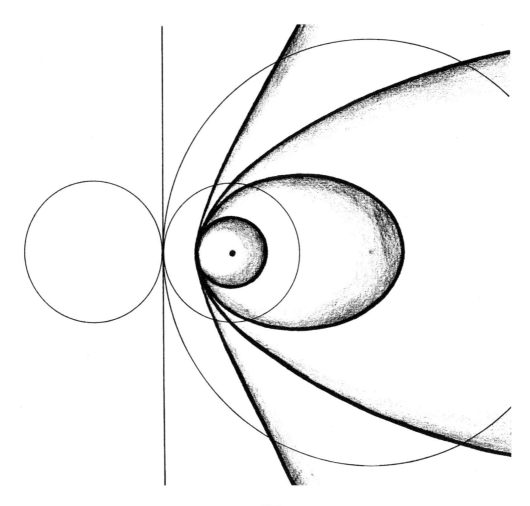

The Curves of Cassini

What is a Cassini curve?

- Above (see *Alternative Definitions*), we showed that an ellipse is the locus of points such that the *sum of the distances* to the two focal points is always the same number (a constant), and that a hyperbola is the locus of points such that the *difference of the distances* to the two focal points is always the same number.

> *A Cassini curve is the locus of points such that*
> ## the product of the distances
> *to the two focal points is constant.*

a times b is always the same number.

Formulas and set-up.

The goal is to have the students produce drawings that look like one of the six possibilities shown on the drawing on the next page. As the theme is transformation of the curve, we will have the students create different curves so that they can look at each other's drawings and see what happens when f (the distance between the focal points) changes. There are two things that determine what the shape of a Cassini curve will be: the distance between the two focal points, f, and the constant, C, that the product of the two distances are always equal to. In order to get the best results, we need to carefully choose values for f and C, even though a Cassini curve could be generated from *any* values for f and C. These values will depend upon the size of the paper. For 8½ by 11 inch paper, I recommend using a C value (the constant product) of 64 (for all the drawings), from which all the variations of the Cassini curves can be nicely created by using f values (the distance between the focal points in cm) of 8, 11.3, 15, 16, 17, and 20. But it is probably better for the students to use 11 by 14 inch paper (from a standard main lesson book), in which case I recommend using a C value of 100, from which all the variations of the Cassini curves can be created by using f values (in cm) of 10, 14.14, 19, 20, 21, and 25. Either way, the whole class uses the same C value.

By using different f values, we are, in effect, allowing the two focal points to drift apart. The result is a sequence of six stages, each one clearly seen in the drawing on the next page, in which the Cassini curve transforms itself from a round oval (not exactly an ellipse), into a flat oval, into an indented oval, into a lemniscate, and finally into two egg-like curves (which is mathematically still one curve). As the focal points drift further apart, these two eggs become smaller and rounder. Amazingly, this transformation looks like the biological process of cell division.

It is helpful to know (but difficult to prove) each of these things:

- The two key transition points of the Cassini curve (the *flat oval* and the *lemniscate*) occur at the instant when $f = \sqrt{2c}$ and when $f = 2\sqrt{c}$, respectively.

- The distance X_{out}, which is measured from a focal point to the neighboring outside-most point of the curve, is given by this formula:
$$X_{out} = \frac{\sqrt{f^2 + 4c} - f}{2}$$

- In the case that the curve is two eggs, the distance X_{in}, which is measured from a focal point to the inside-most point of the egg, is given by this formula:
$$X_{in} = \frac{f - \sqrt{f^2 - 4c}}{2}$$

It is up to the discretion of the teacher to decide whether the students should use these formulas themselves to calculate the X_{out} and X_{in} values, or whether the teacher should simply give the resulting values to the students. Either way, these formulas can help the students to appreciate the power that formulas have to aid engineers and scientists.

The Transformation of a Cassini Curve

Note: f is the distance between the focal points, and C is the constant product. Drawings are 27% of the original size.

$f = 10cm; \quad C = 100$

$f \approx 14.14cm; \quad C = 100; \quad (f = \sqrt{2C})$

$f = 19cm; \quad C = 100$

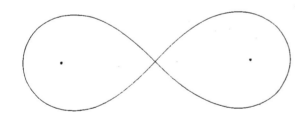

$f = 20cm; \quad C = 100; \quad (f = 2\sqrt{C})$

$f = 21cm; \quad C = 100$

$f = 25cm; \quad C = 100$

Construction of a Cassini Curve

I will now explain, in detail, how to construct one particular Cassini curve. We start by choosing (for 11 by 14inch paper) the values C=100 and f = 19cm, which turns out to be an *indented oval* (see the table on the next page). We then use the above formulas to find out that $X_{out} \approx 4.29$cm, and for X_{in}, we see that what's inside the square root sign ($f^2 - 4c$) turns out to be negative, which is not possible. Therefore, there is no value for X_{in}. (Recall that X_{in} is only valid for the case when the Cassini curve has the shape of two eggs.)

Now, we carefully place the focal points (A and B), so that they are centered horizontally on the paper 19cm apart. Our first point (P_1) on the curve is found (as given by X_{out}) by going 4.29cm to the left of focal point A.

The next two points on the Cassini curve are found by knowing that since the product of the distances to the two focal points must always be 100, there should be a point that is 10cm from each of the focal points. So we set our compass exactly to a width of 10cm, and, by placing the needle, in turn, on each of the two focal points, we draw two arcs. Since each point on an arc is 10cm away from one focal point, we can say that the two points of intersection (P_2 and P_3 in the below drawing) of these two arcs are 10cm away from *each* of the two focal points. (Notice that these two points will not exist if the Cassini curve is *two eggs*; the two drawn arcs will not cross one another.)

We can now locate additional points on our curve by choosing any distance that we please between 4.29cm (X_{out}) and 10cm. We simply draw a circle using the distance we have chosen as the circle's radius, and with the focal point A as its center. The points on the Cassini curve are those two points on this circle that are the proper distance away from the other focal point (B). For example, in the diagram below, we have chosen to draw a circle (the larger one) a distance of 9cm away from focal point A. The question is now: "What must the distance to the other focal point be such that the product of the two distances will be equal to 100?" We find this desired distance by dividing 100 by 9, which gives us approximately 11.11cm. Notice that 9 times 11.11 is (approximately) equal to 100. By using a ruler, we then locate the two points on the circle (P_4 and P_5) that are a distance of 11.11cm to the focal point B.

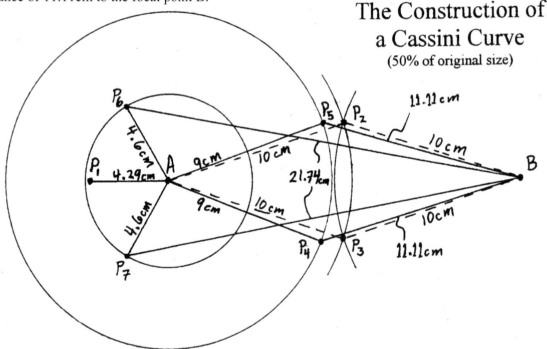

The Construction of a Cassini Curve
(50% of original size)

Similarly, we can choose *any other distance* between 4.29 and 10cm for the radius of the circle around focal point A. In the above diagram, we have chosen a distance of 4.6cm away from focal point A, resulting in the smaller circle. Dividing 100 by 4.6 gives us 21.74. We now find the points P_6 and P_7 by locating the two places on this circle that are 21.74cm away from focal point B. We continue finding more pairs of points by drawing circles a certain distance away from focal point A, calculating what the distance from focal point B must be, and then using our ruler to find where the desired points occur on each circle. Of course, we need to find points that occur around focal point B as well, by drawing circles around the focal point B, and using our ruler to find the calculated distances to focal point A. So we draw the same-sized circles around B as we did around A, and then imagine there is a line of reflection (passing through the points P_2 and P_3) that reflects all the points around focal point A (P_1, P_6, P_7, P_4, P_5 on the next page) to locations around focal point B.

After locating several points by using the method described above, we should be able to clearly see the path of the whole curve. We then carefully draw the curve by connecting the dots. I have used a French curve to assist me in drawing the curve shown here, but the students should do this free-hand, as best as they can.

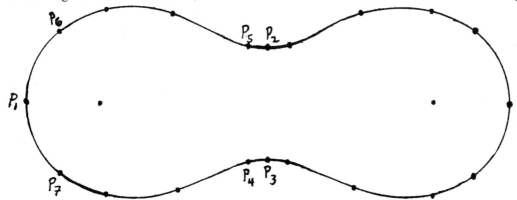

The process for drawing any other Cassini curve is basically the same as described above. In the above example, we just happened to have chosen values for f (equal to 19) and C (equal to 100) that resulted in the Cassini curve having the shape of an indented oval (shown above). The table below summarizes the characteristics of various Cassini curves given certain values of f and a value of C equal to 100 (the whole class should use this value for C). Notice that there is only one specific instant that the curve becomes a "flat oval", namely when the distance between the focal points is approximately 14.14cm. Likewise, there is only one specific instant that the curve becomes a lemniscate, namely when the distance between the focal points is exactly 20cm. These two values (14.14 and 20) are given to us by the formulas $f = \sqrt{2c}$ and $f = 2\sqrt{c}$ with the assumption that C is 100. The f values for the other curves in the table (below) were chosen somewhat arbitrarily. In other words, an oval occurs with any f value less than 14.14; an indented oval occurs with any f value between 14.14 and 20; and two eggs are the result of an f value that is greater than 20. I have chosen to put the f values of 19 and 21 into the table because they nicely show what is happening near the magical transition point of the lemniscate, which is when f equals 20.

c (constant product)	f (distance between focal points, cm)	Shape of Curve	$X_{out} = \frac{\sqrt{f^2+4c} - f}{2}$ (Focal point to outside of curve)	$X_{in} = \frac{f - \sqrt{f^2-4c}}{2}$ (Focal point to inside of curve)	Range (of distances from curve to focal pt.)
100	10 cm	Oval	6.18 cm	n/a	6.18 – 16.18
100	14.14 $(f=\sqrt{2c})$	Flat Oval	5.18	n/a	5.18 – 19.32
100	19	Indented Oval	4.29	n/a	4.29 – 23.29
100	20 $(f=2\sqrt{c})$	Lemniscate	4.14	10 cm	4.14 – 24.14
100	21	Two Eggs	4	7.30cm	4 – 7.30 and 13.70 – 25
100	25	Two Eggs	3.51	5	3.51 – 5 and 20 – 28.51

As a final note regarding Cassini curves, I should mention that this is a great opportunity to integrate two disciplines by having the class do this 6-step transformation of the Cassini curve in eurythmy class. In my school, the eurythmy teacher does the Cassini curves in fourth or fifth grade, but tells the children they will learn about the mathematical significance of these curves in an eighth grade geometry main lesson. In eighth grade, the eurythmy exercise is revisited, but this time the focal points are included. Two of the children, representing the two focal points, stand close together while the rest of the class moves around them in a circular path. The two focal points then move slowly apart, or back together, thereby changing the path the rest of the class must now walk. This creates a process of transformation equivalent to what they experienced in their drawings.

Appendices

Equiangular Spirals
Formed with Inscribed Regular Polygons

Joining the midpoints
of the sides of the polygons.

Joining the quarter-points
of the sides of the squares.

Rotations of Circles
Showing the constructions and the final shaded-in drawings

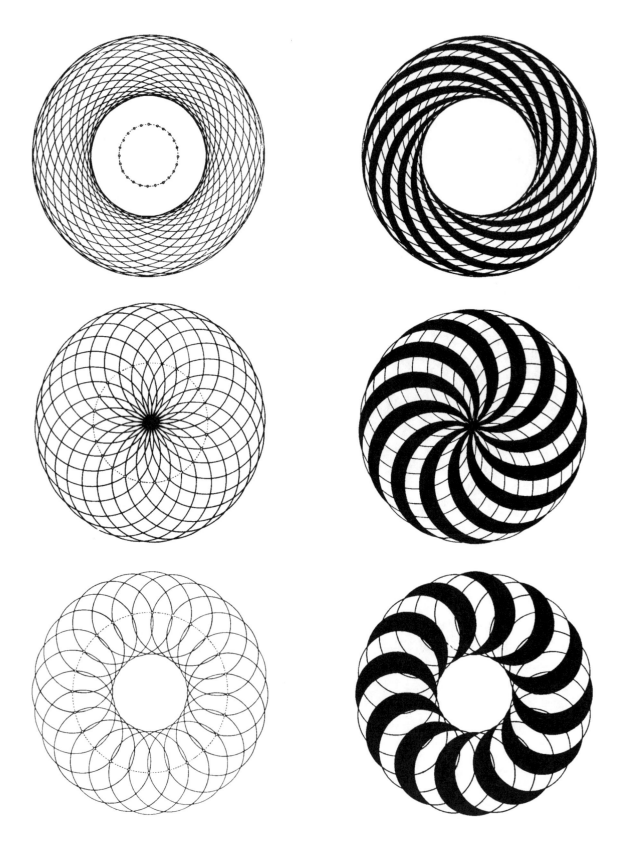

The Metamorphosis of a Limaçon

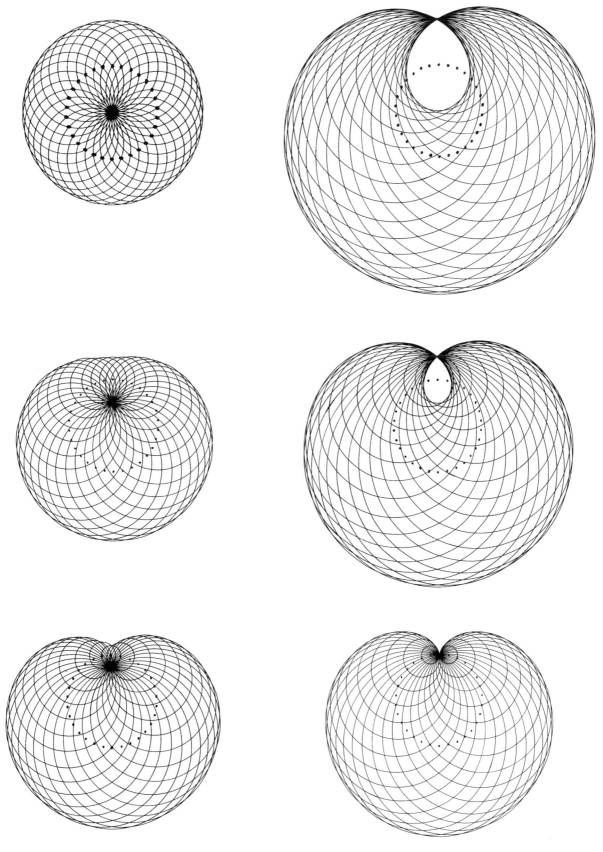

The Hierarchy of Quadrilaterals

Start with any **quadrilateral**. Connect the midpoints to form a **parallelogram**. Bisect the parallelogram angles to get a **rectangle**. Bisect these angles to get a **square**.

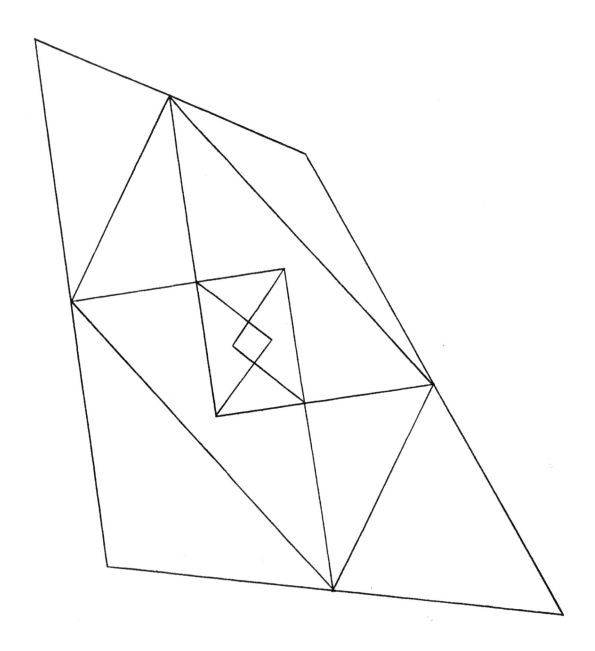

Knots and Interpenetrating Polygons
Using the 8-Division and the 12-Division of the Circle

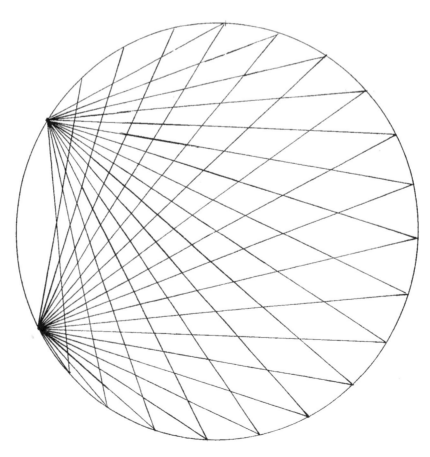

The 24-division with
All of its Diagonals

The King's Crown

Star Patterns with Geometric Division

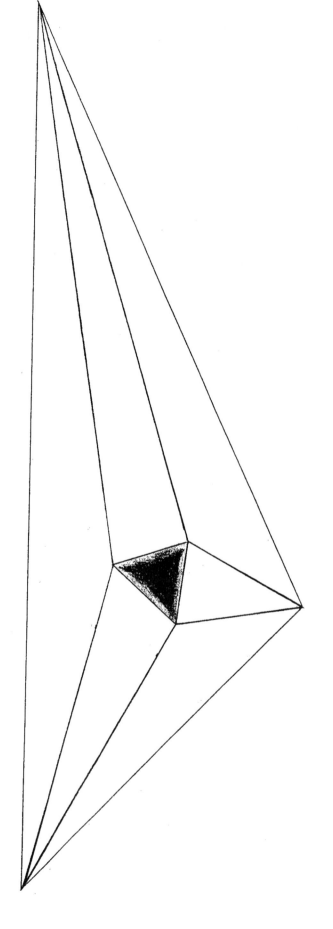

Morley's Theorem

(The 6 angle trisectors of a triangle meet to form an equilateral triangle.)

The Perspective Reduction of a Figure

Explanation: There are six pentagons in this drawing, including those hidden on the backsides of the "houses". The drawing has been done so that each pentagon is 75% of the size of the previous one. This also means that the second pentagon (which has point B at its lower left corner) is 75% as far from the point of perspective (P) as the first pentagon. In order to do this we "double-bisect" the line segment AP by first finding the midpoint (M) of the line segment PA, and then bisecting the resulting line segment MA, thereby locating point B. We use this same method to "bring in" the other four corners of the first pentagon to the other four points of the second pentagon. Similarly, the third pentagon is 75% of the size of the second pentagon, which means that the length of line segment PC is 75% of the length of PB. Likewise, the points D, E, and F are each another step of 25% of the distance toward P. Notice that reductions like 25%, 50%, or 75% are relatively easy, but something random (e.g., 37%) would be quite difficult with just a compass and straightedge.

Questions regarding Repeating Decimals

- This is an investigation of the mathematical laws that arise when a fraction is converted into a decimal, which may repeat.

- With each of the below questions, we are converting a fraction into a decimal by dividing the numerator by the denominator. We assume that we are starting with a *reduced fraction*.

Question: What are the denominators of the fractions that don't become repeating decimals?

Answer: *If the denominator is a 2, 4, 5, 8, 10, 16, 20, 25, 32, 40, 50, 64, 80, 100, 125, etc., then the decimal doesn't repeat.*

Question: What are the rules for when a fraction (or division problem), expressed as a decimal, repeats and when it just ends?

Answer: If we look at the denominators from the question above, then we see that they are all powers of two (e.g., 2, 4, 8, 16, 32, etc.) or powers of five (e.g., 5, 25, 125, 625, etc.) perhaps with zeroes added on to the end. Another way of looking at this, is that their factor trees have only 2's and 5's in them. *Fractions with a denominator having a factor that is anything other than a 2 or a 5 will repeat.* For example, $^{11}/_{60}$ as a decimal repeats because its prime factorization ($2^2 \cdot 3 \cdot 5$) has a three in it. On the other hand, $^{11}/_{80}$ doesn't repeat because its prime factorization is $2^4 \cdot 5$, which contains only twos and fives.

Question: What is the most number of digits that can possibly appear under the repeat bar when a fraction is converted into a decimal?

Answer: *The number of digits under the repeat bar can be at most one less than the number in the denominator.* The explanation is as follows: Using the example of $^4/_7$ we divide 7 into 4. We keep going with the division until it ends (giving a remainder of zero) or until it repeats (giving a remainder that we have already seen). There are only seven possible remainders when dividing by seven, and a remainder of zero would mean that it doesn't repeat at all, which isn't the case. Therefore, we must get a remainder that we have already seen after, at most, 6 digits.

Indeed $^4/_7 = 0.\overline{571428}$, and we can see that it repeats every six digits. Of course it is possible to get a repeated remainder earlier. For example, any fraction with a denominator of 13 ($^5/_{13} = 0.\overline{384615}$) doesn't repeat every 12 digits (that would be the most possible for a denominator of 13), but it happens to repeat after every 6 digits. Likewise, any fraction with a denominator of 11 ($^7/_{11} = 0.\overline{63}$) repeats every two digits instead of every ten digits (which would be the most we could expect). We might expect that $^{19}/_{54}$ repeats every 53 digits, but it repeats only every 3 digits ($^{19}/_{54} = 0.3\overline{518}$). Denominators that "go the maximum distance" before repeating include 17 ($^5/_{17} = 0.\overline{2941176470588235}$), and 19 ($^3/_{19} = 0.\overline{157894736842105263}$).

Question: For those denominators that go the maximum distance before repeating, what patterns do we notice by using different numbers in the numerator? (For example, find the decimal values of $^1/_7$, $^2/_7$, $^3/_7$, etc. What patterns do you see?)

Answer: *The digits under the repeat bar are always the same!* They also appear in the same order, but start off at a different place depending on what the numerator is. For example, $^5/_7 = 0.\overline{714285}$, and $^3/_7 = 0.\overline{428571}$. With both of these, we can imagine that the same 6 digits (under the repeat bar) are repeating again and again, forever. Alternatively, we can rewrite the two as: $^5/_7 = 0.7142\overline{857142}$, and $^3/_7 = 0.42\overline{857142}$ In both cases we see the digits 857142 repeating. $^1/_7$, $^2/_7$, $^4/_7$, and $^6/_7$ can also be expressed with the digits 857142 repeating. Similarly, other denominators that go the maximum distance (e.g., 17, 19, etc.) follow this same law. For example, $^{13}/_{17}$ and $^9/_{17}$ can both be expressed with the same digits in the same order under the repeat bar.

Question: Give an example of a fraction for which there is no equivalent repeating or ending decimal?

Answer: There is no such fraction. *Every fraction either repeats or ends.* This is a very important result in order to understand irrational numbers.

Lesson Plan Outline for
The Square Root Algorithm (7ᵗʰ grade)

Introduction: The following is an outline of a lesson plan that takes about 10 classroom hours to execute. The goal is to teach the students how to efficiently calculate square roots of large numbers (e.g., 223729), and to teach it in such a way that the students gain an understanding of *why* the square root algorithm works.

Method #1: The Guess and Check Method
- This method is simple in concept, but very tedious in practice.
- Guess an approximate value of the answer, than check how good your guess is by squaring it. If your guess squared is bigger (or smaller) than the original problem then the guess was too big (or small). Guess again, by adjusting your guess accordingly, and continue until the guess turns out to be exact, or you have a satisfactory amount of accuracy (e.g., two decimal places).
- Practice these kind of problems: (Don't spend too much time on it. *The idea is largely for the students to come to the realization that we need to find a quicker, more efficient, method.*)
- <u>Large square roots that work out to be whole numbers</u>.
  - $\sqrt{90000}$ (answer: 300)
  - $\sqrt{25000000}$ (answer: 5000)
  - $\sqrt{123201}$ (answer: 351)
  - $\sqrt{7569}$ (answer: 87)
  - $\sqrt{223729}$ (answer: 473)
- <u>Square roots that *don't* work out to be whole numbers</u>. See how far they can go with each one.
  - $\sqrt{263}$ (answer: ≈16.2172747)
  - $\sqrt{2}$ (answer: ≈ 1.41421356237309504880168872420 97)

How can we find a better method?
- *Make a table of squares.* (See table at right.)
- Have the students work in groups and fill out the right column
- Make sure that they understand that our goal is to *go in the other direction* (from the right column to the left) in order to calculate the square root of a number.
- By looking at the table that has now been filled out, the students should try to answer the three questions below, while keeping in mind that we are really taking the square root of some number. We are given a number from the right column and we need to figure out its square root, which is given in the left column.

X	x^2
5	25
9	81
10	100
23	529
38	1444
75	5625
99	9801
100	10,000
216	46,656
347	120409
521	271,441
999	998,001
1000	1,000,000
2012	4,048,144
5204	27,081,616
9999	99,980,001
10000	100,000,000

<u>When calculating a square root that works out evenly</u>:
1. *What can we say about the square root of a number that*:
   has 1 digit?   (Answer: Its square root has 1 digit.)
   has 2 digits?   (Answer: Its square root has 1 digit.)
   has 3 digits?   (Answer: Its square root has 2 digits.)
   has 4 digits?   (Answer: Its square root has 2 digits.)
   has 5 digits?   (Answer: Its square root has 3 digits.)
   has 6 digits?   (Answer: Its square root has 3 digits.)
   has 7 digits?   (Answer: Its square root has 4 digits.)
   has 8 digits?   (Answer: Its square root has 4 digits.)
   has 9 digits?   (Answer: Its square root has 5 digits.)

2. *What can we say about the square root of a number if the number:*
   ends in a 1?   (Answer: its square root ends in a 1 or a 9.)
   ends in a 4?   (Answer: its square root ends in a 2 or a 8.)
   ends in a 5?   (Answer: its square root ends in a 5.)
   ends in a 6?   (Answer: its square root ends in a 4 or a 6.)
   ends in a 9?   (Answer: its square root ends in a 3 or a 7.)
   ends in a 0?   (Answer: its square root ends in a 0.)
   ends in a 2, 3, 7, or 8?   (Answer: its square root can't be exact!)

Square Root Algorithm (continued)

3. *Given a certain number, how can we know exactly what the first digit of its square root is?*
   Answer: Start from the right and move left while grouping the digits in pairs. The left-most "pair" will be just a single digit if the whole number has an odd number of digits. (e.g., 840889 has 84 as its left-most pair, and 54756 has 5 as its left-most pair.) Now, while looking at this left-most pair, ask yourself: "the square root of this left-most pair sits between what two whole numbers?". The lower of these two whole numbers is our desired answer - the first digit of the square root of the entire original number.
   Example: For $\sqrt{393129}$, we ask ourselves "$\sqrt{39}$ sits between what two whole numbers?". The answer to this question is "between 6 and 7", which leads us to the conclusion that $\sqrt{393129}$ has 6 as its first digit.

What have these three questions (above) taught us?

   This should clear up any confusion. Let's use the example of $\sqrt{54756}$. Since 54,756 has "5" as its left-most pair, we know that $\sqrt{5}$ is between 2 and 3. *Therefore, the $\sqrt{54756}$ has 2 as its first digit.* We also know that since the number of digits in the number (54756) is 5, then the number of digits in its square root is 3 (from question #1). Therefore the $\sqrt{54756}$ is two-hundred-and-something. We now have to figure out what the last two digits are (the tens' place and the ones' place). We also know that because the number (54756) ends in a 6, its square root (if it works out evenly) ends in either a 6 or a 4 (from question #2).

Practice Problems (For the concepts given above)

Example: For each problem, give the number of digits that its square root will have (assuming that the answer works out evenly), state what the first digit is, and what the possibilities are for the last digit.
- $\sqrt{529}$ (The answer has 2 digits; the first digit is 2; the last digit is 3 or 7, if exact)
- $\sqrt{695556}$ (The answer has 3 digits; the first digit is 8; the last digit is 4 or 6, if exact)
- $\sqrt{45589504}$ (The answer has 4 digits; the first digit is 6; the last digit is 2 or 8, if exact)
- $\sqrt{3750950025}$ (The answer has 5 digits; the first digit is 6; the last digit is 5, if exact)
- $\sqrt{94352}$ (The answer has 3 digits; the first digit is 3; the answer can't be exact)

An Identity Needed for doing Square Roots

- An identity is a type of equation that states a relationship that is true for all numbers. We are going to use a special identity in order to help us calculate the rest of the digits of a square root.
- The first step is to start with something that we will call **The Squaring Formula:**

$$(a+b)^2 = a^2 + b(2a+b)$$

- Use the above identity for squaring numbers, in order to show students that it works for all numbers:
   Example: 73^2 ($a = 70$; $b = 3$) $\rightarrow$ $70^2 + 3(2 \cdot 70+3)$ $\rightarrow$ $4900 + 3(143)$ $\rightarrow$ 5329
- Stress to students that we need to find a new identity that is more useful for square roots.
- We start by calling the number that is being square rooted, n. We then say that $\sqrt{n}$ can be broken down into the sum of two numbers a and b. For example, we can say that $\sqrt{64}$ (which is 8) is equal to $5 + 3$. This may seem to be strange, but we can see how it leads to our desired identity, shown below:

$$\sqrt{n} = a + b \quad \text{and then squaring both sides}$$
$$n = (a + b)^2 \quad \text{and now using the above identity}$$
$$n = a^2 + b(2a+b) \quad \text{and now subtracting } a^2 \text{ from both sides}$$
$$\underline{-a^2 \quad -a^2} \quad \text{we get...}$$

$$\mathbf{n - a^2 = b(2a+b)} \quad \textbf{We will call this The Square Root Identity}$$

- This identity works for any n, as long as we start with the relationship that $\sqrt{n} = a + b$.
   Example: Using $\sqrt{64} = 5 + 3$, we have $n = 64$, $a = 5$, and $b = 3$, and we can see that the identity works because $64 - 5^2 = 3(2 \cdot 5 + 3)$. Give several examples of this, such as:
- $n = 64$, $a = 6$, $b = 2$ $n = 676$, $a = 18$, $b = 8$
- $n = 64$, $a = 7$, $b = 1$ $n = 676$, $a = 20$, $b = 6$
- The important thing with this identity is that *the students can see that it works, not that they can understand yet how it will be useful in calculating square roots.*
- Mention that with square roots that have a two-digit answer, we will intentionally set a and b to the two digits of the answer. For example, because $\sqrt{169} = 13$, we will set a equal to 10 and set b equal to 3. Similarly with $\sqrt{676}$ we will set a to 20 and b equal to 6.
- Mention that our identity is also valid for square roots that don't work out evenly.

Square Root Algorithm (continued)

Method #2: The Long Algebraic Method
Calculating Square Roots with 2 Digit Answers.
- Have the students practice a good number of these.

   Example: Calculate $\sqrt{6889}$.
   Solution: Here n = 6889. We know that its square root has 2 digits, that the first digit is 8 (because $\sqrt{68}$ is between 8 and 9), and that the last number is a 3 or a 7. We call our first estimate of the answer a, and in this case a = 80. The second digit we call b. Here is the procedure, using the square root identity $\mathbf{n - a^2 = b(2a+b)}$ which is derived from $\sqrt{n}$ = a+b:

$$n - a^2 = b(2a+b)$$
and putting in n = 6889 and a = 80   we get:
$$6889 - 6400 = b(160 + b)$$
$$489 = b(160 + b)$$
Here we try to figure out b (the second digit of the answer).

We try different single digit values for b to see what works. For example, if b = 2, then we try 16$\underline{2}$·2; if b = 5, then we try 16$\underline{5}$·5, hoping that one of them will be equal to (or just under) 489. It turns out that b = 3 works (16$\underline{3}$·3 = 489). Therefore, our answer (which is exact) is **83**.
   Of course, the students should show themselves that the answer is correct - that 83^2 = 6889.

Calculating Answers with more than 2 Digits.
- We now need to do the same procedure as above, but repeat the process a number of times.
- Keep in mind that the a values are the digits that we are certain of at a given point, and the b values are the next digit that we are trying to figure out.
- **Notation:** We will use a_1 to mean the value of a for the first time through the process, and therefore with only one correct digit. a_3 would then represent the value of a the third time through the process, and therefore has three correct digits. The values of b are similarly given as b_1 , b_2 , etc.
- The students should practice several examples, of course doing all the calculations neatly by hand, and keeping the work well organized so that it is easy to follow, building up to something like this example:

   Example: Calculate $\sqrt{7203856}$.

   Step #1 We know that the answer has 4 digits, and the first digit is 2 (because $\sqrt{7}$ is between 2 and 3), so a_1 = 2000, and we use the identity $n-a_1^2 = b_1(2a_1 + b_1)$, where $2a_1$ = 4000.

n	7203856
$\mathbf{a_1^2}$	$- 4000000$ (because 2000^2 = 4000000)
$\mathbf{n-a_1^2}$	3203856 = $b_1(4000 + b_1)$, where b_1 is the 100's place (e.g., 300, 400, etc.)

   $\underline{\mathbf{b_1 = 600}}$ because 700 is too big,
   which means $b_1(2a_1 + b_1)$ = 2760000

   Step #2 We now know that the first two digits are 2 and 6, so a_2 = 2600, and we use the identity $n-a_2^2 = b_2(2a_2 + b_2)$, where $2a_2$ = 5200.

n	7203856
$\mathbf{a_2^2}$	$- 6760000$ (because 2600^2 = 6760000)
$\mathbf{n-a_2^2}$	443856 = $b_2(5200 + b_2)$, where b_2 is the tens' place (e.g., 30, 40, etc.)

   $\underline{\mathbf{b_2 = 80}}$ because 90 is too big,
   which means $b_2(2a_2 + b_2)$ = 422400

   Step #3 We now know that the first three digits are 2, 6, and 8, so a_3 = 2680, and we use the identity $n-a_3^2 = b_3(2a_3 + b_3)$, where $2a_3$ = 5360.

n	7203856
$\mathbf{a_3^2}$	$- 7182400$ (because 2680^2 = 7182400)
$\mathbf{n-a_3^2}$	21456 = $b_3(5360 + b_3)$, where b_3 is the ones' place (e.g., 3, 4, etc.)

   $\underline{\mathbf{b_3 = 4}}$ because 5 is too big,
   which means $b_3(2a_3 + b_3)$ = 21456,

   which means that our final answer is *exactly* $\boxed{2684}$.

Square Root Algorithm (continued)

Method #3: The Short Algebraic Method

The Basic Idea

- This method is the most difficult one, but it is not as crucial for students to understand as the long algebraic method. It serves only as a bridge to seeing why the square root algorithm works. Don't get bogged down.
- <u>Reducing the amount of Calculating.</u> The long algebraic method, described above, requires some tedious, and unnecessary, calculations, which can be eliminated.
- Look at the steps from the long algebraic method shown on the previous page. Looking at the left side of each step, we see, for step #1: $n - a_1^2$, and then for step #2: $n - a_2^2$, etc.
- Since $a_2 = a_1 + b_1$, we can use the *Squaring Formula* $(a+b)^2 = a^2 + b(2a+b)$ to get:

$$a_2^2 = (a_1 + b_1)^2 = a_1^2 + b_1(2a_1 + b_1)$$

<u>This is the key idea:</u> In place of subtracting a_2^2 from n, we can instead subtract the whole of $\{a_1^2 + b_1(2a_1 + b_1)\}$ from n since it is equal to a_2^2. This seems like more work, but it's not - it's less work.

In other words, instead of doing $n - a_2^2$, we can do $n - \{a_1^2 + b_1(2a_1 + b_1)\}$,

which[1] is the same as $(n - a_1^2) - \{b_1(2a_1 + b_1)\}$

In short: instead of doing $n - a_2^2$ we do $(n - a_1^2) - \{b_1(2a_1 + b_1)\}$

Likewise, instead of doing $n - a_3^2$ we do $(n - a_2^2) - \{b_2(2a_2 + b_2)\}$

Likewise, instead of doing $n - a_4^2$ we do $(n - a_3^2) - \{b_3(2a_3 + b_3)\}$

Of course, any sane person would ask, "Haven't we made things more complicated?". The answer to this is, quite surprisingly (and this is where the genius of this method comes in): $(n - a_2^2) - \{b_2(2a_2 + b_2)\}$ is easier to do than $n - a_3^2$ because a_3^2 requires us to square some big ugly number (e.g., 2680), whereas we have already calculated both $(n - a_2^2)$ (which is 443856 on the example on the previous page) and $\{b_2(2a_2 + b_2)\}$ (which is 422400 on the example on the previous page).

Subtracting 443856 − 422400, is easier than squaring 2680!!!!!

- Much of the above may be confusing. So the following example should hopefully clarify things.

Example: In short the whole procedure looks like this (again for $\sqrt{7203856}$):

	n	7203856		our first estimate (a_1) is 2000.
	a_1^2	− 4000000		
step #1	$n - a_1^2$	3203856	$= b_1(4000 + b_1)$ →	$\underline{b_1 = 600}$
	$b_1(2a_1 + b_1)$	− 2760000		
step #2	$n - a_2^2$	443856	$= b_2(5200 + b_2)$ →	$\underline{b_2 = 80}$
	$b_2(2a_2 + b_2)$	− 422400		
step #3	$n - a_3^2$	21456	$= b_3(5360 + b_3)$ →	$\underline{b_3 = 4}$
	$b_3(2a_3 + b_3)$	− 21456		

0 which tells us our answer is *exactly*

$$\boxed{2684}$$

---

[1] $n - \{a_1^2 + b_1(2a_1 + b_1)\}$ is the same as $(n - a_1^2) - \{b_1(2a_1 + b_1)\}$ for the same reason that $40 - (5 + 3 \cdot 2)$ would be the same as $(40 - 5) - (3 \cdot 2)$; i.e., instead of subtracting all of $5 + 3 \cdot 2$ from 40, we can instead subtract 5 first, and afterwards subtract $3 \cdot 2$. Either way the result is the same – in this case 29.

Square Root Algorithm (continued)

Method #4: The Square Root Algorithm (with zeroes)

- This method is basically identical to the *Short Algebraic Method*, but it cuts out all the unnecessary writing, and there is an added shortcut that aids us in determining the values for $2a_1$, $2a_2$, $2a_3$, etc. This new shortcut is as follows:

  With our example of $\sqrt{7203856}$, the values for $2a_1$, $2a_2$, $2a_3$ are 4000, 5200, 5360. The first of these values is found simply by doubling a_1, which is $2000 \cdot 2 = \underline{4000}$. The rest of these values are found by taking the previous value and adding the new **b** value to it, *two times*. So from 4000, we add b_1, which is 600, giving us 4600, and then add 600 again, giving us our next value, $\underline{5200}$. From 5200, we add b_2, which is 80, giving us 5280, and then adding 80 again, gives us our next value, $\underline{5360}$.

- Here is the whole process:

  Step #1: We know that $a_1 = 2000$, so we write down 2000 twice. Multiplying the two 2000's gives us the 4000000 that is written under 7203856, and subtracting, we get 3203856. Then we add 2000 plus 2000 to get 4000, but we put a box in place of the zeroes, and another box underneath the first box. So at this point, everything looks like this:

  ```
  2000        7203856
  2000       − 4000000
  4☐          3203856
   ☐
  ```

  It is important to understand that the boxes represent b_1. So at this point, with both the short and long algebraic method, we had had this equation: $3203856 = b_1(4000 + b_1)$, and we asked ourselves, "what must b_1 be so that $b_1(4000 + b_1)$ is less than 3203856?" Here, with the above situation, we are asking essentially the same thing. We need to fill in the two boxes with the same value (i.e., the value for b_1). And this value must be a certain number of hundreds – resulting in a product of $4100 \cdot 100$, or $4200 \cdot 200$, or $4300 \cdot 300$, etc. Since $4700 \cdot 700$ is bigger than 3203856, we put 600 in the two boxes, and write the product of $4600 \cdot 600$, which is 2760000, under 3203856.

  Step #2: We now add the left column (4600+600), which gives us 5200, and subtract the right column (3203856−2760000), which is 443856. Once again, we write a box in place of the zeroes of 5200, and another box under that one. Everything now looks like this:

  ```
  2000        7203856
  2000       − 4000000
  4600        3203856
   600       − 2760000
  52☐          443856
    ☐
  ```

  Similarly to step #1, we need to put the same number (which is the tens' place of our final answer) into both boxes so that the resulting product is less than 443856. The possibilities are $5210 \cdot 10$, or $5220 \cdot 20$, or $5230 \cdot 30$, etc. Since $5290 \cdot 90$ is a bit too big, we put 80 into both boxes, and write the product of $5280 \cdot 80$, which is 422400, under 443856.

  Step #3: We add the left column and subtract the right column, resulting in 5360 and 21456, respectively. We put a box in place of the zero in 5360, and a box below it (which is *not* shown below). 4 can be put into both boxes, resulting in $5364 \cdot 4$, which is *exactly* 21456. The end result, is that all our work looks like this (quite short, actually!):

```
2000        7203856
2000       − 4000000
4600        3203856
 600       − 2760000
5280         443856
  80       − 422400
5364          21456
   4        − 21456
                  0
```

- The answer, 2684, comes from the underlined digits.

- A remainder of zero tells us that our answer is exact.

- This method of the square root algorithm is slightly different from what is done in eighth grade. (**See 8th grade**, *Square Root Algorithm without zeroes*.)

- Calculating square roots that don't work out evenly (e.g., $\sqrt{30}$) should be delayed until eighth grade.

The Volume of an Octahedron and Tetrahedron

The Volume of an Octahedron

Question: What is the volume of an octahedron that has a 10cm long edge?
Solution: The octahedron can be sliced into two square pyramids. First we will find the height of one of the triangular faces (which is different from the height of the pyramid). We will see why this height is useful in a moment. We find this height (X) by dividing the equilateral triangle in half, thereby creating a right triangle with legs of length 5 and X, and a hypotenuse of length 10. By using the *Leg Formula*, we find x to be $\sqrt{75}$.

To find the volume of one of the pyramids, use the same method as explained in *Mensuration Practice Problems* where the volume of a pyramid is found. The trick is to find the height of the pyramid. This can be found by imagining a triangle sitting inside the pyramid that, when traced, goes from the apex of the pyramid straight down through the center of the pyramid to the center of the base (a square), then goes out to the midpoint of one of the edges of the base, and returns back to the apex by moving up along the middle of a triangular face. This triangle's hypotenuse has a length of $\sqrt{75}$ (from above), and one leg has a length of 5. The missing side of this triangle is the desired height (H) of the whole pyramid. Using the *Leg Formula*, we can see that H^2 is equal to $\sqrt{75}^2 - 5^2$, which makes H equal to $\sqrt{50}$, which is approximately 7.07.

The volume of the pyramid is therefore $V = \frac{1}{3} A_{Base} \cdot H$, and since the area of the square base is 100, this gives a volume of $\frac{1}{3} \cdot 100 \cdot \sqrt{50}$, which is $\frac{100\sqrt{50}}{3}$ or 235.67cm³.

Since the original octahedron consists of two of these pyramids, we can say that its volume is approximately equal to $2 \cdot 235.67$, which is <u>471.33cm³</u>.

The Volume of a Tetrahedron (challenge problem)

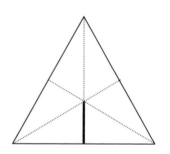

Question: What is the volume of a tetrahedron that has a 10cm long edge?
Solution: Again, we will imagine a right triangle sitting inside the tetrahedron that goes from the apex of the tetrahedron, down to the center of its triangular base, then out to the midpoint of the base's edge, and finally back up to the apex of the tetrahedron. What makes this tricky is determining the length of the leg of the right triangle that goes from the midpoint of the base's edge to the center of the base (shown as a dark line in the drawing). If we draw all three of the angle bisectors of the base triangle, then we can see where the center of this triangle is, and we can see that we have created six 30°-60°-90° triangles. Since the hypotenuse of a 30°-60°-90° triangle is twice the length of the shorter leg, we can say by looking at the drawing that *the distance from the center of the entire base triangle to a vertex of that triangle is twice the distance from the triangle's center to the midpoint of an edge.* Realizing that one of these angle bisectors is the same as the height (or altitude) of the triangle, and is equal to $\sqrt{75}$ (see *Volume of an Octahedron*, above), we can finally conclude that the distance from the midpoint of the triangular base's edge to the center of that triangle is ⅓ the height of the triangle, which is therefore equal to $\frac{1}{3}\sqrt{75}$.

Remember the triangle that we initially "imagined" sitting inside the tetrahedron? We now know the length of its hypotenuse, which is $\sqrt{75}$, and we know that the length of the short leg is $\frac{1}{3}\sqrt{75}$. We can use the Leg Formula of the Pythagorean Theorem to find the longer leg, which is equal to the height (H) of the whole tetrahedron. We get:

$$H^2 = \sqrt{75}^2 - (\tfrac{1}{3}\sqrt{75})^2 \quad \rightarrow \quad H^2 = 75 - \frac{75}{9} \quad \rightarrow \quad H^2 = \frac{600}{9} \quad \rightarrow \quad H = \frac{\sqrt{600}}{3}$$

Now we calculate the area of the base as $A_{Base} = \frac{1}{2} \cdot 10 \cdot \sqrt{75} = 5\sqrt{75}$ and lastly we use the volume formula $V = \frac{1}{3} A_{Base} \cdot H$ in order to finally get the volume of the whole tetrahedron:

$$\tfrac{1}{3}(5\sqrt{75})\frac{\sqrt{600}}{3} = \frac{5\sqrt{45000}}{9} = \underline{117.85\text{cm}^3}, \text{ which is exactly ¼ the volume of the octahedron.}$$

Proof that there exists Only Five Platonic Solids

60°   90°   108°   120°

The number of degrees in each of the regular polygons.

1. Any polyhedron can be made from a *net* on paper, where each of the faces are laid out side by side and then this net is cut out and folded together, all in such a way that the desired three-dimensional solid is formed. We can then see that *every vertex* in any polyhedron has *two properties*:

   (1) *Each vertex must be surrounded by at least three faces.*

   (2) *The sum of the angles* (of the corners of the faces) *coming together at each vertex must be less than 360°.*

   For example, the five triangular faces of an icosahedron can be placed flat on a piece of paper in such a way that they all share a common point, which is the vertex of the solid. When we do this, we notice that there is a "gap". When this gap and the whole net are cut out, and all the folds are made along the edges, this gap is closed in by having the two neighboring edges come together (see arrow, in drawing). This forces the vertex (which is the point where the five triangles come together) to rise up, essentially allowing the form to become three-dimensional. If the vertex is surrounded by angles adding to exactly 360° (e.g., six triangles), then there would be no gap, and the form, when cut out, would not become three-dimensional.

2. By definition, a Platonic solid must have *regular polygonal faces* (e.g., square, or equilateral triangle, pentagon, hexagon, etc.).

3. *If a Platonic solid has equilateral triangles for faces*, then there are three possibilities: there could be three triangles at each vertex (tetrahedron); there could be four triangles at each vertex (octahedron); or there could be five triangles at each vertex (icosahedron). Six triangles at a point is not possible because that would make in the sum of the angles at a vertex 6·60°, or exactly 360°, which is not allowed according to the second property given above.

4. *If a Platonic solid has squares for faces*, then there is only one possibility, namely, three squares at each vertex, which is a cube. Four squares at a point is not possible because that would result in the sum of the angles at a vertex to be 4·90°, or exactly 360°, which is not allowed according to the second property given above.

5. *If a Platonic solid has regular pentagons for faces*, then there is only one possibility, namely, three pentagons at each vertex, which is a dodecahedron. Four regular pentagons at a point is not possible because that would result in the sum of the angles at a vertex to be 4·108°, or 432°, which is greater than 360°, and not allowed according to the second property given above.

6. *A Platonic solid cannot have all regular hexagons for faces* because if three hexagons formed a vertex, the sum of the angles at that vertex would be 3·120°, which is exactly 360°, and is therefore not allowed according to the second property given above. Likewise, polygons with more than six sides (a 7-gon with angles of about 129°; an octagon with angles of 135°, etc.) are also not possible.

7. We have, therefore, exhausted all the possibilities for creating Platonic solids, *so there exist only five Platonic solids*.

The Wonder of Number (for Grades 5 and up)

Square and Triangular Numbers

- **See Appendix E**, *Square and Triangular Numbers,* for a listing of the square and triangular numbers.
- *The square numbers* are 1, 4, 9, 16, etc.
  - They are found by squaring each integer: $1^2, 2^2, 3^2, 4^2$, etc.
  - They can be geometrically made into squares by placing bowling pins into square shapes: three rows of three make 9, four rows of four make 16, etc.
  - They can also be found by adding sequences of odd numbers. For example, the fourth square number can be found by adding the first four odd numbers: 1+3+5+7, which is 16. Similarly, the sixth square number can be found by adding the first six odd numbers: 1+3+5+7+9+11, which is 36.

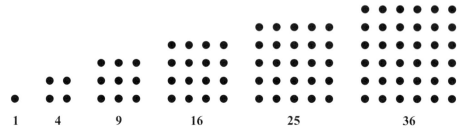

- *The triangular numbers* are 1, 3, 6, 10, 15, 21, 28, 36, etc.
  - The reason that they are called triangular can be explained by looking at the way that the dots are placed in a triangular form, as shown below.

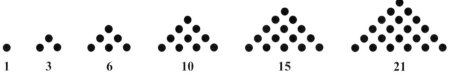

  - The triangular numbers can be found by adding a sequence of numbers. For example, the fourth triangular number is found by adding 1+2+3+4, which is 10, and, similarly, the sixth triangular number is found by adding 1+2+3+4+5+6, which is 21.
  - The sum of two consecutive triangular numbers is a square number! (Can you see why this is so?) This can be quite a thrill for students to discover this on their own!
- There are only seven numbers below 2 billion that are *both* square and triangular. They are
      1   36   1225   41,616   1,413,721   48,024,900   1,631,432,881

Perfect, Abundant and Deficient Numbers

- **See Appendix E**, *Perfect, Abundant, and Deficient Numbers,* for a listing of these numbers.
- *What are perfect, abundant, and deficient numbers?* In general, a whole number is categorized as abundant, deficient or perfect based upon the sum of its factors. In order to determine whether a given whole number is perfect, abundant or deficient, we first list all the number's factors, except for the number itself. Then we sum up the numbers in that list. If this sum is equal to the number itself, then we say that the number is *perfect.* If this sum is less than the number itself, then we say that the number is *deficient.* If the sum is greater than the number itself, then we say that the number is *abundant.*
- *More about perfect, abundant, and deficient numbers* (for the teacher).
- Perfect numbers are extremely rare. There are only three perfect numbers below 5000.

- The first 7 perfect numbers[1] are:
  6; 28; 496; 8128; 33,550,336; 8,589,869,056; 137,438,691,328.
- There are 21 even abundant numbers under 100 and 231 even abundant numbers that occur before 945, which is the first odd abundant number.
- The Greeks (especially the Pythagoreans) believed that certain numbers had special meaning and significance. They studied perfect, abundant, and deficient numbers in detail.
- Early on, the Greeks knew that the first three perfect numbers were 6, 28, and 496. They had troubles finding perfect numbers beyond that because the numbers were getting too large to list and add all the factors. They wanted to find an easier method for determining perfect numbers.
- Euclid discovered a formula for calculating even perfect numbers around 300B.C. This formula (a great topic for seventh or eighth grade algebra) made it possible to discover the next few perfect numbers (perhaps up to the seventh one). In the 1600's, Jean Prestet found the eighth perfect number: 2,305,843,008,139,952,128.
- There are no known odd perfect numbers, and it is one of the great mysteries of mathematics whether or not an odd perfect number could possibly exist.
- *Discovering Perfect Numbers.* Show the students that 10 is a *deficient number* because the sum of its factors (1, 2, 5) is less than 10. Then show the students that 20 is an *abundant number* because the sum of its factors (1, 2, 4, 5, 10) is greater than 20. Then tell the students that there are only two perfect numbers under 100, and let try to find them. (These are 6 and 28.)
- *More perfect numbers?* The students now know that the first two perfect numbers are 6 and 28, and that the next perfect number is greater than 100. Tell them that they will have to wait until seventh grade to learn how to calculate the next perfect numbers by using algebra. (A bit of drama never hurts!)
- *The abundance quotient* is the quotient that results when the sum of factors (without the number itself) is divided by the number itself.

Example: Determine whether the number 10 is perfect, abundant or deficient, and calculate its abundance quotient.

Solution: The list of factors for 10 is 1, 2, 5. The sum of these factors is 8, which is less than the number itself (10), so the number is *deficient*. The abundance quotient is 8÷10, which is 0.8.

Example: Determine whether the number 20 is perfect, abundant or deficient, and calculate its abundance quotient.

Solution: The list of factors for 20 is 1, 2, 4, 5, 10. The sum of these factors is 22, which is greater than the number itself (20), so the number is *abundant*. The abundance quotient is 22÷20, which is 1.1.

Example: Determine whether the number 28 is perfect, abundant or deficient, and calculate its abundance quotient.

Solution: The list of factors for 28 is 1, 2, 4, 7, 14. The sum of these factors is 28, which is equal to the number itself (28), so the number is *perfect*. The abundance quotient (for all perfect numbers) is 1.

Sums and Differences Theorems

- Each of the below theorems express some, rather surprising law about the relationship of numbers. If brought to the children properly, they can engender a real sense of wonder with numbers.
- It is not required to cover these theorems; they should only be brought to the children if the teacher has developed a good connection to it.
- The challenge is to not make it too abstract. Try to make it playful. For example, simply ask the children how many ways they can find to express 90 as the sum of two prime numbers. Have them list the different possibilities that they have found on the board. They will be amazed to see that there are nine ways to express 90 as the sum of two primes, but only two ways to express 68 as the sum of two primes.

- Goldbach's Theorem: *Every even number can be expressed as the sum of two prime numbers.*
  - This has not yet been proven, but is believed to be true.

---

[1] Note that "1" is not considered to be a perfect number for the same reason that it isn't considered to be a prime number: it is the basis of all numbers. Also, our list of factors isn't supposed to include the number itself, so the number 1 doesn't have any numbers in its list of factors.

- • Once we get past the first few even numbers, most all of them can be expressed as the sum of two prime numbers in multiple ways, yet the number of possible ways varies greatly. For example, 68 can only be expressed in two ways, either as 7+61 or 31+37, whereas 90 can be expressed in nine different ways (7+83; 11+79; 17+73; 19+71; 23+67; 29+61; 31+59; 37+53; 43+47).
  - • **See Appendix E,** *Even Numbers as the Sum of Two Primes,* for a list of all the ways that the even numbers from 4 to 150 can be expressed as the sum of two primes.
- • The Greeks were very interested in how numbers could be expressed as the sum or difference of other special numbers (e.g., prime numbers or square numbers). It was the famous French mathematician, Pierre de Fermat, who, around 1640, came up with the following theorems:
  - • *Every prime number, except for 2, can be expressed as the difference of two square numbers in one and only one way.*

    The students should first make a list of consecutive square numbers:

    1   4   9   16   25   36…   We see that the differences/distances between them grows:

    3   5   7   9   11…   ← These are the differences between neighbors.

    Given that the above differences between neighbors form the list of odd numbers, we can easily see how *any odd number can be expressed as the difference of two squares.* For example, we can express 7 as 16−9 (which is $4^2 - 3^2$). Similarly, we can express 15 as $64 - 49$ (which is $8^2 - 7^2$).

    The real surprise with the above theorem is that it says that if the odd number is a prime number then it can be expressed as a difference of two squares in *only one way.* For example, 15 can be expressed as the difference of two squares *in two ways*: either as $8^2 - 7^2$ or as $4^2 - 1^2$. This does not contradict our theorem because 15 is not a prime number. 7, on the other hand, is prime, therefore we know that it can only be expressed as $4^2 - 3^2$.
    - • **See Appendix E,** *Odd Numbers as the Difference of Two Squares*, for a list of all the ways that the odd numbers from 3 to 299 can be expressed as the *difference* of two squares.

  - • *Theorems that deal with the sum of two square numbers:*
    - • **See Appendix E,** *Numbers as the Sum of Two Squares*, for a list of all the ways that the numbers from 2 to 442 can be expressed as the *sum* of two squares.
    - • *If a number is prime and has a remainder of 1 after dividing it by 4, then it can be expressed as the sum of two square numbers in one and only one way.*
      - • The number 73 is both prime and has a remainder of 1 when divided by 4. This theorem tells us that there must be exactly one way to express 73 as the sum of two squares. Looking in Appendix E at *Numbers as the Sum of Two Squares*, we see that 73 can be expressed as $8^2 + 3^2$.
    - • *If a number is prime and has a remainder of 3 after dividing it by 4, then it is not possible to express it as a sum of two square numbers.*
      - • The numbers 43 is both prime and has a remainder of 3 when divided by 4. This theorem tells us that it must be impossible to express 43 as the sum of two squares. Looking in Appendix E at *Numbers as the Sum of Two Squares*, we can see that 43 can't be expressed as the sum of two squares.

- • *If a number is not prime then there are a variety of possibilities − it may be that the number can be expressed as the sum of two square numbers in one way, in multiple ways, or not at all.*
  - • Looking in Appendix E at *Numbers as the Sum of Two Squares*, we can see the following:
    - • 45 can be expressed as the sum of two squares in exactly one way: $6^2 + 3^2$.
    - • 48 can't be expressed as the sum of two squares in any way.
    - • 50 is the first number that can be expressed as the sum of two squares in 2 ways:
      $$5^2 + 5^2 \text{ or } 7^2 + 1^2$$
    - • 325 is the first number that can be expressed as the sum of two squares in 3 ways:
      $$1^2 + 18^2; \quad 6^2 + 17^2; \quad 10^2 + 15^2$$
    - • 1105 is the first number that can be expressed as the sum of two squares in 4 ways:
      $$4^2 + 33^2; \quad 9^2 + 32^2; \quad 12^2 + 31^2; \quad 23^2 + 24^2$$

Perfect, Abundant, and Deficient Numbers

The abundance quotient is the sum of its factors (except for the number itself) divided by the number itself. For example, with 24, the sum of its factors is 36, so the abundance quotient for 24 is 36÷24 = 1.5.

All perfect numbers, by definition, have an abundance quotient exactly equal to one. The first nine perfect numbers are:

6	8,589,869,056
28	137,438,691,328
496	2,305,843,008,139,952,128
8128	2,658,455,991,569,831,744,654,692,615,953,842,176.
33,550,336	

The tenth perfect number has 54 digits! It is still unknown if any odd perfect number exists.

Interestingly, the first 231 abundant numbers are all even numbers. The first odd-numbered abundant number is 945 (quotient = 1.032), and the second one is 1575 (quotient = 1.047). The *abundance quotients* of each of the "biggest" abundant numbers (i.e., having an abundance quotient greater than any previous number) from 6 up to 30,000 are listed below.

12 is abundant with a quotient of 1.333	720 is abundant with a quotient of 2.358
24 is abundant with a quotient of 1.500	840 is abundant with a quotient of 2.429
36 is abundant with a quotient of 1.528	1260 is abundant with a quotient of 2.467
48 is abundant with a quotient of 1.583	1680 is abundant with a quotient of 2.543
60 is abundant with a quotient of 1.800	2520 is abundant with a quotient of 2.714
120 is abundant with a quotient of 2.000	5040 is abundant with a quotient of 2.838
180 is abundant with a quotient of 2.033	10080 is abundant with a quotient of 2.900
240 is abundant with a quotient of 2.100	15120 is abundant with a quotient of 2.937
360 is abundant with a quotient of 2.250	25200 is abundant with a quotient of 2.966
	27720 is abundant with a quotient of 3.052

Here are the abundance quotients for the abundant numbers up to 150:

12 has a quotient of 1.333	80 has a quotient of 1.325
18 has a quotient of 1.167	84 has a quotient of 1.667
20 has a quotient of 1.100	88 has a quotient of 1.045
24 has a quotient of 1.500	90 has a quotient of 1.600
28 has a quotient of 1.000	96 has a quotient of 1.625
30 has a quotient of 1.400	100 has a quotient of 1.170
36 has a quotient of 1.528	102 has a quotient of 1.118
40 has a quotient of 1.250	104 has a quotient of 1.019
42 has a quotient of 1.286	108 has a quotient of 1.593
48 has a quotient of 1.583	112 has a quotient of 1.214
54 has a quotient of 1.222	114 has a quotient of 1.105
56 has a quotient of 1.143	120 has a quotient of 2.000
60 has a quotient of 1.800	126 has a quotient of 1.476
66 has a quotient of 1.182	132 has a quotient of 1.545
70 has a quotient of 1.057	138 has a quotient of 1.087
72 has a quotient of 1.708	140 has a quotient of 1.400
78 has a quotient of 1.154	

Euclid's Formula for Perfect Numbers

$$P = (2^{N-1}) \cdot (2^N - 1)$$

Where N is a whole number. Beginning with N = 2, this formula produces all the even perfect numbers (P) with the condition that $(2^N - 1)$ is a prime number.

Here are the first ten perfect numbers[1]:

1. For N = 2 we get the perfect number <u>6</u>, because $(2^N - 1) = 3$ is prime.
2. For N = 3 we get the perfect number <u>28</u>, because $(2^N - 1) = 7$ is prime.
   For N = 4 we don't get a perfect number, because $(2^N - 1) = 15$ is not prime.
3. For N = 5 we get the perfect number <u>496</u>, because $(2^N - 1) = 31$ is prime.
   For N = 6 we don't get a perfect number, because $(2^N - 1) = 63$ is not prime.
4. For N = 7 we get the perfect number <u>8128</u>, because $(2^N - 1) = 127$ is prime.
   For N = 8 we don't get a perfect number, because $(2^N - 1) = 255$ is not prime.
   For N = 9 we don't get a perfect number, because $(2^N - 1) = 511$ is divisible by 7.
   For N = 10 we don't get a perfect number, because $(2^N - 1) = 1023$ is divisible by 3.
   For N = 11 we don't get a perfect number, because $(2^N - 1) = 2047$ is divisible by 23.
   For N = 12 we don't get a perfect number, because $(2^N - 1) = 4095$ is divisible by 5.
5. For N = 13 we get the perfect number <u>33,550,336</u>, because $(2^N - 1) = 8191$ is prime.
   For N = 14 we don't get a perfect number, because $(2^N - 1) = 16383$ is divisible by 3.
   For N = 15 we don't get a perfect number, because $(2^N - 1) = 32767$ is divisible by 7.
   For N = 16 we don't get a perfect number, because $(2^N - 1) = 65535$ is divisible by 5.
6. For N = 17 we get the perfect number <u>8,589,869,056</u>, because $(2^N - 1) = 131072$ is prime.
   For N = 18 we don't get a perfect number, because $(2^N - 1) = 262143$ is divisible by 3.
7. For N = 19 we get the perfect number <u>137,438,691,328</u>, because $(2^N - 1) = 524287$ is prime.
   For N = 20 we don't get a perfect number, because $(2^N - 1) = 1048575$ is divisible by 5.
   For N = 21 we don't get a perfect number, because $(2^N - 1) = 2097151$ is divisible by 7.
   For N = 22 we don't get a perfect number, because $(2^N - 1) = 4194303$ is divisible by 3.
   For N = 23 we don't get a perfect number, because $(2^N - 1) = 8388607$ is divisible by 47.
   For N = 24 we don't get a perfect number, because $(2^N - 1) = 16777215$ is divisible by 5.
   For N = 25 we don't get a perfect number, because $(2^N - 1) = 33554431$ is divisible by 31.
   For N = 26 we don't get a perfect number, because $(2^N - 1) = 67108863$ is divisible by 3.
   For N = 27 we don't get a perfect number, because $(2^N - 1) = 134217727$ is divisible by 7.
   For N = 28 we don't get a perfect number, because $(2^N - 1) = 268435455$ is divisible by 5.
   For N = 29 we don't get a perfect number, because $(2^N - 1) = 536870911$ is divisible by 233.
   For N = 30 we don't get a perfect number, because $(2^N - 1) = 1073741823$ is divisible by 3.
8. For N = 31 we get the perfect number <u>2,305,843,008,139,952,128</u>, because 2147483647 is prime.

9. For N = 61 we get the perfect number <u>2,658,455,991,569,831,744,654,692,615,953,842,176</u>.

10. For N = 89 we get the perfect number $\approx$<u>$1.916 \cdot 10^{53}$</u> (54 digits long).

---

[1] From Heath's translation of *The Elements*, vol. 2, p426 ; Dover Publications, 1956
<u>Note</u>: that "1" is not considered to be a perfect number for the same reason that it isn't considered to be a prime number: it is the basis of all numbers. "1" can't be said to have any "genuine" factors because to get to "1" we didn't have to multiply by anything.

The First 100 Square Numbers

$1^2 = 1$	$26^2 = 676$	$51^2 = 2601$	$76^2 = 5776$
$2^2 = 4$	$27^2 = 729$	$52^2 = 2704$	$77^2 = 5929$
$3^2 = 9$	$28^2 = 784$	$53^2 = 2809$	$78^2 = 6084$
$4^2 = 16$	$29^2 = 841$	$54^2 = 2916$	$79^2 = 6241$
$5^2 = 25$	$30^2 = 900$	$55^2 = 3025$	$80^2 = 6400$
$6^2 = 36$	$31^2 = 961$	$56^2 = 3136$	$81^2 = 6561$
$7^2 = 49$	$32^2 = 1024$	$57^2 = 3249$	$82^2 = 6724$
$8^2 = 64$	$33^2 = 1089$	$58^2 = 3364$	$83^2 = 6889$
$9^2 = 81$	$34^2 = 1156$	$59^2 = 3481$	$84^2 = 7056$
$10^2 = 100$	$35^2 = 1225$	$60^2 = 3600$	$85^2 = 7225$
$11^2 = 121$	$36^2 = 1296$	$61^2 = 3721$	$86^2 = 7396$
$12^2 = 144$	$37^2 = 1369$	$62^2 = 3844$	$87^2 = 7569$
$13^2 = 169$	$38^2 = 1444$	$63^2 = 3969$	$88^2 = 7744$
$14^2 = 196$	$39^2 = 1521$	$64^2 = 4096$	$89^2 = 7921$
$15^2 = 225$	$40^2 = 1600$	$65^2 = 4225$	$90^2 = 8100$
$16^2 = 256$	$41^2 = 1681$	$66^2 = 4356$	$91^2 = 8281$
$17^2 = 289$	$42^2 = 1764$	$67^2 = 4489$	$92^2 = 8464$
$18^2 = 324$	$43^2 = 1849$	$68^2 = 4624$	$93^2 = 8649$
$19^2 = 361$	$44^2 = 1936$	$69^2 = 4761$	$94^2 = 8836$
$20^2 = 400$	$45^2 = 2025$	$70^2 = 4900$	$95^2 = 9025$
$21^2 = 441$	$46^2 = 2116$	$71^2 = 5041$	$96^2 = 9216$
$22^2 = 484$	$47^2 = 2209$	$72^2 = 5184$	$97^2 = 9409$
$23^2 = 529$	$48^2 = 2304$	$73^2 = 5329$	$98^2 = 9604$
$24^2 = 576$	$49^2 = 2401$	$74^2 = 5476$	$99^2 = 9801$
$25^2 = 625$	$50^2 = 2500$	$75^2 = 5625$	$100^2 = 10000$

The First 75 Triangular Numbers

#1 is 1	#20 is 210	#39 is 780	#58 is 1711
#2 is 3	#21 is 231	#40 is 820	#59 is 1770
#3 is 6	#22 is 253	#41 is 861	#60 is 1830
#4 is 10	#23 is 276	#42 is 903	#61 is 1891
#5 is 15	#24 is 300	#43 is 946	#62 is 1953
#6 is 21	#25 is 325	#44 is 990	#63 is 2016
#7 is 28	#26 is 351	#45 is 1035	#64 is 2080
#8 is 36	#27 is 378	#46 is 1081	#65 is 2145
#9 is 45	#28 is 406	#47 is 1128	#66 is 2211
#10 is 55	#29 is 435	#48 is 1176	#67 is 2278
#11 is 66	#30 is 465	#49 is 1225	#68 is 2346
#12 is 78	#31 is 496	#50 is 1275	#69 is 2415
#13 is 91	#32 is 528	#51 is 1326	#70 is 2485
#14 is 105	#33 is 561	#52 is 1378	#71 is 2556
#15 is 120	#34 is 595	#53 is 1431	#72 is 2628
#16 is 136	#35 is 630	#54 is 1485	#73 is 2701
#17 is 153	#36 is 666	#55 is 1540	#74 is 2775
#18 is 171	#37 is 703	#56 is 1596	#75 is 2850
#19 is 190	#38 is 741	#57 is 1653	

Powers of Two Table

2 to the 1 is 2
2 to the 2 is 4
2 to the 3 is 8
2 to the 4 is 16
2 to the 5 is 32
2 to the 6 is 64
2 to the 7 is 128
2 to the 8 is 256
2 to the 9 is 512
2 to the 10 is 1,024
2 to the 11 is 2,048
2 to the 12 is 4,096
2 to the 13 is 8,192
2 to the 14 is 16,384
2 to the 15 is 32,768
2 to the 16 is 65,536
2 to the 17 is 131,072
2 to the 18 is 262,144
2 to the 19 is 524,288
2 to the 20 is 1,048,576
2 to the 21 is 2,097,152
2 to the 22 is 4,194,304
2 to the 23 is 8,388,608
2 to the 24 is 16,777,216
2 to the 25 is 33,554,432
2 to the 26 is 67,108,864
2 to the 27 is 134,217,728
2 to the 28 is 268,435,456
2 to the 29 is 536,870,912
2 to the 30 is 1,073,741,824
2 to the 31 is 2,147,483,648
2 to the 32 is 4,294,967,296
2 to the 33 is 8,589,934,592
2 to the 34 is 17,179,869,184
2 to the 35 is 34,359,738,368
2 to the 36 is 68,719,476,736
2 to the 37 is 137,438,953,472
2 to the 38 is 274,877,906,944
2 to the 39 is 549,755,813,888
2 to the 40 is 1,099,511,627,776
2 to the 41 is 2,199,023,255,552
2 to the 42 is 4,398,046,511,104
2 to the 43 is 8,796,093,022,208
2 to the 44 is 17,592,186,044,416
2 to the 45 is 35,184,372,088,832
2 to the 46 is 70,368,744,177,664
2 to the 47 is 140,737,488,355,328
2 to the 48 is 281,474,976,710,656
2 to the 49 is 562,949,953,421,312
2 to the 50 is 1,125,899,906,842,624

2 to the 51 is 2,251,799,813,685,248
2 to the 52 is 4,503,599,627,370,496
2 to the 53 is 9,007,199,254,740,992
2 to the 54 is 18,014,398,509,481,984
2 to the 55 is 36,028,797,018,963,968
2 to the 56 is 72,057,594,037,927,936
2 to the 57 is 144,115,188,075,855,872
2 to the 58 is 288,230,376,151,711,744
2 to the 59 is 576,460,752,303,423,488
2 to the 60 is 1,152,921,504,606,846,976
2 to the 61 is 2,305,843,009,213,693,952
2 to the 62 is 4,611,686,018,427,387,904
2 to the 63 is 9,223,372,036,854,775,808
2 to the 64 is 18,446,744,073,709,551,616
2 to the 65 is 36,893,488,147,419,103,232
2 to the 66 is 73,786,976,294,838,206,464
2 to the 67 is 147,573,952,589,676,412,928
2 to the 68 is 295,147,905,179,352,825,856
2 to the 69 is 590,295,810,358,705,651,712
2 to the 70 is 1,180,591,620,717,411,303,424
2 to the 71 is 2,361,183,241,434,822,606,848
2 to the 72 is 4,722,366,482,869,645,213,696
2 to the 73 is 9,444,732,965,739,290,427,392
2 to the 74 is 18,889,465,931,478,580,854,784
2 to the 75 is 37,778,931,862,957,161,709,568
2 to the 76 is 75,557,863,725,914,323,419,136
2 to the 77 is 151,115,727,451,828,646,838,272
2 to the 78 is 302,231,454,903,657,293,676,544
2 to the 79 is 604,462,909,807,314,587,353,088
2 to the 80 is 1,208,925,819,614,629,174,706,176
2 to the 81 is 2,417,851,639,229,258,349,412,352
2 to the 82 is 4,835,703,278,458,516,698,824,704
2 to the 83 is 9,671,406,556,917,033,397,649,408
2 to the 84 is 19,342,813,113,834,066,795,298,816
2 to the 85 is 38,685,626,227,668,133,590,597,632
2 to the 86 is 77,371,252,455,336,267,181,195,264
2 to the 87 is 154,742,504,910,672,534,362,390,528
2 to the 88 is 309,485,009,821,345,068,724,781,056
2 to the 89 is 618,970,019,642,690,137,449,562,112
2 to the 90 is 1,237,940,039,285,380,274,899,124,224
2 to the 91 is 2,475,880,078,570,760,549,798,248,448
2 to the 92 is 4,951,760,157,141,521,099,596,496,896
2 to the 93 is 9,903,520,314,283,042,199,192,993,792
2 to the 94 is 19,807,040,628,566,084,398,385,987,584
2 to the 95 is 39,614,081,257,132,168,796,771,975,168
2 to the 96 is 79,228,162,514,264,337,593,543,950,336
2 to the 97 is 158,456,325,028,528,675,187,087,900,672
2 to the 98 is 316,912,650,057,057,350,374,175,801,344
2 to the 99 is 633,825,300,114,114,700,748,351,602,688
2 to the 100 is 1,267,650,600,228,229,401,496,703,205,376

Prime Numbers up to 2000 (in groups of 250)

2	251	503	751	1009	1259	1511	1753
3	257	509	757	1013	1277	1523	1759
5	263	521	761	1019	1279	1531	1777
7	269	523	769	1021	1283	1543	1783
11	271	541	773	1031	1289	1549	1787
13	277	547	787	1033	1291	1553	1789
17	281	557	797	1039	1297	1559	1801
19	283	563	809	1049	1301	1567	1811
23	293	569	811	1051	1303	1571	1823
29	307	571	821	1061	1307	1579	1831
31	311	577	823	1063	1319	1583	1847
37	313	587	827	1069	1321	1597	1861
41	317	593	829	1087	1327	1601	1867
43	331	599	839	1091	1361	1607	1871
47	337	601	853	1093	1367	1609	1873
53	347	607	857	1097	1373	1613	1877
59	349	613	859	1103	1381	1619	1879
61	353	617	863	1109	1399	1621	1889
67	359	619	877	1117	1409	1627	1901
71	367	631	881	1123	1423	1637	1907
73	373	641	883	1129	1427	1657	1913
79	379	643	887	1151	1429	1663	1931
83	383	647	907	1153	1433	1667	1933
89	389	653	911	1163	1439	1669	1949
97	397	659	919	1171	1447	1693	1951
101	401	661	929	1181	1451	1697	1973
103	409	673	937	1187	1453	1699	1979
107	419	677	941	1193	1459	1709	1987
109	421	683	947	1201	1471	1721	1993
113	431	691	953	1213	1481	1723	1997
127	433	701	967	1217	1483	1733	1999
131	439	709	971	1223	1487	1741	
137	443	719	977	1229	1489	1747	
139	449	727	983	1231	1493		
149	457	733	991	1237	1499		
151	461	739	997	1249			
157	463	743					
163	467						
167	479						
173	487						
179	491						
181	499						
191							
193							
197							
199							
211							
223							
227							
229							
233							
239							
241							

Even Numbers as the Sum of Two Primes

4 = 2+2

6 = 3+3

8 = 3+5

10 = 3+7; 5+5

12 = 5+7

14 = 3+11; 7+7

16 = 3+13; 5+11

18 = 5+13; 7+11

20 = 3+17; 7+13

22 = 3+19; 5+17; 11+11

24 = 5+19; 7+17; 11+13

26 = 3+23; 7+19; 13+13

28 = 5+23; 11+17

30 = 7+23; 11+19; 13+17

32 = 3+29; 13+19

34 = 3+31; 5+29; 11+23; 17+17

36 = 5+31; 7+29; 13+23; 17+19

38 = 7+31; 19+19

40 = 3+37; 11+29; 17+23

42 = 5+37; 11+31; 13+29; 19+23

44 = 3+41; 7+37; 13+31

46 = 3+43; 5+41; 17+29; 23+23

48 = 5+43; 7+41; 11+37; 17+31; 19+29

50 = 3+47; 7+43; 13+37; 19+31

52 = 5+47; 11+41; 23+29

54 = 7+47; 11+43; 13+41; 17+37; 23+31

56 = 3+53; 13+43; 19+37

58 = 5+53; 11+47; 17+41; 29+29

60 = 7+53; 13+47; 17+43; 19+41; 23+37; 29+31

62 = 3+59; 19+43; 31+31

64 = 3+61; 5+59; 11+53; 17+47; 23+41

66 = 5+61; 7+59; 13+53; 19+47; 23+43; 29+37

68 = 7+61; 31+37

70 = 3+67; 11+59; 17+53; 23+47; 29+41

72 = 5+67; 11+61; 13+59; 19+53; 29+43; 31+41

74 = 3+71; 7+67; 13+61; 31+43; 37+37

76 = 3+73; 5+71; 17+59; 23+53; 29+47

78 = 5+73; 7+71; 11+67; 17+61; 19+59; 31+47; 37+41

80 = 7+73; 13+67; 19+61; 37+43

82 = 3+79; 11+71; 23+59; 29+53; 41+41

84 = 5+79; 11+73; 13+71; 17+67; 23+61; 31+53; 37+47; 41+43

86 = 3+83; 7+79; 13+73; 19+67; 43+43

88 = 5+83; 17+71; 29+59; 41+47

90 = 7+83; 11+79; 17+73; 19+71; 23+67; 29+61; 31+59; 37+53; 43+47

92 = 3+89; 13+79; 19+73; 31+61

94 = 5+89; 11+83; 23+71; 41+53; 47+47

96 = 7+89; 13+83; 17+79; 23+73; 29+67; 37+59; 43+53

98 = 19+79; 31+67; 37+61

100 = 3+97; 11+89; 17+83; 29+71; 41+59; 47+53

102 = 5+97; 13+89; 19+83; 23+79; 29+73; 31+71; 41+61; 43+59

104 = 3+101; 7+97; 31+73; 37+67; 43+61

106 = 3+103; 5+101; 17+89; 23+83; 47+59; 53+53

108 = 5+103; 7+101; 11+97; 19+89; 29+79; 37+71; 41+67; 47+61

110 = 3+107; 7+103; 13+97; 31+79; 37+73; 43+67

112 = 3+109; 5+107; 11+101; 23+89; 29+83; 41+71; 53+59

114 = 5+109; 7+107; 11+103; 13+101; 17+97; 31+83; 41+73; 43+71; 47+67; 53+61

116 = 3+113; 7+109; 13+103; 19+97; 37+79; 43+73

118 = 5+113; 11+107; 17+101; 29+89; 47+71; 59+59

120 = 7+113; 11+109; 13+107; 17+103; 19+101; 23+97; 31+89; 37+83; 41+79; 47+73; 53+67; 59+61

122 = 13+109; 19+103; 43+79; 61+61

124 = 11+113; 17+107; 23+101; 41+83; 53+71

126 = 13+113; 17+109; 19+107; 23+103; 29+97; 37+89; 43+83; 47+79; 53+73; 59+67

128 = 19+109; 31+97; 61+67

130 = 3+127; 17+113; 23+107; 29+101; 41+89; 47+83; 59+71

132 = 5+127; 19+113; 23+109; 29+103; 31+101; 43+89; 53+79; 59+73; 61+71

134 = 3+131; 7+127; 31+103; 37+97; 61+73; 67+67

136 = 5+131; 23+113; 29+107; 47+89; 53+83

138 = 7+131; 11+127; 29+109; 31+107; 37+101; 41+97; 59+79; 67+71

140 = 3+137; 13+127; 31+109; 37+103; 43+97; 61+79; 67+73

142 = 3+139; 5+137; 11+131; 29+113; 41+101; 53+89; 59+83; 71+71

144 = 5+139; 7+137; 13+131; 17+127; 31+113; 37+107; 41+103; 43+101; 47+97; 61+83; 71+73

146 = 7+139; 19+127; 37+109; 43+103; 67+79; 73+73

148 = 11+137; 17+131; 41+107; 47+101; 59+89

150 = 11+139; 13+137; 19+131; 23+127; 37+113; 41+109; 43+107; 47+103; 53+97; 61+89; 67+83; 71+79

Odd Numbers as the Difference of Two Squares

$3 = 2^2 - 1^2$

$5 = 3^2 - 2^2$

$7 = 4^2 - 3^2$

$9 = 5^2 - 4^2$

$11 = 6^2 - 5^2$

$13 = 7^2 - 6^2$

$15 = 4^2 - 1^2;\ 8^2 - 7^2$

$17 = 9^2 - 8^2$

$19 = 10^2 - 9^2$

$21 = 5^2 - 2^2;\ 11^2 - 10^2$

$23 = 12^2 - 11^2$

$25 = 13^2 - 12^2$

$27 = 6^2 - 3^2;\ 14^2 - 13^2$

$29 = 15^2 - 14^2$

$31 = 16^2 - 15^2$

$33 = 7^2 - 4^2;\ 17^2 - 16^2$

$35 = 6^2 - 1^2;\ 18^2 - 17^2$

$37 = 19^2 - 18^2$

$39 = 8^2 - 5^2;\ 20^2 - 19^2$

$41 = 21^2 - 20^2$

$43 = 22^2 - 21^2$

$45 = 7^2 - 2^2;\ 9^2 - 6^2;\ 23^2 - 22^2$

$47 = 24^2 - 23^2$

$49 = 25^2 - 24^2$

$51 = 10^2 - 7^2;\ 26^2 - 25^2$

$53 = 27^2 - 26^2$

$55 = 8^2 - 3^2;\ 28^2 - 27^2$

$57 = 11^2 - 8^2;\ 29^2 - 28^2$

$59 = 30^2 - 29^2$

$61 = 31^2 - 30^2$

$63 = 8^2 - 1^2;\ 12^2 - 9^2;\ 32^2 - 31^2$

$65 = 9^2 - 4^2;\ 33^2 - 32^2$

$67 = 34^2 - 33^2$

$69 = 13^2 - 10^2;\ 35^2 - 34^2$

$71 = 36^2 - 35^2$

$73 = 37^2 - 36^2$

$75 = 10^2 - 5^2;\ 14^2 - 11^2;\ 38^2 - 37^2$

$77 = 9^2 - 2^2;\ 39^2 - 38^2$

$79 = 40^2 - 39^2$

$81 = 15^2 - 12^2;\ 41^2 - 40^2$

$83 = 42^2 - 41^2$

$85 = 11^2 - 6^2;\ 43^2 - 42^2$

$87 = 16^2 - 13^2;\ 44^2 - 43^2$

$89 = 45^2 - 44^2$

$91 = 10^2 - 3^2;\ 46^2 - 45^2$

$93 = 17^2 - 14^2;\ 47^2 - 46^2$

$95 = 12^2 - 7^2;\ 48^2 - 47^2$

$97 = 49^2 - 48^2$

$99 = 10^2 - 1^2;\ 18^2 - 15^2;\ 50^2 - 49^2$

$101 = 51^2 - 50^2$

$103 = 52^2 - 51^2$

$105 = 11^2 - 4^2;\ 13^2 - 8^2;\ 19^2 - 16^2;\ 53^2 - 52^2$

$107 = 54^2 - 53^2$

$109 = 55^2 - 54^2$

$111 = 20^2 - 17^2;\ 56^2 - 55^2$

$113 = 57^2 - 56^2$

$115 = 14^2 - 9^2;\ 58^2 - 57^2$

$117 = 11^2 - 2^2;\ 21^2 - 18^2;\ 59^2 - 58^2$

$119 = 12^2 - 5^2;\ 60^2 - 59^2$

$121 = 61^2 - 60^2$

$123 = 22^2 - 19^2;\ 62^2 - 61^2$

$125 = 15^2 - 10^2;\ 63^2 - 62^2$

$127 = 64^2 - 63^2$

$129 = 23^2 - 20^2;\ 65^2 - 64^2$

$131 = 66^2 - 65^2$

$133 = 13^2 - 6^2;\ 67^2 - 66^2$

$135 = 12^2 - 3^2;\ 16^2 - 11^2;\ 24^2 - 21^2;\ 68^2 - 67^2$

$137 = 69^2 - 68^2$

$139 = 70^2 - 69^2$

$141 = 25^2 - 22^2;\ 71^2 - 70^2$

$143 = 12^2 - 1^2;\ 72^2 - 71^2$

$145 = 17^2 - 12^2;\ 73^2 - 72^2$

$147 = 14^2 - 7^2;\ 26^2 - 23^2;\ 74^2 - 73^2$

$149 = 75^2 - 74^2$

$151 = 76^2 - 75^2$

$153 = 13^2 - 4^2;\ 27^2 - 24^2;\ 77^2 - 76^2$

$155 = 18^2 - 13^2;\ 78^2 - 77^2$

$157 = 79^2 - 78^2$

$159 = 28^2 - 25^2;\ 80^2 - 79^2$

$161 = 15^2 - 8^2;\ 81^2 - 80^2$

$163 = 82^2 - 81^2$

$165 = 13^2 - 2^2;\ 19^2 - 14^2;\ 29^2 - 26^2;\ 83^2 - 82^2$

$167 = 84^2 - 83^2$

$169 = 85^2 - 84^2$

$171 = 14^2 - 5^2;\ 30^2 - 27^2;\ 86^2 - 85^2$

$173 = 87^2 - 86^2$

$175 = 16^2 - 9^2;\ 20^2 - 15^2;\ 88^2 - 87^2$

$177 = 31^2 - 28^2;\ 89^2 - 88^2$

$179 = 90^2 - 89^2$

$181 = 91^2 - 90^2$

$183 = 32^2 - 29^2;\ 92^2 - 91^2$

$185 = 21^2 - 16^2;\ 93^2 - 92^2$

$187 = 14^2 - 3^2;\ 94^2 - 93^2$

$189 = 15^2 - 6^2;\ 17^2 - 10^2;\ 33^2 - 30^2;\ 95^2 - 94^2$

$191 = 96^2 - 95^2$

$193 = 97^2 - 96^2$

$195 = 14^2 - 1^2;\ 22^2 - 17^2;\ 34^2 - 31^2;\ 98^2 - 97^2$

$197 = 99^2 - 98^2$

$199 = 100^2 - 99^2$

Numbers as the Sum of Two Squares

(Numbers that are missing cannot be expressed as the sum of two squares.)

$2 = 1^2 + 1^2$

$5 = 1^2 + 2^2$

$8 = 2^2 + 2^2$

$10 = 1^2 + 3^2$

$13 = 2^2 + 3^2$

$17 = 1^2 + 4^2$

$18 = 3^2 + 3^2$

$20 = 2^2 + 4^2$

$25 = 3^2 + 4^2$

$26 = 1^2 + 5^2$

$29 = 2^2 + 5^2$

$32 = 4^2 + 4^2$

$34 = 3^2 + 5^2$

$37 = 1^2 + 6^2$

$40 = 2^2 + 6^2$

$41 = 4^2 + 5^2$

$45 = 3^2 + 6^2$

$50 = 1^2 + 7^2;\ 5^2 + 5^2$

$52 = 4^2 + 6^2$

$53 = 2^2 + 7^2$

$58 = 3^2 + 7^2$

$61 = 5^2 + 6^2$

$65 = 1^2 + 8^2;\ 4^2 + 7^2$

$68 = 2^2 + 8^2$

$72 = 6^2 + 6^2$

$73 = 3^2 + 8^2$

$74 = 5^2 + 7^2$

$80 = 4^2 + 8^2$

$82 = 1^2 + 9^2$

$85 = 2^2 + 9^2;\ 6^2 + 7^2$

$89 = 5^2 + 8^2$

$90 = 3^2 + 9^2$

$97 = 4^2 + 9^2$

$98 = 7^2 + 7^2$

$100 = 6^2 + 8^2$

$101 = 1^2 + 10^2$

$104 = 2^2 + 10^2$

$106 = 5^2 + 9^2$

$109 = 3^2 + 10^2$

$113 = 7^2 + 8^2$

$116 = 4^2 + 10^2$

$117 = 6^2 + 9^2$

$122 = 1^2 + 11^2$

$125 = 2^2 + 11^2;\ 5^2 + 10^2$

$128 = 8^2 + 8^2$

$130 = 3^2 + 11^2;\ 7^2 + 9^2$

$136 = 6^2 + 10^2$

$137 = 4^2 + 11^2$

$145 = 1^2 + 12^2;\ 8^2 + 9^2$

$146 = 5^2 + 11^2$

$148 = 2^2 + 12^2$

$149 = 7^2 + 10^2$

$153 = 3^2 + 12^2$

$157 = 6^2 + 11^2$

$160 = 4^2 + 12^2$

$162 = 9^2 + 9^2$

$164 = 8^2 + 10^2$

$169 = 5^2 + 12^2$

$170 = 1^2 + 13^2;\ 7^2 + 11^2$

$173 = 2^2 + 13^2$

$178 = 3^2 + 13^2$

$180 = 6^2 + 12^2$

$181 = 9^2 + 10^2$

$185 = 4^2 + 13^2;\ 8^2 + 11^2$

$193 = 7^2 + 12^2$

$194 = 5^2 + 13^2$

$197 = 1^2 + 14^2$

$200 = 2^2 + 14^2;\ 10^2 + 10^2$

$202 = 9^2 + 11^2$

$205 = 3^2 + 14^2;\ 6^2 + 13^2$

$208 = 8^2 + 12^2$

$212 = 4^2 + 14^2$

$218 = 7^2 + 13^2$

$221 = 5^2 + 14^2;\ 10^2 + 11^2$

$225 = 9^2 + 12^2$

$226 = 1^2 + 15^2$

$229 = 2^2 + 15^2$

$232 = 6^2 + 14^2$

$233 = 8^2 + 13^2$

$234 = 3^2 + 15^2$

$241 = 4^2 + 15^2$

$242 = 11^2 + 11^2$

$244 = 10^2 + 12^2$

$245 = 7^2 + 14^2$

$250 = 5^2 + 15^2;\ 9^2 + 13^2$

$257 = 1^2 + 16^2$

$260 = 2^2 + 16^2;\ 8^2 + 14^2$

$261 = 6^2 + 15^2$

$265 = 3^2 + 16^2;\ 11^2 + 12^2$

$269 = 10^2 + 13^2$

$272 = 4^2 + 16^2$

$274 = 7^2 + 15^2$

$277 = 9^2 + 14^2$

$281 = 5^2 + 16^2$

$288 = 12^2 + 12^2$

$289 = 8^2 + 15^2$

$290 = 1^2 + 17^2;\ 11^2 + 13^2$

$292 = 6^2 + 16^2$

$293 = 2^2 + 17^2$

$296 = 10^2 + 14^2$

$298 = 3^2 + 17^2$

$305 = 4^2 + 17^2;\ 7^2 + 16^2$

$306 = 9^2 + 15^2$

$313 = 12^2 + 13^2$

$314 = 5^2 + 17^2$

$317 = 11^2 + 14^2$

$320 = 8^2 + 16^2$

$325 = 1^2 + 18^2;\ 6^2 + 17^2;\ 10^2 + 15^2$

$328 = 2^2 + 18^2$

$333 = 3^2 + 18^2$

$337 = 9^2 + 16^2$

$338 = 7^2 + 17^2;\ 13^2 + 13^2$

$340 = 4^2 + 18^2;\ 12^2 + 14^2$

$346 = 11^2 + 15^2$

$349 = 5^2 + 18^2$

$353 = 8^2 + 17^2$

$356 = 10^2 + 16^2$

$360 = 6^2 + 18^2$

$362 = 1^2 + 19^2$

$365 = 2^2 + 19^2;\ 13^2 + 14^2$

$369 = 12^2 + 15^2$

$370 = 3^2 + 19^2;\ 9^2 + 17^2$

$373 = 7^2 + 18^2$

$377 = 4^2 + 19^2;\ 11^2 + 16^2$

$386 = 5^2 + 19^2$

$388 = 8^2 + 18^2$

$389 = 10^2 + 17^2$

$392 = 14^2 + 14^2$

$394 = 13^2 + 15^2$

$397 = 6^2 + 19^2$

$400 = 12^2 + 16^2$

$401 = 1^2 + 20^2$

$404 = 2^2 + 20^2$

$405 = 9^2 + 18^2$

$409 = 3^2 + 20^2$

$410 = 7^2 + 19^2;\ 11^2 + 17^2$

$416 = 4^2 + 20^2$

$421 = 14^2 + 15^2$

$424 = 10^2 + 18^2$

$425 = 5^2 + 20^2;\ 8^2 + 19^2;\ 13^2 + 16^2$

$433 = 12^2 + 17^2$

$436 = 6^2 + 20^2$

$442 = 1^2 + 21^2;\ 9^2 + 19^2$

The first number that can be expressed in 4 ways is...

$1105 = 4^2 + 33^2;\ 9^2 + 32^2;\ 12^2 + 31^2;$
$\qquad\qquad 23^2 + 24^2$

Sixth Grade Math Tricks[1]

1. <u>Multiplication and zeroes.</u> When multiplying two numbers, ignore all ending zeroes, do the multiplication, and then add the zeroes back onto the answer.
   Example: For 4000·300, we multiply 4 times 3, and then add on the 5 zeroes giving a result of 1,200,000.

2. <u>Division and Zeroes.</u> When dividing two numbers that both end in zeroes, cancel the same number of ending zeroes from each of the two numbers, then do the division problem.
   Example: For 24000÷600, we cancel two zeroes from both numbers, and then divide 240 by 6 to get 40.

3. <u>Multiplying and Dividing by 10, 100, 1000, etc.</u> Simply move the decimal point!
   Example: 634.6÷100 = 6.346   We move the decimal point 2 places because there are 2 zeroes in 100.
   Example: 48.37·1000 = 48370   The decimal point gets moved 3 places since there are 3 zeroes in 1000.

4. <u>Adding Numbers by Grouping.</u> Search for digits that add up to 10 or 20.
   Example: For 97 + 86 + 13 + 42 + 54, we see that with the ones' digits we can add 7 + 3 and 6 + 4 to make ten twice, leaving the 2 (from the 42) left over. The sum of the ones' column is therefore 22. In the tens' column, the carry of 2 combines with the 8 to form 10, as does the 9 and the 1. We are left with the 4 and 5. The tens' column is therefore 29. Our answer is 292.

5. <u>Multiplying by 4.</u> You can instead double the number two times.
   Example: For 4·35, we double 35 to get 70, and double again to get a result of 140.

6. <u>Multiplying a 2-digit number by 11.</u> Separate the digits, and then insert the sum of the digits in-between.
   Example: For 62·11, 6 plus 2 is 8, so we place the 8 between the 6 and the 2, giving a result of 682.
   Example: For 75·11, 7 plus 5 is 12, so we place the 2 between the 7 and 5 and carry the 1, giving 825.

7. <u>Multiplying two numbers that are just over 100.</u> First write down a 1, then next to the one we write down the sum of how far above 100 the two numbers are, and then the product of how far above 100 the two numbers are. Both the sum and the product must be two digits.
   Example: For 105·102, add 5 plus 2 (to get 07), and then multiply 5 times 2 (to get 10), giving 10710.
   Example: For 112·107, we do 12 + 7 (19) and then 12·7 (84), which leads to an answer of 11984.

8. <u>Dividing by 4.</u> You can instead cut the number in half, two times.
   Example: For 64÷4, we take half of 64 to get 32, and then take half of that for a result of 16.

9. <u>Subtraction by Adding Distances.</u> Pick an "easy" number between the two numbers, and add the distances from each of the numbers to the easy number.
   Example: For 532−497, choose 500 as the easy number. The distance from 532 to 500 is 32 and the distance from 497 to 500 is 3. The answer is therefore 32+3, which is 35.

10. <u>Division by Nines.</u> When dividing two numbers where the divisor's digits are all nines, we get a decimal where the dividend repeats, but the number of repeating digits must be equal to the number of nines.
    Example: $38 \div 99 = 0.\overline{38}$ **Example:** $417 \div 999 = 0.\overline{417}$ **Example:** $62 \div 999 = 0.\overline{062}$

11. <u>Multiplying by Nines.</u>
    Method #1: Multiply by 10, 100, or 1000, and then subtract the original number.
        Example: For 47·99, we do 100·47 − 47, which is 4700−47, giving an answer of 4653.
    Method #2 (for single digits): Multiply the single digit by 9, which gives us a two-digit answer. Then separate these two digits and insert one less nine than what was in the original problem.
        Example: For 8·9999, we multiply 8 times 9, which gives us 72. Then we insert three nines between the 7 and the 2, giving a final answer of 79,992.

12. <u>Reducing before Dividing.</u> Any division problem is viewed as a fraction that can often be reduced.
    Example: For 3500÷2800, we reduce the fraction to 5/4, which is 1¼ or 1.25.

13. <u>Multiplying by 5.</u> You take half the number, and then add a zero, or move the decimal point.
    Example: For 5·26, we take half of 26 to get 13, and then add a zero, giving us a result of 130.
    Example: For 5·4.18, half of 4.18 is 2.09, and moving the decimal point to the right one place gives 20.9.

14. <u>Dividing by 5.</u> Double the number, and then divide by ten (move the decimal one place to the left).
    Example: For 80÷5, we double 80 and then chop off a zero, giving a result of 16.
    Example: For 93÷5, we double 93 and then move the decimal point one place to the left to get 18.6.

---

[1] See *Rapid Math Tricks and Tips* by Edward H. Julius (John Wiley & Sons, 1992)

Seventh Grade Math Tricks

1. <u>Multiplying two numbers that are just one above and below a number that is easy to square.</u> The answer is one less than the square of the "easy" number between them.
   Example: For 29·31, we square 30, and then subtract 1, giving a result of 899.

2. <u>Multiplying by 25.</u> You can instead take half the number, two times, and then add two zeros.
   Example: For 25·48, take half of 48 to get 24, and half again to get 12. Adding two zeroes gives 1200.

3. <u>Squaring a number ending in 5.</u> Multiply the tens' digit by the next whole number, then place 25 at the end.
   Example: For 65^2, you multiply 6 times 7, which is 42, and then add 25 at the end to get 4225 as a result.

4. <u>Dividing by 25.</u> Instead, double the number two times, then divide by 100 (move decimal left two places).
   Example: For 108÷25, we double 108 to get 216, and then double it again to get 432. Our answer is 4.32.

5. <u>Multiplying a number by 15 (or 15%).</u> Multiply the number by ten, then add that product to half of itself.
   Example: For 32·15, we add 320 with 160 (which is ½ of 320), giving a result of 480.
   Example: For 15% of 420, we add 10% of 420 (which is 42) to half of that (which is 21), resulting in 63.

6. <u>Multiplying an even number by a number ending in 5.</u> Cut the even number in half, and double the number ending in 5. Multiply the results.
   Example: For 14·45, half of 14 is 7, and twice 45 is 90, giving a result of 7 times 90, which is 630.

7. <u>Dividing by a number ending in 5.</u> Double both numbers, then divide.
   Example: For 180÷45, we double both numbers, giving 360÷90, which is 4.

8. <u>Multiplying two numbers that have the same tens' digits and have ones' digits that add to 10.</u> Multiply the tens' digit by the next whole number, and then place the product of the ones' digits at the end, as two digits.
   Example: For 47·43, we do 4 times 5 (= 20), and then 7 times 3 (= 21), giving a result of 2021.

9. <u>Squaring a two-digit number beginning in 5.</u> Add 25 to the ones' digit, then place the square of the ones' digit (as two digits) at the end.
   Example: For 53^2, we add 25 + 3 (which is 28), then we square 3 (which is 09), giving a result of 2809.

10. <u>Multiplying two numbers that are an equal distance from a number that is easy to square.</u> Subtract the square of the distance from the square of the easy number.
    Example: For 34·26, we notice that the numbers are both 4 from 30. The result is $30^2 - 4^2 = 884$.

11. <u>Squaring a two-digit number ending in 1.</u> Write down a 1. Add the tens' digit to itself, and write down the ones' digit of that answer to the left of the 1 that was first written down, and carry a 1 if it was greater than ten. Now multiply the tens' digit by itself, and add 1 if you had a carry, and write down the result to the left of all that was previously written down. It's easier than you think!
    Example: For 71^2, we write down a 1, add 7 plus 7, write down the 4 (to the left of the original 1), and carry the 1. Lastly we multiply 7 times 7, and add the 1 that was carried. The answer is 5041.

12. <u>Multiplying by an "almost easy" number.</u> Do the multiplication with the easy number, and then adjust.
    Example: For 12·39, we see that 39 is almost 40, so we multiply 12 times 40 (which is 480), and then we adjust by subtracting 12 (because 480 is one 12 too much), giving 468 as our result.
    Example: For 25·31, we see that 31 is almost 30, so we multiply 25 times 30 (which is 750), and then add another 25, giving us a result of 775.

13. <u>Cross multiplying when multiplying two 2-digit numbers.</u> Multiply the 2 ones' digits to get the answer's ones' digit. Carry, if necessary. Cross-multiply to get the tens' digit (see example below). Carry, if necessary. Multiply the 2 numbers' tens' digits in order to get the hundreds' place in the answer.
    Example (without carrying): For 12·23, the answer has a ones' digit of 2 times 3 = <u>6</u>. Now we cross-multiply to get the answer's tens' digit, which is 2 times 2, plus 1 times 3, which is <u>7</u>. The answer's hundreds' place is just 1 times 2, which is <u>2</u>. Our final answer (see underlined digits) is then 276.
    Example (with carrying): For 47·28, we first multiply 7 times 8 (which is 56), which means the answer's ones' digit is <u>6</u> with a carry of 5.
    Then, we cross multiply for the tens' digit (see work at right), doing 7 times 2, plus 4 times 8, plus 5 (the carry), to get 51. This means that the answer's tens' place is <u>1</u>, with a carry of 5. Finally, we multiply 4 times 2 and add 5 (the carry), which gives <u>13</u>. The final answer (see underlined digits, above) is 1316.

The Archimedean Solids.... and their Duals

truncated tetrahedron

truncated octahedron

rhombicuboctahedron

truncated icosahedron

rhombicosidodecahedron

cuboctahedron

great rhombicuboctahedron

icosidodecahedron

great rhombicosidodecahedron

truncated cube

snub cube

truncated dodecahedron

snub dodecahedron

triakistetrahedron

tetrakishexahedron

trapezoidal icositetrahedron

pentakisdodecahedron

trapezoidal hexecontahedron

rhombic dodecahedron

triakisoctahedron

rhombic triacontahedron

hexakisoctahedron

hexakisicosahedron

pentagonal icositetrahedron

triakisicosahedron

pentagonal hexecontahedron

Polyhedron Nets

dodecahedron

icosahedron

truncated tetrahedron

truncated octahedron

cuboctahedron

truncated cube

triakistetrahedron

tetrakishexahedron

rhombic dodecahedron

triakisoctahedron

rhombicuboctahedron

great rhombicuboctahedron

snub cube

trapezoidal icositetrahedron

hexakisoctahedron

pentagonal icositetrahedron

truncated icosahedron

icosidodecahedron

truncated dodecahedron

pentakisdodecahedron

rhombic triacontahedron

triakisicosahedron

rhombicosidodecahedron

great rhombicosidodecahedron

snub dodecahedron

trapezoidal hexecontahedron

hexakisicosahedron

pentagonal hexecontahedron

Note: Some of the above nets are *not* drawn exactly to scale.

Patterns for the Archimedean Duals
(and some of the Archimedean Solids)

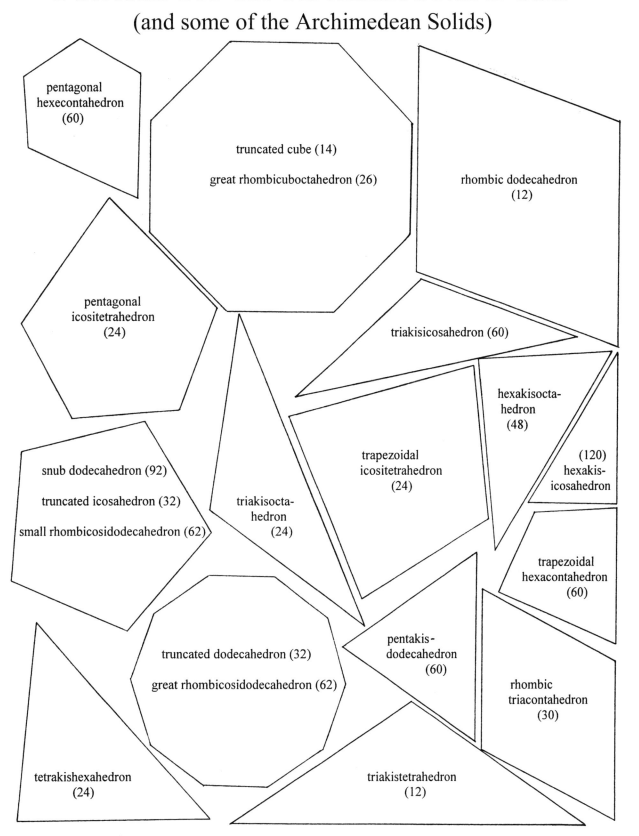

pentagonal
hexecontahedron
(60)

truncated cube (14)

great rhombicuboctahedron (26)

rhombic dodecahedron
(12)

pentagonal
icositetrahedron
(24)

triakisicosahedron (60)

hexakisocta-
hedron
(48)

(120)
hexakis-
icosahedron

snub dodecahedron (92)

truncated icosahedron (32)

small rhombicosidodecahedron (62)

trapezoidal
icositetrahedron
(24)

triakisocta-
hedron
(24)

trapezoidal
hexacontahedron
(60)

truncated dodecahedron (32)

great rhombicosidodecahedron (62)

pentakis-
dodecahedron
(60)

rhombic
triacontahedron
(30)

tetrakishexahedron
(24)

triakistetrahedron
(12)

Note: The number in the parenthesis indicates the number of faces on the solid.

π to 5000 Decimal Places

(Read *entire row* from left to right across the whole page.)

π is 3 point…

```
1415926535 8979323846 2643383279 5028841971 6939937510 5820974944 5923078164 0628620899 8628034825 3421170679
8214808651 3282306647 0938446095 5058223172 5359408128 4811174502 8410270193 8521105559 6446229489 5493038196
4428810975 6659334461 2847564823 3786783165 2712019091 4564856692 3460348610 4543266482 1339360726 0249141273
7245870066 0631558817 4881520920 9628292540 9171536436 7892590360 0113305305 4882046652 1384146951 9415116094
3305727036 5759591953 0921861173 8193261179 3105118548 0744623799 6274956735 1885752724 8912279381 8301194912
9833673362 4406566430 8602139494 6395224737 1907021798 6094370277 0539217176 2931767523 8467481846 7669405132
0005681271 4526356082 7785771342 7577896091 7363717872 1468440901 2249534301 4654958537 1050792279 6892589235
4201995611 2129021960 8640344181 5981362977 4771309960 5187072113 4999999837 2978049951 0597317328 1609631859
5024459455 3469083026 4252230825 3344685035 2619311881 7101000313 7838752886 5875332083 8142061717 7669147303
5982534904 2875546873 1159562863 8823537875 9375195778 1857780532 1712268066 1300192787 6611195909 2164201989

3809525720 1065485863 2788659361 5338182796 8230301952 0353018529 6899577362 2599413891 2497217752 8347913151
5574857242 4541506959 5082953311 6861727855 8890750983 8175463746 4939319255 0604009277 0167113900 9848824012
8583616035 6370766010 4710181942 9555961989 4676783744 9448255379 7747268471 0404753464 6208046684 2590694912
9331367702 8989152104 7521620569 6602405803 8150193511 2533824300 3558764024 7496473263 9141992726 0426992279
6782354781 6360093417 2164121992 4586315030 2861829745 5570674983 8505494588 5869269956 9092721079 7509302955
3211653449 8720275596 0236480665 4991198818 3479775356 6369807426 5425278625 5181841757 4672890977 7727938000
8164706001 6145249192 1732172147 7235014144 1973568548 1613611573 5255213347 5741849468 4385233239 0739414333
4547762416 8625189835 6948556209 9219222184 2725502542 5688767179 0494601653 4668049886 2723279178 6085784383
8279679766 8145410095 3883786360 9506800642 2512520511 7392984896 0841284886 2694560424 1965285022 2106611863
0674427862 2039194945 0471237137 8696095636 4371917287 4677646575 7396241389 0865832645 9958133904 7802759009

9465764078 9512694683 9835259570 9825822620 5224894077 2671947826 8482601476 9909026401 3639443745 5305068203
4962524517 4939965143 1429809190 6592509372 2169646151 5709858387 4105978859 5977297549 8930161753 9284681382
6868386894 2774155991 8559252459 5395943104 9972524680 8459872736 4469584865 3836736222 6260991246 0805124388
4390451244 1365497627 8079771569 1435997700 1296160894 4169486855 5848406353 4220722258 2848864815 8456028506
0168427394 5226746767 8895252138 5225499546 6672782398 6456596116 3548862305 7745649803 5593634568 1743241125
1507606947 9451096596 0940252288 7971089314 5669136867 2287489405 6010150330 8617928680 9208747609 1782493858
9009714909 6759825613 6554978189 3129784821 6829989487 2265880485 7564014270 4775551323 7964145152 3746234364
5428584447 9526586782 1051141354 7357395231 1342716610 2135969536 2314429524 8493718711 0145765403 5902799344
0374200731 0578539062 1983874478 0847848968 3321445713 8687519435 0643021845 3191048481 0053706146 8067491927
8191197939 9520614196 6342875444 0643745123 7181921799 9839101591 9561814675 1426912397 4894090718 6494231961

5679452080 9514655022 5231603881 9301420937 6213785595 6638937787 0830390697 9207734672 2182562599 6615014215
0306803844 7734549202 6054146659 2520149744 2850732518 6660021324 3408819071 0486331734 6496514539 0579626856
1005508106 6587969981 6357473638 4052571459 1028970641 4011097120 6280439039 7595156771 5770042033 7869936007
2305587631 7635942187 3125147120 5329281918 2618612586 7321579198 4148488291 6447060957 5270695722 0917567116
7229109816 9091528017 3506712748 5832228718 3520935396 5725121083 5791513698 8209144421 0067510334 6711031412
6711136990 8658516398 3150197016 5151168517 1437657618 3515565088 4909989859 9823873455 2833163550 7647918535
8932261854 8963213293 3089857064 2046752590 7091548141 6549859461 6371802709 8199430992 4488957571 2828905923
2332609729 9712084433 5732654893 8239119325 9746366730 5836041428 1388303203 8249037589 8524374417 0291327656
1809377344 4030707469 2112019130 2033038019 7621101100 4492932151 6084244485 9637669838 9522868478 3123552658
2131449576 8572624334 4189303968 6426243410 7732269780 2807318915 4411010446 8232527162 0105265227 2111660396

6655730925 4711055785 3763466820 6531098965 2691862056 4769312570 5863566201 8558100729 3606598764 8611791045
3348850346 1136576867 5324944166 8039626579 7877185560 8455296541 2665408530 6143444318 5867697514 5661406800
7002378776 5913440171 2749470420 5622305389 9456131407 1127000407 8547332699 3908145466 4645880797 2708266830
6343285878 5698305235 8089330657 5740679545 7163775254 2021149557 6158140025 0126228594 1302164715 5097925923
0990796547 3761255176 5675135751 7829666454 7791745011 2996148903 0463994713 2962107340 4375189573 5961458901
9389713111 7904297828 5647503203 1986915140 2870808599 0480109412 1472213179 4764777262 2414254854 5403321571
8530614228 8137585043 0633217518 2979866223 7172159160 7716692547 4873898665 4949450114 6540628433 6639379003
9769265672 1463853067 3609657120 9180763832 7166416274 8888007869 2560290228 4721040317 2118608204 1900042296
6171196377 9213375751 1495950156 6049631862 9472654736 4252308177 0367515906 7350235072 8354056704 0386743513
6222447715 8915049530 9844489333 0963408780 7693259939 7805419341 4473774418 4263129860 8099888687 4132604721 ...
```

And we're still not even a millionth of the way done!

Multiplication Tables for Number Bases

Octal Times Table

	0	1	2	3	4	5	6	7
0	0	0	0	0	0	0	0	0
1	0	1	2	3	4	5	6	7
2	0	2	4	6	10	12	14	16
3	0	3	6	11	14	17	22	25
4	0	4	10	14	20	24	30	34
5	0	5	12	17	24	31	36	43
6	0	6	14	22	30	36	44	52
7	0	7	16	25	34	43	52	61

Base-Five Times Table

	0	1	2	3	4
0	0	0	0	0	0
1	0	1	2	3	4
2	0	2	4	11	13
3	0	3	11	14	22
4	0	4	13	22	31

Binary Table

	0	1
0	0	0
1	0	1

Hexadecimal Times Table

	0	1	2	3	4	5	6	7	8	9	A	B	C	D	E	F
0	0	0	0	0	0	0	0	0	0	0	0	0	0	0	0	0
1	0	1	2	3	4	5	6	7	8	9	A	B	C	D	E	F
2	0	2	4	6	8	A	C	E	10	12	14	16	18	1A	1C	1E
3	0	3	6	9	C	F	12	15	18	1B	1E	21	24	27	2A	2D
4	0	4	8	C	10	14	18	1C	20	24	28	2C	30	34	38	3C
5	0	5	A	F	14	19	1E	23	28	2D	32	37	3C	41	46	4B
6	0	6	C	12	18	1E	24	2A	30	36	3C	42	48	4E	54	5A
7	0	7	E	15	1C	23	2A	31	38	3F	46	4D	54	5B	62	69
8	0	8	10	18	20	28	30	38	40	48	50	58	60	68	70	78
9	0	9	12	1B	24	2D	36	3F	48	51	5A	63	6C	75	7E	87
A	0	A	14	1E	28	32	3C	46	50	5A	64	6E	78	82	8C	96
B	0	B	16	21	2C	37	42	4D	58	63	6E	79	84	8F	9A	A5
C	0	C	18	24	30	3C	48	54	60	6C	78	84	90	9C	A8	B4
D	0	D	1A	27	34	41	4E	5B	68	75	82	8F	9C	A9	B6	C3
E	0	E	1C	2A	38	46	54	62	70	7E	8C	9A	A8	B6	C4	D2
F	0	F	1E	2D	3C	4B	5A	69	78	87	96	A5	B4	C3	D2	E1

Place Value (exponent) Table

10	9	8	7	6	5	4	3	2	1	0	BASE
1024	512	256	128	64	32	16	8	4	2	1	2
					3125	625	125	25	5	1	5
					32768	4096	512	64	8	1	8
					100000	10000	1000	100	10	1	10
						65536	4096	256	16	1	16

ASCII Code Table

Note: All codes are given in hexadecimal. Each hexadecimal digit can easily be converted to binary by using the table at the bottom of the page. For example, the character "n" has an ASCII hexadecimal code 6E. Looking at the bottom of the page, we see that 6 is 0110 and that E is 1110. Therefore, the binary ASCII code for "n" is 01101110. Note, also, that this table is incomplete. A full ASCII code table includes 256 codes, since there are 256 possible codes for one byte, which is an 8-digit binary code.

Hex	Char	Hex	Char	Hex	Char	Hex	Char	Hex	Char	Hex	Char
20	space	30	0	40	@	50	P	60	`	70	p
21	!	31	1	41	A	51	Q	61	a	71	q
22	"	32	2	42	B	52	R	62	b	72	r
23	#	33	3	43	C	53	S	63	c	73	s
24	$	34	4	44	D	54	T	64	d	74	t
25	%	35	5	45	E	55	U	65	e	75	u
26	&	36	6	46	F	56	V	66	f	76	v
27	'	37	7	47	G	57	W	67	g	77	w
28	(	38	8	48	H	58	X	68	h	78	x
29	)	39	9	49	I	59	Y	69	i	79	y
2A	*	3A	:	4A	J	5A	Z	6A	j	7A	z
2B	+	3B	;	4B	K	5B	[	6B	k	7B	{
2C	,	3C	<	4C	L	5C	\	6C	l	7C		
2D	-	3D	=	4D	M	5D	]	6D	m	7D	}
2E	.	3E	>	4E	N	5E	^	6E	n	7E	~
2F	/	3F	?	4F	O	5F	_	6F	o	7F	del

Binary/Hexadecimal Conversion Table

Binary	Hexadecimal	Binary	Hexadecimal
0000	0	1000	8
0001	1	1001	9
0010	2	1010	A
0011	3	1011	B
0100	4	1100	C
0101	5	1101	D
0110	6	1110	E
0111	7	1111	F

An Algorithm for Addition

This algorithm is for the addition of two whole numbers.

1. Write the smaller number under the larger number, right justified. Put a "+" sign to the left of the smaller number, and draw a horizontal line under the smaller number.
2. Start with the right-most column of digits.
3. Add together the digits in the current column (assume 0 for any missing digit), including any carry.
4. Write the last digit of the sum under the two digits just added together. If the sum was greater than 10, then carry a one by writing a "1" at the top of the next column.
5. Move to the next column.
6. If there is anything in the column (digits or carry), then goto step 3.
7. The answer (sum of the two numbers) is given below the line.

An Algorithm for Long Division

This algorithm assumes that both the divisor and the dividend are integers greater than zero, and that the dividend is larger than the divisor. If there is a remainder, the answer is written as a mixed number.

1. Draw a short vertical line and write the divisor to the left of it, and the dividend to the right of it. Draw another line starting from the top of the first line, so that it goes over the top of the dividend.
2. Put a small x and a dot just to the left of the left-most digit of the dividend.
3. Move the dot one digit to the right.
4. The number formed by the digits between the dot and the x is called R. If R forms a number that is smaller than the divisor, goto step 3.
5. Above the horizontal line, and directly over the digit just to the left of the dot, write the largest digit that can be multiplied by the divisor giving a product less than R.
6. Write this product under R such that it is right justified with R.
7. Subtract the product from R, and write this difference down underneath the product, right justified. This is the new value for R.
8. If there are more digits to the right of the dot:
   a) Write the next digit of the dividend (the digit just to the right of the dot) at the end of R.
   b) Move the dot one place to the right.
   c) Goto step 5.
9. If R is not equal to zero, then to the right of the digits on top of the horizontal line add a fraction that has R as its numerator, and the divisor as its denominator.
10. The final answer (dividend ÷ divisor) is above the horizontal line.

An Algorithm for Prime Numbers

Follow the directions carefully in order to find all the prime numbers up to 500. Those who want a bit more of a challenge should go up to 1000 (which involves less than 50 multiplications).

1. How far are you going up to? This is N.
2. Find the square root of N. This number without the decimal places is M. (e.g., If N is 500, then M is 22. If N is 1000, then M is 31.)
3. Write down 2 and the odd numbers up to N in a grid. (To save time, the grid is given below. Cross out all the numbers that are larger than N, if N is less than 1000.) Circle 2, which is the first number in the grid.
4. B is the first non-circled, non-crossed-out number. If B is greater than M, then goto step 9.
5. Circle B.
6. If B is less than 12, then cross out multiples of B, starting at B^2 and continuing until you have gone past N. Look for patterns! (This step saves *us* time compared with step 7, but is tough for computers. Why?)
7. If B is greater than 12, then multiply B by all non-crossed numbers starting with B itself (giving B^2) and working up. Cross out each product that you find. (Note: This step needs adjustment if $N \geq 13^3$, which is 2197. This is because this algorithm is not designed to cross out cubes, or larger powers, of primes.)
8. Go to step 4.
9. Circle all non-crossed-out numbers. The numbers that are circled are the prime numbers.

```
  2   3   5   7   9  11  13  15  17  19  21  23  25  27  29  31  33  35  37  39
 41  43  45  47  49  51  53  55  57  59  61  63  65  67  69  71  73  75  77  79
 81  83  85  87  89  91  93  95  97  99 101 103 105 107 109 111 113 115 117 119
121 123 125 127 129 131 133 135 137 139 141 143 145 147 149 151 153 155 157 159
161 163 165 167 169 171 173 175 177 179 181 183 185 187 189 191 193 195 197 199
201 203 205 207 209 211 213 215 217 219 221 223 225 227 229 231 233 235 237 239
241 243 245 247 249 251 253 255 257 259 261 263 265 267 269 271 273 275 277 279
281 283 285 287 289 291 293 295 297 299 301 303 305 307 309 311 313 315 317 319
321 323 325 327 329 331 333 335 337 339 341 343 345 347 349 351 353 355 357 359
361 363 365 367 369 371 373 375 377 379 381 383 385 387 389 391 393 395 397 399
401 403 405 407 409 411 413 415 417 419 421 423 425 427 429 431 433 435 437 439
441 443 445 447 449 451 453 455 457 459 461 463 465 467 469 471 473 475 477 479
481 483 485 487 489 491 493 495 497 499 501 503 505 507 509 511 513 515 517 519
521 523 525 527 529 531 533 535 537 539 541 543 545 547 549 551 553 555 557 559
561 563 565 567 569 571 573 575 577 579 581 583 585 587 589 591 593 595 597 599
601 603 605 607 609 611 613 615 617 619 621 623 625 627 629 631 633 635 637 639
641 643 645 647 649 651 653 655 657 659 661 663 665 667 669 671 673 675 677 679
681 683 685 687 689 691 693 695 697 699 701 703 705 707 709 711 713 715 717 719
721 723 725 727 729 731 733 735 737 739 741 743 745 747 749 751 753 755 757 759
761 763 765 767 769 771 773 775 777 779 781 783 785 787 789 791 793 795 797 799
801 803 805 807 809 811 813 815 817 819 821 823 825 827 829 831 833 835 837 839
841 843 845 847 849 851 853 855 857 859 861 863 865 867 869 871 873 875 877 879
881 883 885 887 889 891 893 895 897 899 901 903 905 907 909 911 913 915 917 919
921 923 925 927 929 931 933 935 937 939 941 943 945 947 949 951 953 955 957 959
961 963 965 967 969 971 973 975 977 979 981 983 985 987 989 991 993 995 997 999
```

The Square Root Algorithm (without zeroes)
(Written in the style of a computer program. For Eighth grade.)

Note: As you follow the algorithm below you will need to carefully keep track of the following variables:
R, X, Y, *Difference, Sum, Product*

1. Enclose the number in a "house" as you would enclose a long division problem. Starting at the decimal point, and working out in both directions, draw short vertical lines that separate the number into pairs of two digits. Make sure that there are at least as many digit-pairs after the decimal place as the number of decimal places that are needed in the answer. Add ending zeroes, if needed. (e.g., In order to calculate $\sqrt{45}$ to three decimal, we would need to add three pairs of ending zeroes and do $\sqrt{45.\,00\,00\,00}$.)

2. Let R be equal to the left-most digit-pair (which may be a single digit) that is inside the "house". Circle it. Draw a small box, large enough to hold one digit, well to the left of R.

3. Let X be a single digit (somewhere from 0 to 9), such that it is as large as possible, but X^2 is still less than or equal to R. Write X both in the box, and immediately below the box.

4. Underneath the digit that is below the box, write down the *Sum* of X plus X. Write the result of squaring X below R, and below that, write the *Difference* of R minus the square of X.

5. If there are no more digit pairs to bring down, then goto step 11.

6. Bring down the next digit-pair, combining it with, and writing it next to, the *Difference* (that was just found). This now forms the new value for R. Circle it.

7. Draw a small box to the right of the *Sum*. If the digit-pair just brought down is the first one after the decimal place, then write a decimal point above this box.

8. We must now choose a special single digit (somewhere between 0 and 9) that will be written both in the box and directly below the box. This special digit below the box will be called Y, and the new value for X will be the result of taking the *Sum* (found to the left of the box), and attaching to the end of it, the special digit in the box. (This means that Y will be equal to the last digit of the new value for X.) This special digit is chosen such that the result of X times Y is as large as possible, but still less than or equal to R. Write the correct choice for this special digit both in the box and below the box.

9. Underneath R, write the *Product* of X times Y, and then subtract it from R, writing this new *Difference* underneath it all.

10. Underneath X and Y, write the *Sum* of X plus Y. Goto step 5.

11. The answer to the square root problem is found by reading the digits in the boxes from top to bottom, with the decimal point possibly in the middle. If the *Difference* is zero, then the answer is exact; otherwise it is an approximation.

Example: Calculate $\sqrt{780.0849}$

Solution: The work is shown below. The values for R are circled. The Y values (2, 7, 9, 3) are the single digits immediately below the boxes. The X values (2, 47, 549, 5583) are the numbers ending with the digit in the box. Each step number corresponds to the step number in the above algorithm.

Step1: The number is divided into 4 digit-pairs. Step2: R=7. Step3: X=2. Step4: *Sum*=4, *Difference*=3. Step6: R=380. Step8: Trying different "special" digits, we see that 48·8 is bigger than R, and 47·7 is less than R. The correct special digit is therefore 7, which we write both in the

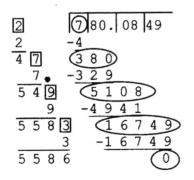

box and below the box. Step9: The product of 47·7 (329) is written below R. The *Difference* is 51. Step10: The *Sum* of 47+7 (54) is written below. We go back up to step5. Step6: R=5108. Step7: We write a decimal point above the box. Step8: The special digit is 9, making X=549 and Y=9. Step9: *Difference*=167. Step10: *Sum*=558. Step6: R=16749. Step8: X=5583, Y=3. Step9: *Difference*=0. Step10: *Sum*=5586, goto step5. Step5: goto step11. Step11: **Our final answer is 27.93** (exactly).

Table of Squares

$1^2 = 1$	$21^2 = 441$	$41^2 = 1681$	$61^2 = 3721$	$81^2 = 6561$
$2^2 = 4$	$22^2 = 484$	$42^2 = 1764$	$62^2 = 3844$	$82^2 = 6724$
$3^2 = 9$	$23^2 = 529$	$43^2 = 1849$	$63^2 = 3969$	$83^2 = 6889$
$4^2 = 16$	$24^2 = 576$	$44^2 = 1936$	$64^2 = 4096$	$84^2 = 7056$
$5^2 = 25$	$25^2 = 625$	$45^2 = 2025$	$65^2 = 4225$	$85^2 = 7225$
$6^2 = 36$	$26^2 = 676$	$46^2 = 2116$	$66^2 = 4356$	$86^2 = 7396$
$7^2 = 49$	$27^2 = 729$	$47^2 = 2209$	$67^2 = 4489$	$87^2 = 7569$
$8^2 = 64$	$28^2 = 784$	$48^2 = 2304$	$68^2 = 4624$	$88^2 = 7744$
$9^2 = 81$	$29^2 = 841$	$49^2 = 2401$	$69^2 = 4761$	$89^2 = 7921$
$10^2 = 100$	$30^2 = 900$	$50^2 = 2500$	$70^2 = 4900$	$90^2 = 8100$
$11^2 = 121$	$31^2 = 961$	$51^2 = 2601$	$71^2 = 5041$	$91^2 = 8281$
$12^2 = 144$	$32^2 = 1024$	$52^2 = 2704$	$72^2 = 5184$	$92^2 = 8464$
$13^2 = 169$	$33^2 = 1089$	$53^2 = 2809$	$73^2 = 5329$	$93^2 = 8649$
$14^2 = 196$	$34^2 = 1156$	$54^2 = 2916$	$74^2 = 5476$	$94^2 = 8836$
$15^2 = 225$	$35^2 = 1225$	$55^2 = 3025$	$75^2 = 5625$	$95^2 = 9025$
$16^2 = 256$	$36^2 = 1296$	$56^2 = 3136$	$76^2 = 5776$	$96^2 = 9216$
$17^2 = 289$	$37^2 = 1369$	$57^2 = 3249$	$77^2 = 5929$	$97^2 = 9409$
$18^2 = 324$	$38^2 = 1444$	$58^2 = 3364$	$78^2 = 6084$	$98^2 = 9604$
$19^2 = 361$	$39^2 = 1521$	$59^2 = 3481$	$79^2 = 6241$	$99^2 = 9801$
$20^2 = 400$	$40^2 = 1600$	$60^2 = 3600$	$80^2 = 6400$	$100^2 = 10000$

Pythagorean Triples

3,4,5
5,12,13
8,15,17
7,24,25
20,21,29
12,35,37
9,40,41
28,45,53
11,60,61
16,63,65
33,56,65
48,55,73
13,84,85
36,77,85
39,80,89
65,72,97

Table of Square Roots

$\sqrt{1} = 1.000$	$\sqrt{21} = 4.583$	$\sqrt{41} = 6.403$	$\sqrt{61} = 7.810$	$\sqrt{81} = 9.000$
$\sqrt{2} = 1.414$	$\sqrt{22} = 4.690$	$\sqrt{42} = 6.481$	$\sqrt{62} = 7.874$	$\sqrt{82} = 9.055$
$\sqrt{3} = 1.732$	$\sqrt{23} = 4.796$	$\sqrt{43} = 6.557$	$\sqrt{63} = 7.937$	$\sqrt{83} = 9.110$
$\sqrt{4} = 2.000$	$\sqrt{24} = 4.899$	$\sqrt{44} = 6.633$	$\sqrt{64} = 8.000$	$\sqrt{84} = 9.165$
$\sqrt{5} = 2.236$	$\sqrt{25} = 5.000$	$\sqrt{45} = 6.708$	$\sqrt{65} = 8.062$	$\sqrt{85} = 9.220$
$\sqrt{6} = 2.449$	$\sqrt{26} = 5.099$	$\sqrt{46} = 6.782$	$\sqrt{66} = 8.124$	$\sqrt{86} = 9.274$
$\sqrt{7} = 2.646$	$\sqrt{27} = 5.196$	$\sqrt{47} = 6.856$	$\sqrt{67} = 8.185$	$\sqrt{87} = 9.327$
$\sqrt{8} = 2.828$	$\sqrt{28} = 5.292$	$\sqrt{48} = 6.928$	$\sqrt{68} = 8.246$	$\sqrt{88} = 9.381$
$\sqrt{9} = 3.000$	$\sqrt{29} = 5.385$	$\sqrt{49} = 7.000$	$\sqrt{69} = 8.307$	$\sqrt{89} = 9.434$
$\sqrt{10} = 3.162$	$\sqrt{30} = 5.477$	$\sqrt{50} = 7.071$	$\sqrt{70} = 8.367$	$\sqrt{90} = 9.487$
$\sqrt{11} = 3.317$	$\sqrt{31} = 5.568$	$\sqrt{51} = 7.141$	$\sqrt{71} = 8.426$	$\sqrt{91} = 9.539$
$\sqrt{12} = 3.464$	$\sqrt{32} = 5.657$	$\sqrt{52} = 7.211$	$\sqrt{72} = 8.485$	$\sqrt{92} = 9.592$
$\sqrt{13} = 3.606$	$\sqrt{33} = 5.745$	$\sqrt{53} = 7.280$	$\sqrt{73} = 8.544$	$\sqrt{93} = 9.644$
$\sqrt{14} = 3.742$	$\sqrt{34} = 5.831$	$\sqrt{54} = 7.348$	$\sqrt{74} = 8.602$	$\sqrt{94} = 9.695$
$\sqrt{15} = 3.873$	$\sqrt{35} = 5.916$	$\sqrt{55} = 7.416$	$\sqrt{75} = 8.660$	$\sqrt{95} = 9.747$
$\sqrt{16} = 4.000$	$\sqrt{36} = 6.000$	$\sqrt{56} = 7.483$	$\sqrt{76} = 8.718$	$\sqrt{96} = 9.798$
$\sqrt{17} = 4.123$	$\sqrt{37} = 6.083$	$\sqrt{57} = 7.550$	$\sqrt{77} = 8.775$	$\sqrt{97} = 9.849$
$\sqrt{18} = 4.243$	$\sqrt{38} = 6.164$	$\sqrt{58} = 7.616$	$\sqrt{78} = 8.832$	$\sqrt{98} = 9.899$
$\sqrt{19} = 4.359$	$\sqrt{39} = 6.245$	$\sqrt{59} = 7.681$	$\sqrt{79} = 8.888$	$\sqrt{99} = 9.950$
$\sqrt{20} = 4.472$	$\sqrt{40} = 6.325$	$\sqrt{60} = 7.746$	$\sqrt{80} = 8.944$	$\sqrt{100} = 10.000$

Note: If there are ending zeroes inside the square root, then you can remove an even number of zeroes from inside, which will result in half as many zeroes (or moving the decimal place half as many places) in your answer.

Examples:

With $\sqrt{25000000}$ we remove 6 zeroes, then adding 3 zeroes to $\sqrt{25}$, gives an answer of 5000.

With $\sqrt{60000}$ we remove 4 zeroes. Since $\sqrt{6}$ is 2.449, we move 2 decimal places to get 244.9.

With $\sqrt{600000}$ we remove 4 zeroes. Since $\sqrt{60}$ is 7.746, we move 2 decimal places to get 774.6.

Note: This table should not be used if, after removing an <u>even</u> number of zeroes, there are more than two digits inside the square root. For example, it *can* be used for $\sqrt{58000000}$, but *cannot* be used for $\sqrt{58700}$ or for $\sqrt{580}$ or for $\sqrt{5800000}$.

Growth Rate Table giving values for $(1+r)^t$ from the formula $P = P_0(1+r)^t$

$(1+r)$

t	1.01	1.02	1.025	1.03	1.035	1.04	1.05	1.06	1.07	1.08	1.09	1.1	1.15	1.2	1.25	1.3	1.4	1.5	2
2	1.0201	1.0404	1.05063	1.0609	1.07123	1.0816	1.1025	1.1236	1.1449	1.1664	1.1881	1.21	1.3225	1.44	1.5625	1.69	1.96	2.25	4
3	1.0303	1.06121	1.07689	1.09273	1.10872	1.12486	1.15763	1.19102	1.22504	1.25971	1.29503	1.331	1.52088	1.728	1.95313	2.197	2.744	3.375	8
4	1.0406	1.08243	1.10381	1.12551	1.14752	1.16986	1.21551	1.26248	1.3108	1.36049	1.41158	1.4641	1.74901	2.0736	2.44141	2.8561	3.8416	5.0625	16
5	1.05101	1.10408	1.13141	1.15927	1.18769	1.21665	1.27628	1.33823	1.40255	1.46933	1.53862	1.61051	2.01136	2.48832	3.05176	3.71293	5.37824	7.59375	32
6	1.06152	1.12616	1.15969	1.19405	1.22926	1.26532	1.34009	1.41852	1.50073	1.58687	1.6771	1.77156	2.31306	2.98598	3.8147	4.82681	7.52954	11.3906	64
7	1.07214	1.14869	1.18869	1.22987	1.27228	1.31593	1.4071	1.50363	1.60578	1.71382	1.82804	1.94872	2.66002	3.58318	4.76837	6.27485	10.5414	17.0859	128
8	1.08286	1.17166	1.2184	1.26677	1.31681	1.36857	1.47746	1.59385	1.71819	1.85093	1.99256	2.14359	3.05902	4.29982	5.96046	8.15731	14.7579	25.6289	256
9	1.09369	1.19509	1.24886	1.30477	1.3629	1.42331	1.55133	1.68948	1.83846	1.999	2.17189	2.35795	3.51788	5.15978	7.45058	10.6045	20.661	38.4434	512
10	1.10462	1.21899	1.28008	1.34392	1.4106	1.48024	1.62889	1.79085	1.96715	2.15892	2.36736	2.59374	4.04556	6.19174	9.31323	13.7858	28.9255	57.665	1024
11	1.11567	1.24337	1.31209	1.38423	1.45997	1.53945	1.71034	1.8983	2.10485	2.33164	2.58043	2.85312	4.65239	7.43008	11.6415	17.9216	40.4957	86.4976	2048
12	1.12683	1.26824	1.34489	1.42576	1.51107	1.60103	1.79586	2.0122	2.25219	2.51817	2.81266	3.13843	5.35025	8.9161	14.5519	23.2981	56.6939	129.746	4096
13	1.13809	1.29361	1.37851	1.46853	1.56396	1.66507	1.88565	2.13293	2.40985	2.71962	3.0658	3.45227	6.15279	10.6993	18.1899	30.2875	79.3715	194.62	8192
14	1.14947	1.31948	1.41297	1.51259	1.61869	1.73168	1.97993	2.2609	2.57853	2.93719	3.34173	3.7975	7.07571	12.8392	22.7374	39.3738	111.12	291.929	16384
15	1.16097	1.34587	1.4483	1.55797	1.67535	1.80094	2.07893	2.39656	2.75903	3.17217	3.64248	4.17725	8.13706	15.407	28.4217	51.1859	155.568	437.894	32768
16	1.17258	1.37279	1.48451	1.60471	1.73399	1.87298	2.18287	2.54035	2.95216	3.42594	3.97031	4.59497	9.35762	18.4884	35.5271	66.5417	217.795	656.841	65536
17	1.1843	1.40024	1.52162	1.65285	1.79468	1.9479	2.29202	2.69277	3.15882	3.70002	4.32763	5.05447	10.7613	22.1861	44.4089	86.5042	304.913	985.261	131072
18	1.19615	1.42825	1.55966	1.70243	1.85749	2.02582	2.40662	2.85434	3.37993	3.99602	4.71712	5.55992	12.3755	26.6233	55.5112	112.455	426.879	1477.89	262144
19	1.20811	1.45681	1.59865	1.75351	1.9225	2.10685	2.52695	3.0256	3.61653	4.3157	5.14166	6.11591	14.2318	31.948	69.3889	146.192	597.63	2216.84	524288
20	1.22019	1.48595	1.63862	1.80611	1.98979	2.19112	2.6533	3.20714	3.86968	4.66096	5.60441	6.7275	16.3665	38.3376	86.7362	190.05	836.683	3325.26	1048576
25	1.28243	1.64061	1.85394	2.09378	2.36324	2.66584	3.38635	4.29187	5.42743	6.84848	8.62308	10.8347	32.919	95.3962	264.698	705.641	4499.88	25251.2	3.4E+07
30	1.34785	1.81136	2.09757	2.42726	2.80679	3.2434	4.32194	5.74349	7.61226	10.0627	13.2677	17.4494	66.2118	237.376	807.794	2620	24201.4	191751	1.1E+09
40	1.48886	2.20804	2.68506	3.26204	3.95926	4.80102	7.03999	10.2857	14.9745	21.7245	31.4094	45.2593	267.864	1469.77	7523.16	36118.9	700038	1.1E+07	1.1E+12
50	1.64463	2.69159	3.43711	4.38391	5.58493	7.10668	11.4674	18.4202	29.457	46.9016	74.3575	117.391	1083.66	9100.44	70064.9	497929	2E+07	6.4E+08	1.1E+15
60	1.8167	3.28103	4.39979	5.8916	7.87809	10.5196	18.6792	32.9877	57.9464	101.257	176.031	304.482	4384	56347.5	652530	6864377	5.9E+08	3.7E+10	1.2E+18
80	2.21672	4.87544	7.20957	10.6409	15.6757	23.0498	49.5614	105.796	224.234	471.955	986.552	2048.4	71750.9	2160228	5.7E+07	1.3E+09	4.9E+11	1.2E+14	1.2E+24
100	2.70481	7.24465	11.8137	19.2186	31.1914	50.5049	131.501	339.302	867.716	2199.76	5529.04	13780.6	1174313	8.3E+07	4.9E+09	2.5E+11	4.1E+14	4.1E+17	1.3E+30
150	4.44842	19.4996	40.605	84.2527	174.202	358.923	1507.98	6250	25560.3	103172	411126	1617718	1.3E+09	7.5E+11	3.4E+14	1.2E+17	8.3E+21	2.6E+26	1.4E+45
200	7.31602	52.4849	139.564	369.356	972.904	2550.75	17292.6	115126	752932	4838950	3.1E+07	1.9E+08	1.4E+12	6.9E+15	2.4E+19	6.1E+22	1.7E+29	1.7E+35	1.6E+60

Note: The cell on the bottom right is 1.6E+60, which means $1.6 \cdot 10^{60}$, and is scientific notation for
The last column is where (r+1) is 2, or r = 1, which means 100% annual growth, or doubling.

Conversion Table

* Denotes that it should be memorized as given in parentheses.

Weight
* * 1 lb = 16 oz
* * 1 kg ≈ 2.2046 (2.2) lb
* * 1 oz ≈ 28.35 g
*   1 g ≈ 0.0353 oz
*   1 lb ≈ 0.4536 kg
* * 1 U.S. ton = 2000 lb
* * 1 metric ton = 1000 kg

Volume
* * 1 tablespoon = 3 teaspoons
* * 1 fl oz = 2 tablespoons
* * 1 cup = 8 fl oz
* * 1 pt = 2 cups = 16 fl oz
* * 1 qt = 2 pt = 32 fl oz
* * 1 gal = 4 qt = 128 fl oz ≈ 3.785 ℓ
* * 1 mℓ = 1cm^3 (exactly!)
* * 1 ℓ ≈ 1.0567 (1.06) qt ≈ 33.8 fl oz
*   1 fl oz ≈ 29.58 mℓ ≈ 1.804 in^3
*   1 qt ≈ 57.75 in^3 ≈ 0.9464 ℓ
*   1 gal ≈ 231.0 in^3 ≈ 0.134 ft^3
*   1 ft^3 = 1728 in^3 ≈ 7.481 gal
*   1 in^3 ≈ 0.554 fl oz ≈ 16.39 cm^3
*   1 m^3 = 1000 ℓ ≈ 35.31 ft^3
*   1 cord (of wood) = 128 ft^3

Area
* * 1 acre ≈ area of square with side of 70 yards
* * 1 hectare = 10,000 m^2 (100m·100m) ≈ 2.471 acres
*   1 acre = 4840 yd^2 ≈ 0.405 hectare
*   1 mile^2 = 640 acres ≈ 2.590 km^2
*   1 ft^2 = 144 in^2
*   1 m^2 = 10,000 cm^2 ≈ 10.764 ft^2
*   1 in^2 ≈ 6.452 cm^2

Length
* * 1 yd = 36 in
* * 1 in ≈ 2.5400 (2.54) cm
* * 1 m ≈ 3.2808 (3.28) ft
* * 1 mile = 5280 feet ≈ 1.6093 (1.61) km
* * 1 km ≈ 0.6214 (0.62) mi
*   1 cm ≈ 0.39370 in
*   1 m ≈ 39.370 in ≈ 1.09yd
*   1 ft ≈ 0.3048m

Speed
1 m/s = 3.6 km/h ≈ 2.237 mph ≈ 3.281 ft/sec

Density[1]
Density conversion factors:

$$1\frac{g}{cm^3} = 1000\frac{kg}{m^3} \approx 62.43\frac{lb}{ft^3} \approx 0.578\frac{oz}{in^3}$$

$$1\frac{oz}{in^3} \approx 1.73\frac{g}{cm^3}$$

Water[1] (at a maximum density of 4°C)

$$= 1\frac{g}{cm^3} \text{ or } 1\frac{kg}{\ell} \text{ or } 1000\frac{kg}{m^3}$$

$$\approx 0.578\frac{oz}{in^3} \text{ or } 1.043\frac{oz}{fl oz}$$

$$\approx 62.43\frac{lb}{ft^3} \text{ or } 8.345\frac{lb}{gal}$$

Air	1.29$\frac{oz}{ft^3}$ or 1.29$\frac{kg}{m^3}$ (coincidentally!)	
Aluminum	169$\frac{lb}{ft^3}$ or	2.70$\frac{g}{cm^3}$
Iron	443$\frac{lb}{ft^3}$ or	7.10$\frac{g}{cm^3}$
Mercury	843$\frac{lb}{ft^3}$ or	13.5$\frac{g}{cm^3}$
Gold	1204$\frac{lb}{ft^3}$ or	19.3$\frac{g}{cm^3}$

Useful Distances

Average Radius of the Earth:	3960 mi (6371 km)
Polar Circumference of Earth:	24859 mi (40,005 km)
Equatorial Circum. of Earth:	24902 mi (40,076 km)
Surface Area of the Earth:	197,000,000 mi^2 (510,000,000 km^2)
Total land area of the Earth:	57,500,000 mi^2 (149,000,000 km^2)
Radius of the Sun:	432,000 mi (696,000 km)
Radius of the Moon:	1080 mi (1738 km)
Distance to the Moon:	239,000 mi (384,400 km)
Distance to the Sun:	93,000,000 mi (150,000,000 km)
One light year:	5.8784x10^{12} mi (9.46x10^{12} km)
Distance to the nearest star:	2.53x10^{13} mi (4.07x10^{13} km)

Temperature Conversions
$$C = {}^5/_9 (F - 32)$$
$$F = {}^9/_5 C + 32$$

---

[1] Density always reads as weight per volume. For example, the density of gold is 1204 lb/ft^3, which tells us that a cubic foot of gold weighs 1204 pounds. The density of gold can also be given as 19.3 g/cm^3, which says that a cubic centimeter weighs 19.3 grams.
* Note that water has a density of exactly 1 oz/fl.oz. at 212°F when it is *least* dense.
* It is perhaps more useful to give densities in terms of g/cm^3 because we can easily compare it to water, which has a density of exactly 1 g/cm^3 (1 cm^3 of water weighs 1 gram). For example, with gold's density of 19.3 g/cm^3, we can say that gold is 19.3 times heavier than water.

Suggested Reading

von Baravalle, Hermann. <u>Geometric Drawing and the Waldorf Plan</u>. Rudolf Steiner College Publications, 1991
ISBN: 0-945803-16-8.

von Baravalle, Hermann. <u>The Waldorf Approach to Arithmetic</u>. Parker Courtney Press, 1996
ISBN: 1-888182-51-2.

von Baravalle, Hermann. <u>Perspective Drawing</u>. Rudolf Steiner College Press, 2000. ISBN: 0-945803-50-8.

Diggins, Julia. <u>String, Straightedge, and Shadow – The Story of Geometry</u>. Jamie York Press, 2003.

Franceschelli, Amos. <u>Algebra, Mathematics for grades 6, 7,and 8</u>. AWSNA and Mercury Press, 1985.

Holden, Alan. <u>Shapes, Space, and Symmetry</u>. Dover Publications, 1995. ISBN: 0-486-26851-9.

Jarman, Ron. <u>Teaching Mathematics in Rudolf Steiner Schools for Classes I – VIII</u>. Hawthorn Press, 1998.
ISBN: 1-869890-92-2.

Julius, Edward H. <u>Rapid Math Tricks and Tips</u>. John Wily & Sons, 1992. ISBN: 0-471-57563-1.

Kretz, Harry. <u>Solid Geometry</u>. AWSNA Publications Committee, 1999. ISBN: 1-888365-27-7.

Lockwood, E. H. <u>A Book of Curves</u>. Cambridge University Press, 1961.

Lundy, Miranda. <u>Sacred Geometry</u>. Walker Publishing Company, 2002. ISBN 0-8027-1382-3.
www.walkerbooks.com.

Schuberth, Ernst. <u>Introduction of Advanced Arithmetical Operations for Waldorf School 7th Grades</u>.
AWSNA Publications Committee, 1999.

Schuberth, Ernst. <u>Mathematics Lessons for the Sixth Grade</u>. AWSNA Publications Committee, 2002.

Swanson, Herb. <u>Geometry for the Waldorf High School</u>. AWSNA Publications Committee, 1987.
(Also quite useful for middle school.)

Sheen, Renwick. <u>Geometry and the Imagination</u>. AWSNA Publications Committee, 1994.
ISBN: 0-9623978-2-2.

Stockmeyer, Karl. <u>R. Steiner's Curriculum for Waldorf Schools</u>. Steiner Schools Fellowship Publications,
1991. ISBN: 0-9510331-2-3.

Sutton, Daud. <u>Platonic and Archimedean Solids</u>. Walker Publishing Company, 2002. ISBN: 0-8027-1386-6.
www.walkerbooks.com.

Ulin, Bengt. <u>Finding The Path</u>. AWSNA, 1991. ISBN: 0-9623978-1-4.

Williams, Robert. <u>Natural Structure</u>. Dover Publications (1-516-294-7000), 1979. ISBN: 0-486-23729-X.

Special symbols used in this book

$\approx$	means "approximately".
$=$	means "equal to".
$\equiv$	means "equivalent to".
$\neq$	means "not equal to".
$\angle B$	means "angle B".
$4{\cdot}5$	means "4 times 5".
$4{:}5$	means "4 to 5" with a ratio.
km/hr	means "kilometers <u>per</u> hour".
3^4	means "3 to the 4th power", which is $3{\cdot}3{\cdot}3{\cdot}3 = 81$.
$\sqrt{25}$	means "the square root of 25". It is asking: "What number times itself is 25?" (Answer: 5)
$\sqrt[4]{81}$	means "the 4th root of 81". It is asking: "What number times itself 4 times is 81?" (Answer: 3)
7ft^2	means "7 square feet" (area), and the 7 is *not* being squared.
$5.4\overline{681}$	means "five point 4 six-eight-one repeating", is equal to 5.4681681681681…

Glossary

Note: Thorough explanations for many of these terms can be found by looking in the *index*.

Abundance quotient	The sum of a number's factors divided by the number itself.
Abundant number	A number that has its sum of factors greater than itself.
Acute angle	An angle that is less than 90°.
Acute triangle	A triangle that has all acute angles.
Algorithm	Step-by-step instructions usually associated with computer programming.
al-Khwarizmi (ca. 820AD)	The father of algebra. Wrote a book titled, *Hisab al-jabr wal-muqabala*.
Alternate interior angles	When two parallel lines are crossed by a transversal, two angles that are both inside the parallel lines, but on opposite sides of the transversal.
Arc	A part of a circle's circumference.
Archimedean Dual	A solid where all the faces and the dihedral angles are the same.
Archimedean Solid	A solid with regular (but different) faces, where all the vertices are the same.
Archimedes (ca. 250BC)	Greatest of the Greek minds. Discovered many things, including: formula for the volume of a sphere, Archimedes' principle (hydraulics), the Law of the Lever, method for calculating π, and made the first steps toward calculus.
ASCII code	Computer codes for storing characters, (e.g., from the keyboard).
Binary (numbers)	Another word for *base-two*.
Bisect	To cut something into two equal parts.
Bit	The smallest unit of storage in a computer's memory. It is either 0 (off) or 1 (on).
Cardioid	A heart-shaped curve, and a specific case of a limaçon.
Cassini curve	A loci curve that can either be an oval, an indented oval, a lemniscate, or two eggs.
Casting out nines	The process of "throwing out" all digits that add to nine.
Chord	A line that connects two points on a circle.

Circumscribe	To draw a figure on the outside of another one, so that it passed through its vertices.
Coefficient	A number that occurs before, and is multiplied by, a variable, (e.g., The "4" in $4x^2+5$).
Commensurable	The notion that two lengths can be expressed *exactly* as a ratio in whole number form.
Complementary angles	Two angles that add to 90°.
Compound fraction	A fraction that has one, or more, fractions in the numerator or denominator.
Compound interest	Interest that is calculated on both the initial deposit and the accruing interest.
Concentric circles	Circles that have the same center.
Congruent	Another word for equal. Congruent figures are exactly the same shape and size.
Conic section	A curve that results from taking the cross section of a double cone. There are three types of conic sections: ellipse, parabola, and hyperbola.
Constant	Usually a whole number or fraction that is separate from the variable term, (e.g., The "5" in $4x^2 + 5$).
Corresponding angles	Angles that are in the same relative location of the two "intersections" created when two parallel lines are crossed by a transversal.
Deficient number	A number that has its sum of factors less than itself.
Denominator	The bottom part of a fraction.
Density	The weight of a material per unit of volume. Density = weight ÷ volume.
Dihedral angle	The angle at which two planes meet along an edge.
Dimensional analysis	The study of units of measurement.
Dividend	The number that is being divided by the divisor. It is "inside" the house when doing long division.
Divisor	The number that divides into the dividend. It is "outside" the house when doing long division.
Dodecahedron	A Platonic solid that has twelve equilateral pentagons for faces.
Ellipse	A conic section curve that resembles an oval.
Equiangular polygon	A polygon that has all equal angles.
Equilateral polygon	A polygon with all equal sides.
Eratosthenes	A Greek mathematician and astronomer who accurately calculated the circumference of the earth.
Euclid (ca. 300BC)	A Greek who gathered all known mathematics into one book, *The Elements*.
Eurythmy	A type of body movement art (somewhat resembling a form of dance) that results in "visible speech". Eurythmy is taught in most Waldorf schools.
Evenly divisible	When one number divides into another without leaving a remainder.
Exponential growth	Growth that is based on a geometric progression. Also "constant percentage growth."
GCF	Greatest common factor, (e.g., The GCF of 48 and 36 is 12).
Geometric progression	A progression where each number is a given percentage larger than the previous one.
Golden ratio/mean	The ratio of the lengths of the diagonal and side of a regular pentagon.
Golden rectangle	A rectangle where the ratio of its base and height is equal to the golden ratio.
Half-wheel theorem	The theorem stating that the angles in a triangle add to 180°, so named because the proof resembles a "half-wheel".
Hexadecimal	Another word for *base-sixteen*.
Hexahedron	Another word for "cube". A Platonic solid that has six squares for faces.
Hyperbola	A conic section curve that has two branches, where each branch approaches the lines of an "X".

Hypotenuse	The longest side, and the side opposite the right angle, of a right triangle.
Hypotenuse Formula	The version of the Pythagorean Theorem that allows us to calculate the length of the hypotenuse of a right triangle, if the other two sides are given. The formula is: $c^2 = a^2 + b^2$. (See, also, *Leg Formula*.)
Icosahedron	A Platonic solid that has twenty equilateral triangles for faces.
Improper fraction	A fraction where the numerator is greater than the denominator, (e.g., $^7/_3$).
Inscribe	To draw a figure inside another one so that it is barely touching it.
Integer	A positive or negative whole number. (…-3, -2, -1, 0, 1, 2, 3…)
Inversely proportional	If we say that two things are inversely proportional, then we mean that if one goes up (or down), then the other does the opposite, (e.g., "The amount of time you spend getting somewhere is inversely proportional to your speed.").
Irrational number	A number that cannot be expressed as a whole-number fraction, (e.g., π, $\sqrt{20}$, etc.).
Isosceles triangle	A triangle with two equal sides, and two equal angles.
Kite	A quadrilateral with two pairs of equal adjacent sides.
LCM	Least common multiple, (e.g., The LCM of 12 and 8 is 24).
Leg	One of the two shorter sides of a right triangle.
Leg Formula	The version of the Pythagorean Theorem that allows us to calculate the length of a right triangle's leg (i.e. one of the two shorter sides of the triangle), if the other two sides are given. The formula is: $a^2 = c^2 - b^2$. (See, also, *Hypotenuse Formula*.)
Lemniscate	A figure-eight curve.
Limaçon	A variation of a cardioid, or heart-shaped curve.
Loci	The study of curves on a plane.
Mensuration	The study of measurement, especially area and volume.
Mixed number	A whole number combined with a *proper* (or *simple*) *fraction* (e.g., $3\frac{1}{2}$, or $5^4/_7$).
Net	A two-dimensional pattern that folds up into a three-dimensional shape.
Number bases	The study of number systems that use a base other than ten.
Numerator	The top part of the fraction.
Obtuse angle	An angle that is more than 90°.
Obtuse triangle	A triangle that has an obtuse angle in it.
Octahedron	A Platonic solid that has eight equilateral triangles for faces.
Octal (numbers)	Another word for *base-eight*.
Parabola	A conic section curve that has the shape of the path followed by a rock thrown in the air.
Parallelogram	A quadrilateral with opposite sides that are both parallel and equal.
Pentagram	A five-pointed star.
Perfect number	A number that has its sum of factors equal to itself.
Perpendicular bisector	A line that bisects another line and meets it at a right angle.
Perpendicular lines	Two lines that cross at 90° angles.
Platonic Solid	A regular and "perfectly symmetrical" three-dimensional solid.
Polygon	A closed figure that is bounded by three or more straight lines.
Polyhedron	A solid that is bounded by four or more faces that are flat polygons.
Prime factorization	A breakdown of a number into a product of its prime factors.
Prime number	A whole number that can be divided evenly only by itself and one.
Prism	A solid that has rectangles for sides and a top and bottom that are the same.
Progression	A sequence of numbers where each one gets progressively bigger than the previous one.
Proportion	(1) Meaning "fraction", (e.g., "What *proportion* of the class is boys?"). (2) An equation where there is *one* fraction on each side.

Proportional	If we say that two things are proportional, then we mean that if one goes up (or down), then the other does the same, (e.g., "How far you drive is directly proportional to the amount of time.").
Protractor	A small tool that allows one to measure the numbers of degrees in an angle.
Pythagoras (ca. 540BC)	The first great Greek mathematician and philosopher. His secret brotherhood/school discovered the Pythagorean Theorem and proved the existence of irrational numbers.
Quadrilateral	A polygon with four sides.
Quotient	The answer to a division problem. The number of times that the divisor goes into the dividend.
Rational number	A number that can be expressed as a whole-number fraction, including decimals.
Reciprocal	To find the reciprocal of a fraction, we flip it. With decimals, we divide the number into 1.
Rectangle	A quadrilateral with four right angles, where opposite sides are equal.
Regular	Means that all sides, angles, and faces are equal, (e.g., equilateral triangle, square).
Repeating decimal	A decimal where a pattern repeats forever, (e.g., $5.3\overline{72}$ means 5.372727272…).
Rhombic dodecahedron	An Archimedean dual solid that has 12 rhombuses for faces.
Rhombus	A quadrilateral with four equal sides and with equal opposite angles. It is commonly called a diamond.
Right angle	An angle equal to 90°.
Right triangle	A triangle that has a right angle in it.
Same-side interior angles	When two parallel lines are crossed by a transversal, the two angles that are both inside the parallel lines, and on the same sides of the transversal.
Secant	A line that crosses a circle in two places.
Segment of a circle	A "piece of pie" from a circle.
Scalene triangle	A triangle that has all three sides with different lengths.
Shear and stretch	The process of slicing something into thin strips or sheets, and then shifting it so that the area or volume is kept the same.
Similar figures	Two figures that have the same shape, but (probably) different sizes.
Simple interest	Interest that is based upon only the initial deposit, as opposed to compound interest.
Square Root Algorithm	A procedure, similar to long division, which allows for calculating the decimal value of the square root of a number.
Supplementary angles	Two angles that together form a straight line, or 180°.
Tangent	When a line (or curve) touches, but does not cross a curve.
Tetrahedron	A Platonic solid that has four equilateral triangles for faces.
Transversal	A line that crosses two parallel lines.
Trapezoid	A quadrilateral with one pair of parallel sides.
Truncate	With solid geometry, it means that we cut off the vertices (corners).
Variable	A letter representing an unknown number or quantity, (e.g., the "x" in $4x^2 + 5$).
Vertex	The corner of a polygon or polyhedron (solid), or the point of an angle.
Vertices	Plural of vertex.
Vertical angles	Two angles that are opposite one another when two lines intersect.

Index